PEARSON

ISBN-13: 978-0-13-208004-0
ISBN-10: 0-13-208004-4

Printed and bound in Canada

1 2 3 4 5 TC 12 11 10 9 8

PROJECT MANAGER: Yvonne Van Ruskenveld (Edvantage Press)

DEVELOPMENTAL EDITORS: Janis Barr, David Gargaro, Susan Girvan, Georgina Montgomery,
    Eileen Pyne-Rudzik, Ph.D., Rosemary Tanner

CONTRIBUTING WRITER: Erin Khelouiati, Ken Peck

COPY EDITOR: Moira Calder

PROOFREADERS: Maja Grip, Christine McPhee

INDEXER: Jennifer Hedges

PRODUCTION COORDINATORS: Sharlene Ross, Shonelle Ramserran

SENIOR MANUFACTURING COORDINATOR: Jane Schell

DESIGN: Alex Li

COMPOSITION: Carolyn E. Sebestyen

ILLUSTRATORS: Kevin Cheng, David Cheung, Deborah Crowle, Jeff Dixon, Jane Whitney

PHOTO RESEARCHERS: Nancy Cook, Rosie Gowsell, Alison Lloyd-Baker

PUBLISHER: Reid McAlpine

MANAGING EDITOR: Cecilia Chan

RESEARCH AND COMMUNICATION MANAGER: Deborah Nelson

This book was printed using paper containing recycled fibre content.

Acknowledgements

Consultants and Reviewers

Program

Marietta (Mars) Bloch
Director, Education Services
Let's Talk Science

Assessment

Derek Totten
Curriculum Consultant
York Region District School Board

Literacy

Sandra Mirabelli
Academic Consultant, Literacy, Grades 4 - 8
Dufferin-Peel Catholic District School Board

Catherine Costello
Education Consultant
formerly Curriculum Coordinator, Literacy
York Region District School Board

Environmental Education

Jane Forbes
Instructor, Science and Technology
Ontario Institute for Studies in Education, University of Toronto

Differentiated Instruction

Karen Hume
Student Success Leader
Durham District School Board

Technology

Josef Martha
Science Education Consultant and Writer
formerly Northern Gateway Public Schools, AB

Numeracy

Sue Continelli
Grapeview Public School
District School Board of Niagara

Character Education

Dennis Caron
St. Maurice Catholic School
Toronto Catholic District School Board

Leda Ostafichuk
Josyf Cardinal Slipyj Catholic Elementary School
Toronto Catholic District School Board

Raymond Weirsma
Lord Elgin Public School
Thames Valley District School Board

Combined Grades

Maureen Sims
St. Timothy Catholic School
Toronto Catholic District School Board

ELL/ESL

Jane E. Sims
Education Consultant
formerly Sir Sandford Fleming Academy
Toronto District School Board

Maureen Sims
St. Timothy Catholic School
Toronto Catholic District School Board

Safety

Peter Bloch
Northern Secondary School
Toronto District School Board

Expert Reviewers

Randy Dumont
McMaster University

Dr. Monika Havelka
University of Toronto (Mississauga)

Marina Milner-Bolotin
Ryerson University

Steven Sadura
University of Guelph

Dr. Rashmi Venkateswaran
University of Ottawa

Unit Reviewers

Daniel Birkenbergs
St. Edmund Campion Senior School
Dufferin-Peel Catholic District School Board

Paul Bosacki
John P. Robarts Public School
Thames Valley District School Board

Laura Christian
R.A. Riddel School
Hamilton Wentworth District School Board

Acknowledgements

Ian Christie
Aldershot School
Halton District School Board

Julie Grando
Academic Consultant, Science and Mathematics, Grades 7-12
Dufferin-Peel Catholic District School Board

Jodie Hancox-Meyer
Doon Public School
Waterloo District School Board

Jocelyn Harrison
D.A. Morrison Junior Middle School
Toronto District School Board

Shawna Hopkins
Consultant, Science, 7-12
District School Board of Niagara

Stephanie Insley
Chippewa Public School
Thames Valley District School Board

Kristina Kernohan
Applecroft Public School
Durham District School Board

Tait Luste
Glenhaven Senior Public School
Peel District School Board

Heather A. Mace
Featherston Drive Public School
Ottawa-Carleton District School Board

Michael J. Newnham
Learning Coordinator, 7-12 Science
Thames Valley District School Board

Bruno Pullara
All Saints and St. Christopher Schools
Dufferin-Peel Catholic District School Board

Micheline Tamminen
Five Mile Public School
Lakehead Public Schools

Margaret Ward
Orchard Park Public School
Halton District School Board

Matthew Wilson
Port Weller Public School
District School Board of Niagara

Field-Test Teachers

Chris Atkinson
St. Francis Xavier Catholic School
Catholic District School Board of Eastern Ontario

Jody Bonner-Vickers
J.W. Walker School
Rainy River District School Board

Anne Bradley
St. James the Greater Catholic School
Catholic District School Board of Eastern Ontario

Helen Brown
Gordon B. Attersley Public School
Durham District School Board

Patricia Cava
Sacred Heart High
Ottawa Catholic District School Board

Brenda Collins
St. Jude Catholic School
London Catholic District School Board

Joan D'Elia
Ruth Thompson Middle School
Peel District School Board

Chris di Tomasso
Sacred Heart Catholic School
Catholic District School Board of Eastern Ontario

Jessica Egelnick
Royal Orchard Middle School
Peel District School Board

Jody Ferdinand
A.J. Charbonneau Public School
Renfrew County District School Board

Heidi Ferguson
Our Lady of Sorrows Catholic School
Renfrew County Catholic District School Board

Alison Fernandes
St. Sebastian Catholic Elementary School
Dufferin-Peel Catholic District School Board

Andy Forgrave
Harmony Public School
Hastings and Prince Edward District School Board

Donna Forward
Sacred Heart Intermediate School
Ottawa Catholic District School Board

David Gillespie
Roland Michener Public School
Durham District School Board

Jocelyn Harrison
Dixon Grove Junior Middle School
Toronto District School Board

Pat Hogan
St. Francis de Sales Catholic School
Catholic District School Board of Eastern Ontario

Bill Hrynkiw
Nottingham Public School
Durham District School Board

Nizam Hussain
Military Trail Public School
Toronto District School Board

Colleen Hutcheson
Glashan Public School
Ottawa-Carlton District School Board

Terry Jay
Assikinack Public School
Simcoe County District School Board

Matt Johnston
Birch Cliff Public School
Toronto District School Board

Kristi Johnston Bates
St. Michael Catholic High School
Catholic District School Board of Eastern Ontario

Tom Karrow
Wellesley Public School
Waterloo Region District School Board

Kristina Kernohan
Applecroft Public School
Durham District School Board

Irene Kicak
Glenview Senior Public School
Toronto District School Board

Heather Lanning
General Crerar Public School
Toronto District School Board

Jeff Laucke
Rosedale Public School
Lambton Kent District School Board

Nicholas Lemire
Humberwood Downs Junior Middle Academy
Toronto District School Board

Tait Luste
Glenhaven Senior Public School
Peel District School Board

Hugh MacLean
Centennial Public School
Waterloo Region District School Board

Marjory Masson
Earl Beatty Junior and Senior Public School
Toronto District School Board

Irene McCuaig
Lakewood School
Keewatin-Patricia District School Board

Mary Sue McIntyre
Monsignor Clair School
Simcoe Muskoka Catholic District School Board

Brian Murrant
Victoria Harbour Elementary School
Simcoe County District School Board

Tom Rhind
Lakewood School
Keewatin-Patricia District School Board

Phil Sanders
Northdale Central Public School
Thames Valley District School Board

Rey Sandre
St. Mark Catholic School
Toronto Catholic District School Board

Ryan Seale
Sacred Heart Catholic School
Catholic District School Board of Eastern Ontario

John Starratt
Monsignor Michael O'Leary School
Simcoe Muskoka Catholic District School Board

Corinna Taverna-Rossi
Kateri Tekakwitha Catholic Elementary School
York Catholic District School Board

Stacy van Boxtel
St. Andrew's School
Renfrew County Catholic District School Board

Cathy Viscount
Stanley Park Public School
Waterloo Region District School Board

Janice Whiton
Kateri Tekakwitha Catholic Elementary School
York Catholic District School Board

Rebecca Widler
Prince of Wales Public School
Simcoe County District School Board

Raymond Wiersma
Chippewa Public School
Thames Valley District School Board

Craig Winslow
St. Martin School
Niagara Catholic District School Board

Students

The authors and Pearson Education Canada would like to thank all the students who participated in focus groups and field tests during the development of this book.

Contents

Contents

Contents

Contents

Contents

Contents

Contents

Contents

Common-Sense Science Safety in Your Classroom

You will be doing many activities in this book. Before you begin an activity, read through it and watch for "Caution" notes. These notes will tell you how to take extra care as you work through the activity. Make sure you understand what the cautions mean.

When doing an activity, it is very important that you follow the safety rules below. Your teacher may have safety instructions to add to this list. As you read the rules, discuss with a partner or note why each one is an example of common-sense safety.

Before You Begin

1. Read and make sure you understand the instructions in the text or in any handouts your teacher may provide. Follow your teacher's direction always. Never change or start an activity without approval.

2. Learn to recognize the warning symbols for hazardous materials shown in Toolkit 1, pages 377–378.

3. Keep your work area uncluttered and organized.

4. Know the location of fire extinguishers and other safety equipment.

5. Always wear safety goggles and any other safety clothing as requested by your teacher or this book.

6. If you have long or loose hair, tie it back. Roll up long shirt sleeves.

7. Inform your teacher if you have any allergies or medical conditions, or anything else that might affect your work in the science classroom.

During the Activity

8. Report any safety concerns you have, or hazards you see (such as spills) to your teacher.

9. Don't eat, drink, or chew gum in your science classroom.

10. Never taste any substance.

11. Never smell any substance directly. Instead, gently wave your hand over it to bring its vapours toward your nose, as shown in the photo below.

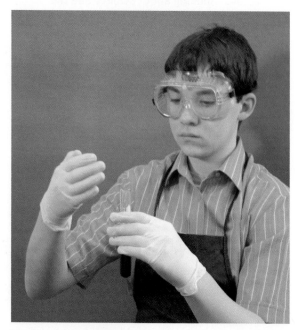

Smell an odour by wafting it toward you.

12. Handle all glassware carefully. If you see broken glass, ask your teacher how to dispose of it properly.

13. Handle knives and other sharp objects with care. Always cut away from yourself, and never point a sharp object at another person.

14. Heat solids and liquids only in open heat-resistant glass containers and test tubes. Use tongs or protective gloves to pick up hot objects.

15. When you heat test tubes, make sure that the open end is pointing away from you and anyone else in the room. The photo below shows the correct way to do this.

The open end of the test tube should point away from you when you heat it.

16. When heating a substance, make sure the container does not boil dry.

17. Keep water or wet hands away from electrical outlets or sockets.

18. Use tools safely when cutting, joining, or drilling. Make sure you know how to use any tools properly.

19. If any part of your body comes in contact with a chemical, wash the area immediately and thoroughly with water. If you get anything in your eyes, do not touch them. Wash them immediately and continuously with water for 15 minutes. Inform your teacher.

20. Treat all living things with respect. Follow your teacher's instructions when working with living things in the classroom or on a field trip.

21. On a field trip, do not disturb the area any more than you need to. If you have to take any plant material, take as little as possible and remove it carefully.

When You Finish the Activity

22. Make sure you close the containers of chemicals immediately after you use them.

23. Follow your teacher's instructions to safely dispose of all waste materials.

Wear the proper safety equipment when doing science activities.

24. Always wash your hands well with soap, preferably liquid soap, after handling chemicals or other materials. Always wash your hands after touching plants, soil, or any animals and their cages or containers.

25. When you have finished an experiment, clean all the equipment before putting it away. Be careful with hot plates and equipment that have been heated as they may take a long time to cool down.

Say "Yes!" to Safety

✓ Follow the safety instructions outlined by your teacher and this book.

✓ Keep an eye open for possible hazards, and report them immediately.

✓ Show respect and concern for your own safety and the safety of your classmates and teachers.

After Reading

Thinking Literacy

Share Your Knowledge

With a partner or small group, think of a way you could share your knowledge of safety in the science classroom through a poster or a skit. For example, you could create a poster about the correct way to smell a substance or how to heat a liquid in a container. Or, you could plan and present a skit about getting yourselves and your workspace ready for a science activity.

Exploring Your Textbook

Investigating Science and Technology 7

Explore the different ways *Investigating Science and Technology 7* is organized by finding the answers to the following questions.

Titles and Organizers

1. How many units will you study in *Science and Technology 7*? List their titles. For each unit, describe what you think it's about.

2. Turn to the Unit Overview at the beginning of one of the units. What information about the unit can you find there?

3. Who is Jay Ingram? What is the title of the page with information from him? (HINT: look near the end of Chapter 3.)

Symbols

1. What is the symbol in the upper right hand corner of a During Reading feature? What is the purpose of a During Reading feature?

2. Find an Inquiry Lab in Chapter 8 and sketch two of the safety symbols found in the activity. Where can you find more information about the safety symbols in your textbook?

Colours

1. Name three different types of activities printed on blue backgrounds. Find an example of each type in Unit A.

2. At the end of each chapter there is a Chapter Review printed on a yellow background. What are the different parts of a Chapter Review called?

3. There is a Unit Task described at the beginning of each unit. Find the Unit Task for Unit C and summarize it. Look at the end of each chapter in Unit C for the Unit Task Links printed on blue backgrounds. How many Unit Task Links are there in Unit C?

Words and Skills

1. Find the list of key terms for Chapter 2. Where can you find the definitions for all of the key terms in your textbook?

2. You will use many different skills as you work through this book. Find the list of skills you will use in Chapter 7. Choose one and describe how you could practise that skill.

3. Find an example of a Words Matter margin feature in Chapter 7. What can you learn about from a Words Matter?

4. Look for an activity in Chapter 4 that refers you to Toolkit 4. Where can you go in your textbook to find the Toolkit section? What can you learn about in Toolkit 4?

Interactions in the Environment

Unit Overview

Fundamental Concepts

In Grade 7 Science and Technology, six fundamental concepts occur throughout. This unit addresses the following two:

- Systems and Interactions
- Sustainability and Stewardship

Big Ideas

As you work through this unit, you will develop a deeper understanding of the following big ideas:

- Ecosystems are made up of biotic (living) and abiotic (non-living) elements that depend on each other to survive.

- Ecosystems are in a constant state of change. The changes may be caused by nature or by human intervention.

- Human activities have the potential to alter the environment. Humans must be aware of these impacts and try to control them.

Overall Expectations

By the end of this unit, you will be expected to:

1. assess the impacts of human activities and technologies on the environment and evaluate ways of controlling these impacts

2. investigate interactions within the environment and identify factors that affect the balance between different components of an ecosystem

3. demonstrate an understanding of interactions between and among biotic and abiotic elements in the environment

All living things survive by interacting with other elements in their ecosystem.

Exploring

A walk in an ecosystem will bring you into close contact with many living things.

You have come to walk along the forest path in a river valley. You spy a white-tailed deer snacking on a small shrub. A pheasant nearby loudly beats its wings and flies off. Insects are buzzing in the air. The plants, the insects, the birds, and the animals are all living things, just like you. You have something else in common with them. You are all part of an ecosystem. **Ecosystems** are the places where living things interact with other living and non-living things.

Interactions in the Environment is about how living things survive on Earth. You will find out how ecosystems work.

Just as important, you will assess the impact of human activities on ecosystems and learn how activities and technology are changing as people take action to protect ecosystems.

The Rouge River Valley

Over 500 years ago, the Rouge River was known locally as Katabokokonk, which meant "river of easy entrance." The valley was home to the People of the Longhouse, who used the river's water for cooking, drinking, and fishing as well as transportation. Villagers grew crops in the valley, including beans that kept the soil healthy and increased the production of other plants. The Iroquois lived in longhouses made of wooden poles, branches, and bark from the forests. These early inhabitants of the valley depended on the living and non-living elements of the valley for their survival.

When Europeans settled the area, they established farms and built mills to use the water power to grind local grain. Communities, businesses, and roads were added as the city of Toronto expanded.

The Rouge River and the smaller ones that flow into it begin in the Oak Ridges Moraine and empty into Lake Ontario. The ecosystems in the Rouge Valley include mature forests, a large marsh, bluffs, meadows, and beach shoreline.

Creating the Rouge Park

By 1975, local people were concerned about the impact of human activities on the valley's ecosystems. They suspected that increased development would damage them. Roads and housing would destroy habitats, animals, and plants, and cars would contribute to air pollution. Some water sources would be diverted, and others would be polluted.

The locals formed a group to preserve the Rouge Valley and protect it from development. It took 20 years of meetings, petitions, and rallies before the Rouge Park was created.

The Rouge Park now covers 47 km². and protects many ecosystems. Local people work co-operatively with federal, provincial, and municipal governments to manage the park. Their goal is to limit the impact of human activities and technologies on the Rouge Valley.

...MORE TO EXPLORE

Interactions and Connections

Purpose

Ecosystems contain a variety of living things that depend on the water, soil, air, and other living and non-living things for survival. The class is going to model the connections among living things.

Materials & Equipment

- 3 large balls of wool: red, blue, green
- 1 pair of scissors

Procedure

1. Most of the class will form a circle. Four students will be in the middle, and two students will be on the outside.

2. The student pairs in the circle represent soil and water. The soil team will have the red wool; the water team will have the blue. One member holds the end of the wool in the centre of the circle; each "runner" has the ball.

3. Each student in the circle will represent a different organism from a local ecosystem.

4. Students representing a living thing interacting with soil (an oak or an earthworm) will indicate their connection. The "soil" runner will use the red wool to make continuous links between each of those living things with the centre.

5. Those with a connection to water will be linked to the centre with blue wool. (Runners should stay low to avoid tangles.)

6. The students outside the circle will connect living things that depend on each other. For example, they will cut a piece of green wool long enough to connect the earthworm to the robin that eats it.

Questions

7. Describe some of the ways living things and non-living things may be connected.

8. How would the loss of soil or water or some of the plants or animals affect the ecosystem?

A2 *Thinking about Science, Technology, Society, and the Environment*

Fundamental Concept Focus: What is stewardship?

A steward is someone who looks after and takes care of something that belongs to someone else. People often talk about stewardship when they talk about Earth because Earth does not belong to us.

Consider This

As a class, answer the following questions:

1. Who do you think is responsible for Earth?

2. What can you do to help look after Earth?

Contents

Unit Task

You know the size of your foot, but do you know the size of your ecological footprint? Like all living things, you require some of Earth's resources to keep yourself alive. In the Unit Task you are going to measure the amount of Earth's resources you are using. You will be able to compare your ecological footprint with others in your class and assess the impact of your needs for Earth's resources.

Essential Question

What is the environmental impact of your activities?

Getting Ready to Read

Thinking Literacy

Anticipation Guide

Your teacher will give you a list of statements. Circle "Agree" or "Disagree" beside each statement before you read your textbook. As you read this unit, note page numbers that relate to each statement. When you have finished reading, you can check to see whether your opinion has changed based on what you have learned.

All living things find what they need to survive in their local ecosystem.

What You Will Learn

In this chapter, you will:

- explain what living things need to survive
- describe an ecosystem
- describe interactions of producers, consumers, decomposers, and non-living things in ecosystems

Skills You Will Use

In this chapter, you will:

- follow established safety procedures for investigating ecosystems
- design and construct a model ecosystem

Why This Is Important

Living things — like you, a fish in a river, or a tomato plant — depend on interactions with other living and non-living things to survive. These interactions (acting on each other) happen in ecosystems.

Before Reading

Thinking Literacy

Previewing Text Features
Textbooks use a variety of text features to organize key concepts and main ideas, and to highlight important details. Scan this chapter to preview the headings and scientific vocabulary. Look at how colour and the size and shape of the type are used. Thinking about the ways these two features are presented can help you understand what you will be reading.

Key Terms
- ecosystem
- abiotic
- population
- consumers
- biotic
- producers
- community
- decomposers

Figure 1.1 Aboriginal peoples shared their land with animals like this deer.

Figure 1.2 Aboriginal peoples respect all things in nature.

North American Aboriginal peoples have lived off the land as fishers, hunters, and farmers for generations. Wherever they have lived, they have paid close attention to the local plants, birds, animals, and other natural resources they used to survive. The Northern Cree knew that if they killed too many geese, there would be no more goose for dinner. If the Mohawk took too many trees, they might lose their shelters or source of heat. If the local water sources were ruined, the Ojibwa community would have to relocate or risk death.

Traditional Aboriginal practices taught the people to waste nothing when they used plants or killed animals. They hunted animals such as deer for food (Figure 1.1). Then they used the skin, bones, and other parts for tools, clothing, shelter, or medicine. These traditional interactions with the natural world are based on the beliefs that both life and water are sacred. They believe that everything is connected through interactions. Aboriginal peoples consider themselves to be part of the ecosystem they live in. These beliefs have led to a deep respect and gratitude for Earth. Traditional ways of living require that everything in nature be treated with respect and used wisely.

Today, Aboriginal elders continue to share their respect for Earth as they work with environmental scientists. Together, they combine traditional knowledge with scientific research in order to improve the management of local ecosystems.

A3 Quick Lab

Ecosystems Are Everywhere

Figure 1.3

Figure 1.4

Wherever you look, you will see elements of ecosystems. In a city, you see birds, insects, nests, trees, grasses, squirrels, and raccoons. In a less populated area, you may see a pond with wildlife living in it or visiting it. Each ecosystem has a variety of living things such as plants and animals and non-living things such as soil, rocks, and water.

Living things get what they need to survive from the ecosystem they live in. Ecosystems can be huge or tiny. They can be wet or dry; they can be cold or hot.

Purpose

To identify interactions that occur in ecosystems

Materials & Equipment
■ photos   ■ paper and pencil

Procedure

1. Take a blank piece of paper and make two charts, each with two columns headed Living Things and Non-living Things. Look at the pictures of the ecosystems in Figures 1.3 and 1.4 above. Use the chart to classify everything you see.

2. With a partner, make a list of the ways the living things interact with the environment.

Questions

3. With a classmate or as a class, discuss the following questions.

   (a) How would you interact with each of these ecosystems?

   (b) How would your interaction affect each ecosystem?

Here is a summary of what you will learn in this section:

- A living thing is known as a biotic element.
- A non-living thing is known as an abiotic element.
- Biotic elements need five basic things in order to survive.
- Biotic elements interact with both biotic and abiotic elements in order to meet their basic needs.

You and your classmates are busy 24 hours a day keeping yourselves alive. You may not think of it that way, but it is true! What are some of the activities that you — and most other living things — do to survive? You breathe air. You drink water. You eat food. You get rid of waste. Your body makes energy so that it can carry out activities such as digesting food and moving around. You and other living things have basic needs that are essential to your survival. To meet these basic needs, you interact with living and non-living things.

A4 *Starting Point* Skills

Living and Non-living Things in Ecosystems

In Activity A3, you made a list of the living and non-living things you could see in the photographs. How did you decide which was which?

Look at the three photographs here. Which of these elements are living and which are non-living? Discuss with a classmate how to decide whether something is living or non-living. Make a list of the factors you used to make your decision.

Figure 1.6

Figure 1.7

Figure 1.5

Basic Needs of Biotic Elements

Scientists call living things **biotic** elements. Non-living things are **abiotic** elements. Biotic elements have five basic needs for survival. Most biotic elements — polar bears, mosquitoes, dandelions, maple trees, and you — need these same five basic things:

1. oxygen
2. water
3. food
4. energy
5. suitable habitat (place to live)

As you read about these five basic needs, think about how meeting each one requires interaction with other biotic and abiotic elements.

Take It *Further*

Some biotic elements live in habitats without oxygen. Find out what living things live in an environment without oxygen and how they survive. Begin your research at PearsonScience.

A5 | *During Reading*

Thinking Literacy

Let the Titles Guide You

As you read about the basic needs of living things, you can use the headings to guide your understanding of the information. In your notes, make a list of the headings. For each one, write a question you would like answered using words such as Why? Where? What? or How? Keep these questions in mind as you read to help you understand how interactions with non-living things help living things meet their basic needs.

Oxygen	Water	Food	Energy	Habitat
How do I get oxygen?	What does water do for me?			

Oxygen

Oxygen is a gas in Earth's atmosphere. You take it into your body when you breathe in. Oxygen helps your body release and use energy made from the food you eat. Almost every biotic element takes in oxygen in order to survive (Figure 1.8).

Water

Your body is about 70% water. Many of the chemical reactions that keep you alive take place in the water inside your body. Animals (including humans) must take in clean water to survive. Plants need water to make food.

Figure 1.8 Fish use gills to get the oxygen they need from water.

Figure 1.9 An orange contains nutrients that help to keep your body healthy.

Figure 1.10 Your body needs energy to keep its systems working. You also need energy for your activities.

Figure 1.11 The habitat of this beaver supplies oxygen, water, food, and shelter.

Food

You need to eat food to get the nutrients your body needs (Figure 1.9). **Nutrients** are the components of food that your body converts into energy. They are also the materials a living thing needs to keep living. Nutrients include carbohydrates, fats, proteins, vitamins, and minerals. Your body needs these materials to make energy to move, grow, and repair and maintain your body's millions of cells. Most biotic elements get food from their environment.

Energy

Oxygen, water, and nutrients from food interact in your body to produce energy. Energy is what moves your body (Figure 1.10). It keeps your heart beating. It powers your breathing. You do not think about these activities, but they keep you alive. Your brain uses about 20 % of all the energy your body produces. It uses this energy to control most of your body and its activities.

Suitable Habitat

As a living thing, you must live in a place where you can obtain everything you need to survive. **Habitat** provides living things with oxygen, water, food, shelter, and anything else that they need for survival. For example, the beaver in Figure 1.11 lives in a pond filled with plants that provide food and shelter. The pond also provides the water the beaver needs to survive.

Interactions to Meet Basic Needs

Plants use sunlight, soil, and water to grow. Animals use leaves, branches, trees, or soil for shelter and other living things for food. These are examples of interactions of biotic and abiotic elements in ecosystems. In a pond, the plants, soil, and water create suitable habitat for many different birds, insects, and fish. Some animals, such as deer, eat plants. Other animals, such as bears, eat fish and berries. Feeding interactions give living things the nutrients they need to survive.

Interactions of Living and Non-living Things

In Activity A3, you looked at photographs of two natural spaces and identified biotic and abiotic elements. Now you are going to take a closer look at a natural space you are familiar with to discover some of the ways that the biotic elements there meet their basic needs through interactions.

Purpose

To explore the interactions between biotic and abiotic elements in a local area

Materials & Equipment

- area of schoolyard
- clipboard
- digital camera (optional)
- paper and pencil
- magnifier

Procedure

1. Your class will be going into the schoolyard to observe and record biotic and abiotic elements. Before going outside, work with a partner to create a list of Courtesy Guidelines to ensure that everyone respects the habitats of the different plants and animals in the schoolyard. Everyone should follow these guidelines when working and playing in the schoolyard.

2. Once in the schoolyard or a location your teacher specifies, get to know your surroundings. Stand quietly for a few moments. Listen to the sounds around you, and try to identify any new sounds or smells.

3. Draw a rough sketch or take a picture of the area where you will make your observations. Your written observations should include anything you can detect with your senses of sight, smell, and hearing. Do not taste or touch anything.

4. Create a chart like the one below, and list everything that you observe. If you are not sure whether something belongs under Living or Non-living, put it in the Not sure column.

Living	Non-living	Not Sure

5. Continue recording your observations until your teacher asks you to return to the school.

Questions

6. Compare your chart with your classmates' charts. Create a class chart of biotic and abiotic elements you observed in your schoolyard. Are there observations you disagree with? Why would you place them in a different category?

7. As a class, discuss and reclassify the things recorded in the Not Sure column.

8. In your chart, draw a line between a living and non-living thing if you think there are interactions between them. You may have observed this interaction, or you may think there is one. For example, if you observed a worm (biotic) and soil (abiotic), you could draw a line connecting the two things. This would connect the worm to the soil it uses for its habitat. In the margin, identify the basic need the interaction meets.

9. From your chart, select two different biotic elements. Describe how they meet all their needs through interactions in their habitat.

Key Concept Review

1. (a) What are your basic needs for survival?

   (b) How do your needs compare with those of other living things?

2. Describe interactions you have with the environment that you depend on to meet your basic needs.

3. (a) List four biotic elements in the pond shown below.

   (b) List four abiotic elements in this pond.

4. Describe how interactions help the following living things survive: dandelion, hawk, honeybee.

Connect Your Understanding

5. Describe why Canada geese migrate to meet their basic needs.

6. Identify and briefly describe two ecosystems in your community that are beyond your schoolyard. For each of these ecosystems, list three biotic and three abiotic elements.

7. Explain how one of the biotic elements in an ecosystem you identified interacts with other elements to meet its needs.

Practise Your Skills

8. Create a chart or graphic organizer illustrating the five basic needs of biotic elements.

For more questions, go to PearsonScience.

A7 *Thinking about Science and the Environment*

Your Ecosystems Mind Map

You are studying how living things interact to survive on Earth. This chapter looks at how ecosystems support life. Later chapters describe the transfer of energy and cycling of matter, and changes in ecosystems. Use a mind map to help you record this information.

To start your mind map, take a blank piece of paper and write the word *Ecosystems* in the centre as shown here. On the right side of the page, make a column to write new words that you see as you go through the unit. This can be your personal Word Wall.

As you connect the words and your understanding of interactions in ecosystems, indicate the connections on your mind map.

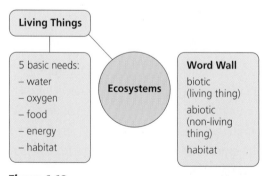

Figure 1.12

Here is a summary of what you will learn in this section:

- Plants interact with the Sun's light and heat to support life on Earth.
- Plants are the only organisms that can use the Sun's energy to produce food.
- Other living things interact with plants as food or to find or make shelter.

On a sunny day, you can feel the warmth of the Sun on your face. You might even have to shade your eyes because of its bright light. Plants also interact with the Sun's heat and light. You can notice this in the spring when the Sun's heat melts the snow and warms the soil. Plants start to poke up through the warm soil. They grow rapidly as the days get longer and more light is available.

The Sun is an essential abiotic element in most ecosystems (Figure 1.13). The two forms of energy from the Sun — light and heat — are important to most life forms on Earth.

Figure 1.13 Living things interact with the light and heat from the Sun.

A8   *Starting Point*   Skills Ⓐ Ⓒ

The Year With No Summer

In 1815, Mount Tambora erupted in the Pacific Ocean, east of Java, spewing 150 million tonnes of volcanic dust high into Earth's atmosphere. The ash gradually surrounded Earth and filtered the Sun's light for months. The summer months of 1816 were known as "the year with no summer" in North America and parts of Europe. Snow covered areas around Montreal, Quebec City, and the New England states for brief periods in June. Crops sprouted very late and were killed by an early hard frost in September. Families had no food for themselves or their livestock for the coming winter.

1. How would the lack of sunlight affect the normal interactions between living and non-living things?

2. Historical documents report that people had to abandon their farms and towns. Do you think that would happen again if the Sun's rays were blocked?

Figure 1.14 Volcanoes can spew huge quantities of dust and gases high into the air.

How Producers Use the Sun's Energy

Plants are called **producers**. Producers can make their own food to supply the matter and energy they need to survive. All sizes and types of green plants, from tiny algae to the largest trees, are producers (Figure 1.15).

Photosynthesis

Producers use a process called photosynthesis to make food. **Photosynthesis** is a chemical reaction that takes place in the leaves of plants when the Sun's light is present. The green colour visible in most leaves is a compound called chlorophyll, which is needed to make the chemical reaction. Through photosynthesis, producers combine carbon dioxide from the air and water from the soil to make a sugar product called glucose and a waste product — oxygen (Figure 1.16). The oxygen is released back into the air through tiny pores in the plants' leaves.

Figure 1.15 The algae floating on this pond and the larger plants in the upper part of the photo are all producers.

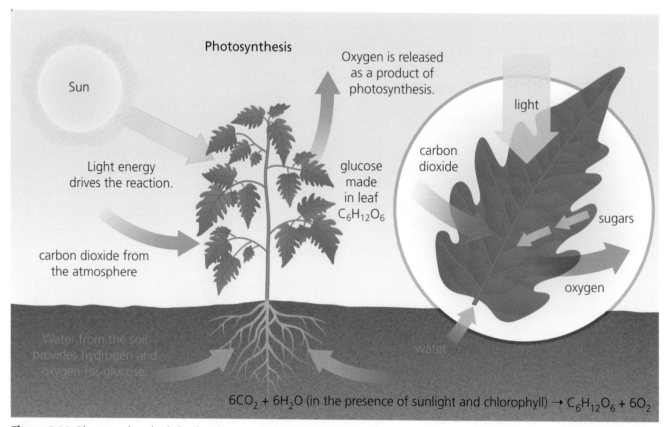

Photosynthesis

Oxygen is released as a product of photosynthesis.

Sun

Light energy drives the reaction.

carbon dioxide from the atmosphere

glucose made in leaf $C_6H_{12}O_6$

light

carbon dioxide

sugars

oxygen

Water from the soil provides hydrogen and oxygen for glucose.

water

$6CO_2 + 6H_2O$ (in the presence of sunlight and chlorophyll) $\rightarrow C_6H_{12}O_6 + 6O_2$

Figure 1.16 Plants produce both food and oxygen during photosynthesis.

Producers' Roles

All ecosystems have producers. Producers are part of the interactions that support biotic elements in an ecosystem. Producers have three roles in an ecosystem:

1. They produce oxygen.
2. They supply food.
3. They provide shelter.

Producers Produce Oxygen

Plants and plant-like biotic elements maintain Earth's supply of oxygen. Oxygen is one of the basic needs of living things.

Producers Supply Food

Producers are the only biotic elements that can make their own food. All other living things must find food to eat in order to get all the matter and energy they need to survive. Some of these living things eat only producers. For example, some insects, deer, rabbits, and cows eat only plants. Others eat the living things that eat producers. Birds eat insects. Foxes eat rabbits. Humans eat cows. This means that all feeding interactions begin with producers.

Producers Provide Shelter

In ecosystems, living things often shelter in plants or use plants to make their shelters. Birds nest in tree branches. Squirrels and chipmunks nest in hollowed-out tree trunks. Insects can live in or on trees, bushes, shrubs, and mosses. Fish shelter in the cover of aquatic plants in ponds and rivers.

Decaying logs, beaver dams, and birds' nests are a very few examples of the shelter provided by or supported by plants in ecosystems.

Figure 1.17 A variety of animals dine on many different parts of producers.

Interactions in Ecosystems

Ecosystems are busy places, as biotic elements interact with other elements to meet their basic needs. Producers take in the Sun's energy while they also take in water and nutrients from the soil. Photosynthesis is under way. Meanwhile, other biotic elements take shelter or feed.

Some interactions in an ecosystem can harm one of the participants. For example, when a garter snake eats a frog, the frog dies, while the garter snake takes in nutrients (Figure 1.18). Other interactions benefit both participants. For example, when a bee feeds on nectar, it also gathers and distributes pollen. This helps the plants to reproduce.

These constant interactions are part of all ecosystems. Canada's Aboriginal peoples describe these interactions as "connections." These connections mean that when something changes one element of an ecosystem, the change will have an effect on many other elements in the ecosystem. For example, when a beaver builds a dam and floods an area, the plants that cannot survive in wet conditions will die. The living things that depend on those plants may have trouble surviving.

Figure 1.18 Some interactions in ecosystems harm one of the participants.

A9 | *Learning Checkpoint*

Plants and the Sun

1. Describe the interaction between the Sun and producers.

2. Explain why this interaction is important.

3. What is the name of the interaction?

4. What are the roles of producers in an ecosystem?

5. Why does a fox need to be in an ecosystem that includes grass?

Figure 1.19 The population of ducks is part of a pond community.

Populations and Communities

As you consider interactions in ecosystems, you will not be looking at individual organisms. Instead you will be looking at populations and communities. **Populations** are groups of individuals that belong to the same species and live in the same area. **Species** are the most closely related groups of living things in an ecosystem. The members of a species can reproduce with each other.

A community is made up of populations of different species that live in the same ecosystem. The interactions of the populations with each other and the local abiotic elements make up the ecosystem.

For example, the mallard ducks in Figure 1.19 are members of a population. Around them is a pond habitat, with populations of various plants, geese and other birds, insects, and mammals. Together these populations make up the pond community. The pond ecosystem includes the community's interaction with abiotic elements in the pond, such as the water, rocks, and soil, and with each other. Within each ecosystem, the biotic elements depend on other biotic elements and abiotic elements for survival.

Take It Further

Even though humans are omnivores, some people choose to be herbivores. Find out how vegetarians get all the nutrients they need from plants. Begin your research at PearsonScience.

A10 *During Reading*

Thinking Literacy

Reading like a Writer

Understanding the organizational pattern used in a piece of non-fiction writing can help you as a reader. Much of the information presented in this chapter is written as a description. Writers use descriptive text pattern when they want to share the characteristics of something, such as a concept, animal, plant, or place. Descriptive text paints a visual picture with words.

Give this type of writing a try. The following paragraph describes a species, population, and community of producers in an ecosystem.

In Ontario, farmers grow many different types of fruits and vegetables. One popular type of fruit is the McIntosh apple. Many farms grow large populations of McIntosh apples. On other farms, the McIntosh apple is just one of the many different fruit and vegetables that are grown in that farm community.

Using the information you have read in this section, add details to this paragraph using the three Es of writing. The table below summarizes the three Es and key questions you can ask.

When you have finished adding details to your paragraph, exchange it with a partner and read each other's writing. Suggest one or two details that could be added to the paragraph.

Incorporate your partner's suggestions into your paragraph.

Es for Stretching Ideas	Key Questions to Consider
Expand	How is this so?
Extend	Such as? For example?
Elaborate	And an example is . . .
	This looks like . . .
	Tell me more about . . .

How an Abiotic Element Affects Producers

Purpose

To find out how sunlight affects Canada's producers

Materials & Equipment

- potato production statistics (by province)
- wheat production statistics (by province)
- apple production statistics (by province)

Procedure

1. Look at the map in Figure 1.20 below showing the average annual hours of sunshine in Canada. What patterns do you notice among provinces with similar hours of sunshine? Different hours of sunshine?

2. Compare the production of farm products to the average hours of sunshine of the areas where they are most commonly grown. What trends do you notice?

Questions

3. How was the amount of sunshine related to the growth of plants?

4. What other abiotic elements could affect plant growth? Give some examples and describe their possible impact.

5. How does organizing the statistical information in a graph or a chart help you state and defend a clear conclusion?

6. What are some of the factors farmers need to consider when looking for new land to grow crops on?

7. How does the growing season (hours of sunlight) have an effect on where people would choose to live?

8. What role does Canada's climate play in industries related to producers?

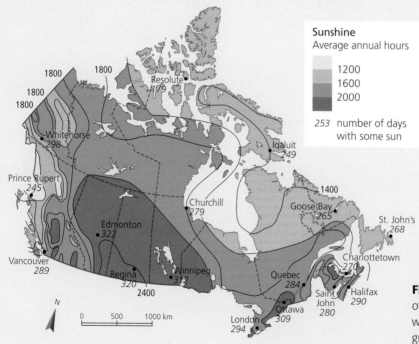

Sunshine
Average annual hours

1200
1600
2000

253 number of days with some sun

Figure 1.20 The average amount of sunshine that an area receives will affect the crops that are grown there.

Key Concept Review

1. List two ways the Sun supports life.

2. Explain how the plants in and around a meadow provide habitat for these animals: butterfly, field mouse, owl.

3. Explain why photosynthesis is important for ecosystems everywhere.

Connect Your Understanding

4. Forests and meadows are often cut down to make way for farms or campgrounds. What are some of the elements of ecosystems that are lost when plants in these areas are removed?

5. How would planting a variety of plants in a vacant lot help establish an ecosystem in that location?

6. Plants that live in shallow water have the same roles as plants on dry land. Describe the roles of plants like the ones shown below. Give an example of an interaction between one of the plants shown and another biotic element in the ecosystem.

Practise Your Skills

7. How can gathering and organizing information about ecosystems help you better understand the interactions among the different elements in an ecosystem?

For more questions, go to PearsonScience.

A12 *Thinking about Science and the Environment*

Connections

On page 17, you read about "the year with no summer." That was 1815, when many eastern North Americans could not grow enough food for the next winter. No one knew then that the eruption of a volcano in the Pacific Ocean had caused their troubles.

Scientists now understand that the connections among all biotic and abiotic elements on Earth make survival of biotic elements possible. These connections can be global or within a tiny ecosystem in a puddle. A change in one element in an ecosystem has a ripple effect — like a pebble dropped in a pond — on all the other elements in an ecosystem.

Consider This

1. Do you think it is acceptable for someone to release old chemicals into a stream? Explain your answer.

2. Do you think it is acceptable for large industries to release chemicals into the air? Explain your answer.

Here is a summary of what you will learn in this section:

- Animals cannot make their own food and must consume other living things to get nutrients.
- A food chain is a summary of feeding interactions among producers and consumers.
- Decomposers are a special type of consumer. They break down dead organic materials so that the nutrients can be returned to the ecosystem.

Figure 1.21 The sheep are consumers that feed on the grass. The grass is a producer in this ecosystem.

Producers can make their own food from the Sun's energy, water, and nutrients, so they do not feed on other biotic elements. All other living things in an ecosystem rely on feeding interactions to supply their food needs. These living things are known as **consumers** because they have to consume other living things. "Consume" means to eat or use. Consumers could not exist in an ecosystem without producers. In Figure 1.21, the sheep are consumers that are eating producers.

A13   *Starting Point*   Skills P C

Where Does Their Food Come From?

1. Identify six different living things in the pond ecosystem in Figure 1.22.

2. Classify the six living things into two groups:

   Group 1: can make their own food

   Group 2: cannot make their own food

   Write these two lists in a T-chart in your notebook. Label each of the two groups in your T-chart.

Figure 1.22

Types of Consumers

Consumers eat living things to get the nutrients they need. Some eat fruit. Some eat seeds. Some eat roots. Others eat fish, birds, small animals, or large ones. Consumers are classified by the type of living things they eat. **Herbivores** eat plants. **Carnivores** eat meat. **Omnivores** eat both meat and plants.

Table 1.1 Consumers

Type of Consumer	Food Eaten	Examples
Herbivores	Plants	Moose and aphids
Carnivores	Meat	Lake trout and wolf
Omnivores	Meat and plants	Humans and bears

A14 *During Reading*

Origins of Scientific Words

Knowing the meaning of prefixes and root words can help you make sense of unfamiliar terms. Scientists often use words from the ancient languages of Greek or Latin when they create new terms. The root of the words "herbivore," "carnivore," and "omnivore" comes from the Latin word *vorare*, which means to devour. *Herba* is the Latin word for plant, so a herbivore devours plants. *Carnis* is the Latin word for meat or flesh, and so a carnivore is a meat eater. In Latin, *omni* means all or everything, and so an omnivore eats both plants and animals.

Often scientific words will appear as bold or italicized text. Look for the "Words Matter" feature boxes in this textbook to find information about the origins of some scientific words.

Use a dictionary to create a list of other words that begin with *herba*, *carnis*, and *omni*.

Predators and Prey

One type of interaction in an ecosystem is the one between a carnivore and the animal it eats. An animal that is hunted for food is called the *prey*. The animal that hunts and consumes the prey is called the *predator* (Figure 1.23). When a coyote eats a deer, the coyote is the predator and the deer is the prey. When a wolf eats a coyote, the wolf is the predator and the coyote is the prey.

Figure 1.23 In meadow ecosystems, birds are predators.

Special Consumers: Scavengers, Detrivores, and Decomposers

All living things eventually die. As well, all consumers generate waste materials from the food they eat. Our planet would be littered with dead bodies and waste materials if not for special groups of consumers. Some of these consumers are scavengers. Some are detrivores. Others are decomposers.

Scavengers are consumers that do not usually kill their own food. Instead, they feed off the remains of dead animals (Figure 1.24). Crows, ravens, and housefly larvae (maggots) are examples of scavengers.

Detrivores are consumers that feed off waste (detritus). Snails and earthworms are common examples of detrivores. Earthworms eat their way through soil and organic matter (Figure 1.25). As they do so, their digestive systems break the material down into nutrients they can absorb and waste matter they leave behind. The waste matter is full of nutrients that can be absorbed by plants through their roots. Without the help of earthworms, plants would not be able to survive.

Helping or Harming?

Decomposers are consumers that break down (decompose) dead plants and animals. Fungi, such as mushrooms and the mould you see growing on bread, fruits, and vegetables, are decomposers. Other decomposers, such as bacteria, are visible only through a microscope.

E. coli (short for *Escherichia coli*) are bacteria found in your large intestine. These bacteria break down the food you eat in order to get their own food. In the process, they manufacture several vitamins that your body needs to stay healthy. Your body needs these bacteria. *E. coli bacteria 0157:H7* (Figure 1.26) is a form of *E. coli* sometimes found in common food products such as ground beef, milk, and apple juice. When these decomposers break down food, they produce highly toxic chemicals that can cause food poisoning.

Figure 1.24 Vultures and other scavengers get their nutrients by consuming the remains of dead animals.

Figure 1.25 Worms are another specialized group of consumers, known as detrivores.

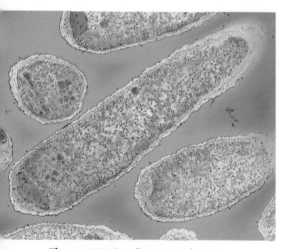
Figure 1.26 *E. coli 0157:H7* bacteria

Essential to All Ecosystems

Detrivores and decomposers are more than just nature's "clean-up crew." Their actions mean that plants always have a supply of nutrients available to them. In fact, detrivores and decomposers connect the biotic elements of ecosystems to the abiotic elements.

Food Chains

The feeding interaction between producers and consumers can be shown visually as a food chain (see Figure 1.27). A food chain always begins with a producer. Then an arrow points to a consumer that eats the producer. In most cases, there is another consumer to eat the first one. These feeding interactions are a key part of all ecosystems.

(a)

(b)

Take It *Further*

Whales are the top consumers in some ocean food chains. Find out about the food chains that support these large mammals in and around Antarctica. Begin your research at PearsonScience.

Figure 1.27 In the meadow food chain shown, an oak tree produces acorns, which are food for the squirrel. The squirrel is food for the fox. In the aquatic food chain shown, the algae use the Sun to produce food. The consumers are the insect larva and the fish.

Food Chains and You

You and the food you eat are part of many different food chains.

Purpose

To identify the food chains that brought you your lunch

Materials & Equipment

- paper
- pencils

Procedure

1. Consider all the different parts of the meal you ate at lunch today or yesterday. For example, perhaps you had a piece of pizza, apple juice for a drink, a piece of cheese, or a doughnut. List them all on a single piece of paper. Leave lots of room around each one, and draw a box around it.

2. For those foods that have separate ingredients, write the ingredients that you know of around the entry. For example, pizza may have tomato sauce, flour in the crust, mushrooms on top. Link each of these ingredients to the word "pizza" with arrows. Continue until you have listed the main ingredients in your lunch.

3. Now add the source of the main ingredients you have listed, and link it to the ingredient. Was the source a producer or a consumer? If it was a consumer, add its food source. For example, if you had cheese on your pizza, it comes from milk, which comes from a cow. A cow feeds on grass. Link each of these items in a food chain that leads to your lunch item.

4. Repeat the process until you have identified the producer at the beginning of each food chain.

5. When you have completed the food chains for the meal you chose, look for any patterns in the lines and arrows.

Questions

6. Where do all the food chains that fed you begin?

7. How many producers and consumers are involved in the meal you chose?

Figure 1.28

Ecosystem in a Jar, Part 1

Question

What living and non-living things can you put into a sealed container to make a healthy ecosystem?

Materials & Equipment

- glass jar or clear container with lid
- clean gravel or small rocks
- pond water
- distilled water or tap water that has sat for 24 h
- small aquatic organisms such as pond snails
- aquatic plants such as duckweed or *Elodea*
- duct tape

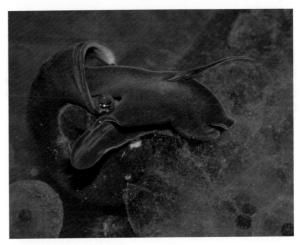

Figure 1.29 Pond snail

Procedure

1. Look at the things your teacher has brought in as possible items to go into the ecosystem jar. With your group, determine the following:
   (a) which things are living
   (b) which things are non-living

2. In your group, identify which living things and which non-living things should be placed in the sealed jar.

3. Before creating your ecosystem, identify any precautions you should take when preparing your materials. For example, should the jar be cleaned with soap or just rinsed with water?

4. Organize your group to make sure that everyone has a role in preparing the sealed-jar ecosystem.

5. Assemble your ecosystem and seal it. Store it in a place where it can be observed easily.

6. Make a sketch or take a photograph of your sealed ecosystem to record its appearance at the beginning of this activity.

Analyzing and Interpreting

7. Discuss with your group the biotic and abiotic elements of your ecosystem and how you think they will interact over the next three weeks. Record these ideas and prepare a drawing of what you think the jar will look like after three weeks.

8. Create a chart that will allow you to record any changes you observe in the sealed-jar ecosystem over the next three weeks. Include a section in your chart to describe any observations of the types of interactions that can occur in an ecosystem.

Skill Builder

9. How does what you already know about ecosystems help you make reasonable predictions?

Forming Conclusions

10. For any changes you observe in the ecosystem, suggest reasons that might explain what is happening.

Key Concept Review

1. What is the main difference between a producer and a consumer? Give an example to support your answer.

2. Explain what you think happens to a food chain when one part of it is removed or eliminated.

3. Every fall many people put leaves that have fallen from local trees on their gardens. By the following summer, many of these leaves seem to have disappeared. What happened to them?

Connect Your Understanding

4. Describe what you think would happen to an ecosystem if it did not have any decomposers.

5. Explain how a vulture consuming the remains of a dead raccoon on the side of a highway is helping an ecosystem.

6. Many people have fish in an aquarium. Discuss with a classmate how an aquarium is not a real ecosystem. Be sure to identify what parts of an ecosystem are missing. Would it be possible to design and build an aquarium as an ecosystem? Explain your answer.

Practise Your Skills

7. Choose an ecosystem near your school. Draw a diagram to show two different food chains that can be found in that ecosystem.

For more questions, go to PearsonScience.

A17   *Thinking about Science and the Environment*

Mapping Consequences

Connections among biotic and abiotic elements in ecosystems ensure that no change happens in isolation. The possible consequences of a change can be charted in a consequences map, which is similar to a mind map. Instead of connecting ideas, the graphic connects possible consequences.

Use a consequences map to show what could happen if there was no rain in a meadow ecosystem. What do you think would happen to the biotic and abiotic elements?

What to Do

1. Make a list of biotic and abiotic elements that could be found in a meadow.

2. Draw possible food chains based on your list.

3. List roles that producers and consumers play in an ecosystem.

Consider This

5. What do you think would happen to the biotic elements in the meadow after a dry summer? In a box on the left hand side of your page, write "dry summer." Map out the consequences on your page.

The Wainfleet Bog

The Wainfleet Bog began to form thousands of years ago in an expanse of open water that could not drain into nearby Lake Erie. As plants died, organic material built up in stagnant water that had little oxygen to support the tiny organisms needed for decomposition. Instead, peat formed and the water became highly acidic.

As towns grew up around the bog in the last 200 years, farms and roads were built, and people removed peat for use as fuel and fertilizer. Water became less acidic, and different plants began to grow. These changes altered the original bog ecosystem and reduced populations of native plants and animals.

Saving the Bog

The types of plants that can survive in this ecosystem cannot live anywhere else. Local conservation and nature clubs, universities, and different levels of government co-operated to re-establish the bog ecosystem. Non-native trees were cut down and replaced with plantings suited to the bog conditions. Canals draining the bog were blocked to restore water levels, and shallow holes were dug in open areas to keep water in the bog.

Figure 1.30 Local residents joined in the effort to save the bog.

Maintaining the Bog

The Niagara Peninsula Conservation Authority monitors the water levels and changes in plant communities and animal populations to learn more about a healthy bog ecosystem. Groundwater levels are now more consistent, the native plants are thriving, and peat is once again accumulating. Populations of birds and wildlife suited to the bog ecosystem have increased.

People living around the bog continue to keep some of their land as supportive habitat. It took the efforts of many different groups of people to preserve this unique ecosystem in southern Ontario.

Questions

1. What ecosystems are preserved in the conservation area closest to your community?

2. Should unique ecosystems be preserved? Explain your reasoning.

3. The people in the community around the Wainfleet Bog worked together to save it. Describe an environmental project in your community that you could become involved in.

Figure 1.31 The rich, acidic soil of the bog supports a variety of mosses and plants.

Key Concept Review

1. What is an example of an ecosystem in your area? What are the abiotic and biotic elements that make up that ecosystem? How do they interact? ⓚ ⓐ

2. Explain how the following organisms meet their basic needs for living: (a) snake (b) cardinal (c) white pine tree (d) mushroom. ⓚ ⓒ

3. Give examples of two different types of interactions that can occur in an ecosystem. Explain why these interactions are important. ⓚ

4. Why are producers essential to all ecosystems? What would happen if there were no producers? ⓚ ⓣ

Connect Your Understanding

5. Use the photo of the meadow below to answer the following questions.

   (a) Draw three food chains that you would find in the meadow. Identify the different elements in the food chains.

   (b) What would happen to the food chains if:

   (i) A toxin was released into the local water supply, and the mice in the meadow died.

   (ii) There was an increase in the hawk population. ⓚ ⓐ

After Reading — Thinking Literacy

Reflect and Evaluate

When readers understand that text features occur in predictable patterns, they can use the features to guide their comprehension. This lets them spend more time thinking about the content of what they are reading. At the beginning of this chapter, you looked at colour and the size and shape of the type. What other text features have you noticed in this chapter? How can previewing text features help you read other types of print and electronic text?

ACHIEVEMENT CHART CATEGORIES
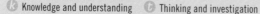 ⓚ Knowledge and understanding   ⓣ Thinking and investigation   ⓒ Communication   ⓐ Application

6. A forest is a habitat for many different living things. What happens to these different living things if the forest is harvested? 🕼🅒

7. Earth's climate has changed in the past few decades. Northern areas are becoming warmer. Other parts of the world are experiencing serious droughts and storms. What effect do you think these changes will have on the ability of living things, including humans, to feed themselves? 🅣🅐

Practise Your Skills

8. If you set up a model ecosystem, how would knowing the following information help you decide what to put in it?

(a) basic needs of living things

(b) biotic and abiotic elements of ecosystems

(c) interactions between different elements in ecosystems
🅣🅒

Unit Task Link

Humans, like all biotic elements, interact with other biotic and abiotic elements in order to survive. In your science notebook, start a list of your own interactions with the biotic and abiotic elements around you. Which ones are necessary to keep you alive? Which ones are not?

A18 *Thinking about Science and the Environment*

Zoos and Ecosystems

A visit to a zoo gives you a chance to see animals from around the world. However, some people believe that zoos are not good for the animals.

Zoos do more than take care of and display animals. They are also part of conservation projects and are preserving and breeding animals whose populations are threatened.

Critics of zoos think that conservation efforts and protecting ecosystems where the animals actually live would be a better solution than keeping animals in captivity. Do you think zoos have a role in conserving and protecting animals?

What to Do

1. Do some research to find out what types of conservation efforts zoos are involved in.

2. Research some of the concerns people have about keeping animals in zoos.

Consider This

With a classmate or as a whole class, discuss the following questions.

3. What are some of the advantages of having animals in zoos?

4. What are some of the disadvantages of having animals in zoos?

5. What future activities do you think zoos should be involved in?

All ecosystems feature biotic and abiotic interactions, the transfer of energy and the cycling of matter.

What You Will Learn

In this chapter, you will:

- describe the transfer of energy in ecosystems
- describe the cycling of matter in ecosystems
- explain how changes in ecosystems affect sustainability and the balance of interactions

Skills You Will Use

In this chapter, you will:

- investigate occurrences that affect the balance within a local ecosystem
- use appropriate science and technology vocabulary in oral and written communication

Why This Is Important

Studying the transfer of energy and the cycling of matter can help you understand ecosystems. You can then determine how your actions might affect both the biotic and abiotic elements in the ecosystems around you.

Before Reading

Thinking Literacy

Predict-Read-Verify

Making predictions about what you think a chapter will be about helps you stay focussed as you read. Before you start reading this chapter, scan each section (2.1, 2.2, 2.3). Look for information that is presented visually in photographs, diagrams, charts, and maps. Read their captions. List two or three main ideas for each section. After you study each section in class, revisit these main ideas to confirm or modify them as needed.

Key Terms

- energy pyramid
- organic matter
- limiting factors
- food web
- cycling of matter
- sustainability

Figure 2.1 Ecosystems need rainfall as well as sunlight in order to support biotic elements.

Water is one of the basic needs of all living things. Earth's water has been moving through the water cycle for thousands of years. The same water has been a liquid in the ground or in rivers, lakes, or oceans. It has evaporated and been a gas in the form of vapour. It may have become tiny droplets in clouds or fog. The moisture has circulated in the atmosphere around Earth and come back down as rain or snow.

The water may stay deep in the ground for decades or be frozen in a glacier for centuries before it is cycled back into the atmosphere as a gas and returned to Earth again. The water that comes down

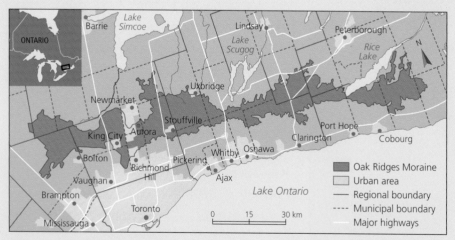

Figure 2.2 The Oak Ridges Moraine lies just north of Lake Ontario.

on you as rain or snow has fallen to Earth before, in another time and another place.

If you live in southern Ontario, the water you drink may flow through the Oak Ridges Moraine. The moraine, shown in Figure 2.2, was formed over 13 000 years ago from the sand and gravel left behind by melting glaciers. It filters and distributes the water that flows in the many rivers and streams that supply water to ecosystems in wetlands, creeks, marshes, ponds, meadows, forests, and human communities.

As human populations grow, their communities need more land. This expansion by humans affects the ecosystems around them, including how water recycles through the land. This could affect the water supplies of many Ontario towns and cities. An understanding of cycling in ecosystems helps in making important decisions about human activities.

A19 Quick Lab

Recycling Paper

Recycling programs started in the 1980s to reduce the amount of waste going into landfills. The goal is to re-use some of the resources used to make tin, aluminum, paper, and glass products. Re-using these materials means reducing waste and saving the resources. Paper is something that can be recycled and re-used fairly easily in order to save trees.

Purpose

To identify ways schools can use paper more wisely

Materials & Equipment
■ paper and pencil

Procedure

1. With a partner, estimate how many sheets of paper each of you throws away in one week. Compare your estimates with those of two other pairs of classmates.

2. Use your estimate to calculate the amount of paper used and thrown out by your whole class in one week

3. Use this figure to estimate the amount of paper thrown out by your school in one month.

4. With your partner, make a list of ways the school could reduce its use of paper.

Questions

5. What happens to the paper that is thrown out at school? By the community?

6. Could reducing the amount of paper used be as important as recycling the paper that is used? Explain your reasoning.

Here is a summary of what you will learn in this section:

- Food chains show how energy is transferred in an ecosystem.
- At each step in a food chain, less energy is available to the next consumer.
- A group of interconnected food chains is called a food web.

Figure 2.3 When a predator like this raccoon eats its prey, it is getting the energy it needs to survive. A food chain represents the transfer of energy from the prey to the predator (consumer).

Some of the light and heat that flows from the Sun is absorbed by producers. Through photosynthesis, the producers change that energy into sugars that they use for food. Herbivores and omnivores then eat some of the producers. These consumers can convert the sugar in the producers to energy they can use.

Food chains are a way to show how energy and matter flow from one biotic element to another. The energy transfer in an ecosystem always begins with the Sun and producers. It then continues through a series of consumers in a food chain (Figure 2.3).

A20 *Starting Point*   Skills

Representing Food Chains

Illustrating food chains in different ways helps you understand the interactions among producers, consumers, and decomposers. Your teacher will give you a worksheet that identifies the following components of an ecosystem:

carnivores   omnivores
decomposers   scavengers
herbivores   Sun
producers

Use the worksheet to complete the following steps.

1. Write the definition for each term in the space provided.

2. Using scissors, carefully cut out each component.

3. Arrange all the components in a way that illustrates your understanding of a food chain. Remember you must use all the components in your diagram.

4. Glue each of the components to a sheet of paper and add any labels or illustrations you think would better illustrate your thinking.

5. Describe any patterns or shapes that you observe.

6. Share your findings with your class.

Energy Transfer

Food chains show how energy travels through an ecosystem on a one-way path. Energy goes from the Sun to producers to herbivores and omnivores and then to carnivores and omnivores. At each level of a food chain, some of the energy is used for living, a lot is given off as heat, and some is stored. It is only the stored energy that is available to the next level. Ecologists estimate that about 10 percent of the energy taken in by a food source is available to the organism that consumes it.

Primary consumers eat producers. Both herbivores and omnivores are primary consumers. They are the first level of consumers in a food chain. Carnivores and omnivores that eat primary consumers are **secondary consumers**. They are the second level of consumers. Secondary consumers may be eaten by other carnivores or omnivores, called **tertiary consumers**. They are the third level. As a food chain gets longer, less and less of the Sun's energy is transferred from one biotic element to the next.

Energy Pyramids

Figure 2.4 is a type of graphic representing an energy pyramid. An **energy pyramid** shows the amount of energy transferred in a food chain. There are fewer organisms at each level as you move up the pyramid. This occurs because only about 10 percent of the energy consumed at one level is transferred to the next level. Less energy means fewer organisms, which is why this type of graphic is called an energy pyramid.

Figure 2.4 In this energy pyramid, 6 000 000 producers have 1000 units of energy. These producers can support only about 700 000 primary consumers. There are fewer primary consumers because they can obtain only 100 units of energy by consuming the producers.

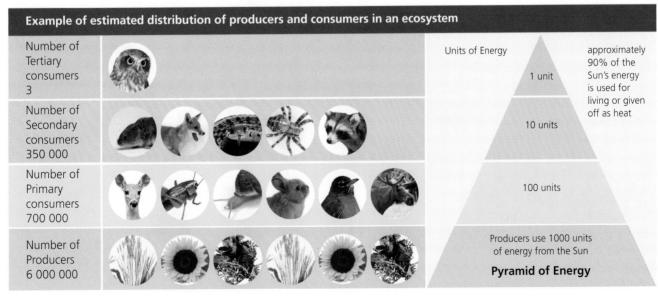

Example of estimated distribution of producers and consumers in an ecosystem

		Units of Energy	
Number of Tertiary consumers 3		1 unit	approximately 90% of the Sun's energy is used for living or given off as heat
Number of Secondary consumers 350 000		10 units	
Number of Primary consumers 700 000		100 units	
Number of Producers 6 000 000		Producers use 1000 units of energy from the Sun **Pyramid of Energy**	

Reading like a Writer

Sometimes writers help their readers understand complex ideas and concepts by presenting some information graphically as photographs, charts, diagrams, or maps. Graphics usually have text such as labels and captions. Information displayed in this way is more concise because graphics can say a lot in a small space. How do the chart on page 39 and the diagram on this page help you understand energy transfer and food webs better?

Food Webs

An ecosystem contains a number of different food chains. A single food source can be a part of many of the food chains that are interconnected. For example, many different herbivores, such as rabbits, squirrels, and mice, eat the grass or seeds in a meadow. Carnivores such as owls prey on the mice and other herbivores. Some omnivores, such as the red fox, might also think of mice as a tasty meal.

A **food web** shows interconnected food chains. A food web is more complex than a food chain. It is also a more accurate way of showing how energy is transferred in feeding interactions in an ecosystem. Figure 2.5 shows a model of a food web in a meadow.

Take It Further

The Grand Banks off the coast of Newfoundland have been home to a rich and diverse ecosystem. Find out more about the food webs that have existed for centuries. Begin your research at PearsonScience.

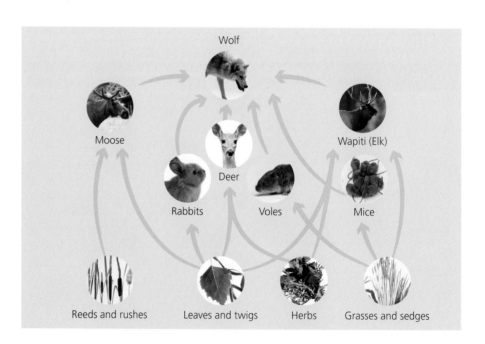

Figure 2.5 In a meadow, energy flows from the Sun to different producers. The producers turn the energy into sugars. The energy is then transferred to a variety of consumers through feeding interactions.

Pass It On

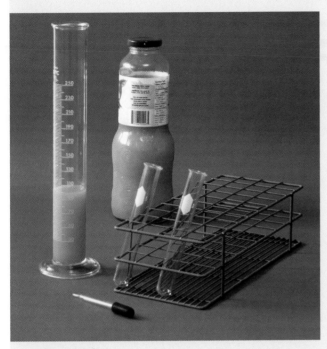

Figure 2.6

Purpose

To demonstrate how energy is transferred through a food chain

---

Materials & Equipment

- 1 L container of fruit juice
- 250 mL graduated cylinder
- 2 test tubes
- medicine dropper

Procedure

1. Have a student hold the graduated cylinder. Pour 100 mL of the juice from the 1 L container into the graduated cylinder. Put the remaining 900 mL of juice still in the container to the side.

2. Have a second student hold a test tube. Pour 10 mL of juice from the graduated cylinder into the first test tube.

3. Have a third student hold the other test tube. Use the medicine dropper to remove 1 mL of juice from the first test tube and drop it into the second test tube.

Questions

4. The 1 L of juice represents 1000 units of energy from the Sun. What did the 100 mL of juice in the graduated cylinder represent?

5. How does the amount of juice in the two test tubes represent energy moving through the next two levels of the food chain?

6. What does the energy (juice) that is not passed on to the next level of consumer represent?

7. About how much of the original energy from the Sun did the final consumer get?

Figure 2.7 This demonstration shows how much energy is transferred from producers to consumers in a food chain like the one shown here.

Key Concept Review

1. How is the Sun's energy passed along in an ecosystem?

2. Why is a food web a more accurate representation of feeding interactions in an ecosystem than a food chain is?

3. There is less energy available to consumers at higher levels in a food chain. Why?

Connect Your Understanding

4. How are food webs on land and in the water similar? How are they different?

5. Draw a diagram to show how the Sun's energy is transferred in a food chain that ends with a chicken sandwich and you.

Practise Your Skills

6. A freshwater lake has hundreds of plants along its shore. They provide habitat and food for animals and insects. The insects are eaten by dragonflies and fish. The dragonflies and fish are consumed by heron. Draw an energy pyramid of this lake ecosystem.

For more questions, go to PearsonScience.

A23 *Thinking about Science and the Environment*

Holes in the Food Web

An endangered species has a population so small that the species is struggling to meet basic needs and reproduce. This may be due to disease, change in climate, destruction of habitat, or loss of a main food source. A species is described as endangered when it is likely to disappear from all ecosystems.

The Committee on the Status of Endangered Wildlife in Canada reports that the barn owl and the American chestnut tree are two endangered species in Ontario. Suitable habitat and food sources for barn owls are disappearing. The American chestnut has been almost wiped out by disease.

Consider This

With a classmate or as a whole class, discuss the following questions.

1. What happens to a food web when one or more of its organisms disappear? Study the meadow food web in Figure 2.5 on page 40. Trace what will happen when one organism disappears. How many organisms are affected? What if two organisms disappear?

2. Compare what would happen to a food web if two producers disappear to what would happen if two tertiary level consumers disappear. Predict the effect on the food web.

Here is a summary of what you will learn in this section:

- Decomposers break down organic matter in order to recycle basic elements.
- Carbon, nitrogen, and phosphorus atoms are basic elements of matter that are cycled in ecosystems.
- Cycling interactions are part of the constant change in ecosystems.

When you clean out your locker and find a very old sandwich under your science notebook, you will likely find decomposers at work. They are busy breaking down the organic matter of your sandwich into abiotic elements. **Organic matter** is made up of, or comes from, organisms. ("Organism" is another word for a biotic element.)

You may find decomposers in action in containers in the back of your refrigerator, in the composter in your yard, or in any natural environment. The decomposers are breaking organic matter down into abiotic elements that can be reabsorbed by biotic elements. This over-and-over-again movement of matter from abiotic elements into biotic elements and back to abiotic elements is called a **cycle**. Decomposers are the engines of Earth's recycling program for nutrients.

Figure 2.8 Many communities have green bin programs for the disposal of organic matter.

A24 *Starting Point*  Skills

Organic Wastes and You

In nature, organic wastes are broken down for recycling by decomposers. What happens to the organic wastes you produce — apple cores, potato peelings, and other food materials? These things used to be thrown out with the garbage that went to landfills. Recently communities have started programs to keep this organic matter out of the landfills and create compost that returns minerals and nutrients to the soil more quickly (Figure 2.8).

1. What is organic waste?

2. Research a community that recycles organic waste. What are citizens asked to do with their organic garbage?

3. List the benefits of a community organic waste disposal program.

4. Find out how your school recycles organic waste.

Cycling Organic Matter

Water is an abiotic element that moves through a cycle in ecosystems. Other abiotic elements also flow in cycles. These include carbon, oxygen, hydrogen, nitrogen, and phosphorus. Carbon is in carbon dioxide in the air, and oxygen and hydrogen are in the air and water. Nitrogen is in the air and in soil. Phosphorus is in soil.

The **cycling of matter** is a series of steps in a cycle that allows abiotic elements to be used over and over again. These abiotic elements are absorbed and used by producers to form organic matter. Consumers then absorb the organic matter through feeding interactions and use it for growth. As they grow, they produce organic waste. Decomposers break down the organic waste from living or dead organisms into abiotic elements that producers can use again (Figure 2.9).

The cycling of matter makes sure that there will be a constant supply of abiotic elements available for interactions in ecosystems.

Figure 2.9 Decomposers will slowly reduce these carrots to mush that can be stirred back into the soil. The carrots will be broken down into nutrients to be reabsorbed by other organisms.

A25 Learning Checkpoint

Going in Circles

1. When a bear leaves the remains of a salmon carcass in the forest, decomposers break it down into abiotic elements, including carbon and nitrogen and other nutrients. Describe how these different abiotic elements from the dead salmon are then reintroduced into an ecosystem.

2. Describe the difference between the way energy moves through ecosystems and the way abiotic elements such as carbon and nitrogen move through ecosystems.

Figure 2.10 The parts of the salmon that the bear did not eat will be broken down into abiotic elements and used again in the ecosystem.

Changes Resulting from the Cycling of Matter

As energy is transferred and matter is cycled, ecosystems are changed in very small ways. When you look at an ecosystem, it may not appear to change from one hour or day to the next. Over time, however, you will notice changes. From one season to the next or one year to the next, plants grow, perhaps shed leaves, or die. Animals build nests, reproduce, and then abandon their nests. Seeds sprout. Insects, birds, and animals die. Organic matter piles up. These changes are the result of the normal process of cycling matter.

The cycling of matter is continuous, in the same way that the transfer of energy is continuous. Small changes to the ecosystem are also continuous. Only by visiting an undisturbed ecosystem over a number of years will you see the results of all of the tiny changes taking place there (Figure 2.11).

Take It Further

A variety of abiotic elements move in cycles through ecosystems. These include carbon, nitrogen, and phosphorus. Choose one and find out why the way it cycles is important in ecosystems. Begin your research at PearsonScience.

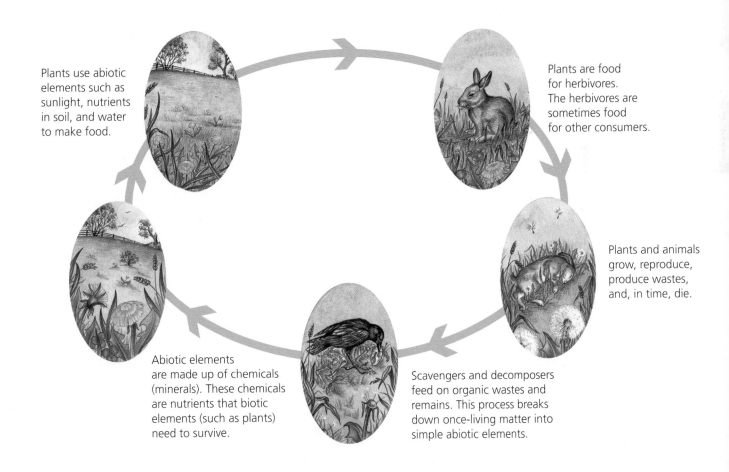

Plants use abiotic elements such as sunlight, nutrients in soil, and water to make food.

Plants are food for herbivores. The herbivores are sometimes food for other consumers.

Plants and animals grow, reproduce, produce wastes, and, in time, die.

Scavengers and decomposers feed on organic wastes and remains. This process breaks down once-living matter into simple abiotic elements.

Abiotic elements are made up of chemicals (minerals). These chemicals are nutrients that biotic elements (such as plants) need to survive.

Figure 2.11 The cycling of matter

A26 *Problem-Solving Activity*

Toolkit 3

SKILLS YOU WILL USE
- Identifying a problem
- Designing, building, and testing

Redesign a Package

Recognize a Need

Most goods sold in Canada must be shipped long distances. The goods must arrive in perfect condition and often require a lot of label information. Most packaging ends up as waste in landfills or ecosystems. If it is not made of organic matter, decomposers cannot break it down.

Figure 2.12

Problem

How can you make a secure package that can be broken down by decomposers?

Materials & Equipment

- a plastic vase of flowers with water, or
- a pyramid of marbles, or
- 4 hard-boiled eggs (not in carton)
- packaging materials of your choice

Criteria for Success

The model addresses the following issues:

- the package can be broken down by decomposers
- goods are not damaged in transit
- labelling requirements (required customer information) are met
- the package is appealing to customers

Brainstorm Ideas

1. Research the packaging for any one of the items listed. Answer the following questions: How is the item protected? How is it transported? How is it sold? What happens to the packaging?

2. What is the impact of the packaging on the environment? Can decomposers break it down? How long will it take?

3. What packaging alternatives would be better for the environment?

Build a Model

4. Create a package that meets the criteria for success but at the same time reduces the amount of packaging that would end up as waste.

Test and Evaluate

5. Using your new package, transport your item along the hall and up or down the stairs to another floor at the other end of the school using a custodian's two-wheeled device to transport it. Did your package meet the criteria for success?

6. Share and compare your ideas and findings with your classmates' plans and findings. Did anyone have ideas exactly like yours? Similar to yours? Completely different from yours? How do your results compare with theirs?

Communicate

7. Prepare a poster, computer slide show presentation, or a packaging "fair" to display alternatives. Or present your findings to the class in a form suggested by your teacher.

Key Concept Review

1. What is organic matter?

2. Describe the cycling of matter. Give an example.

3. How can humans help with the cycling of basic nutrients in ecosystems?

4. Would you expect an ecosystem that had not been disturbed for 20 years to remain the same? Explain why or why not.

5. What kinds of changes would you expect to see in an ecosystem over time?

6. "Earth's ecosystems recycle." Is this statement true or false? Explain your reasoning.

Connect Your Understanding

7. What do you think would eventually happen in an ecosystem if there were no decomposers?

8. Why is the movement of basic elements in ecosystems different from the transfer of energy?

Practise Your Skills

9. Design a test for a package of yogurt. Define your criteria for a successful package. Include in your criteria that it can be broken down by decomposers. List the tasks the test would include.

For more questions, go to PearsonScience.

A27 Thinking about Science and the Environment

Chemicals in Food Chains

In 1938, a Swiss scientist discovered that a chemical called DDT could kill insects that destroyed crops and caused diseases such as malaria. For years, DDT was used around the world to kill millions of insects.

Decomposers broke down the dead insects and other organic matter treated with DDT. However, DDT itself was not broken down. Instead, it stayed in the organic matter and became part of local food chains. DDT in organic matter, on the soils, and in the water was absorbed or consumed by every organism in the areas where it was used.

Birds and other consumers ate plants, seeds, and insects that had been sprayed. DDT was stored in their bodies and passed on to the next level of consumers.

As DDT became part of food chains, the populations of many organisms decreased. The DDT they consumed either killed them or damaged them enough to make it difficult for them to reproduce. DDT was banned in North America in the 1980s, but it is still used in countries with a malaria problem.

Consider This

1. Communities where malaria is still a problem face a difficult choice. What factors should they consider when deciding whether to use DDT or not? What would you suggest?

2. Weed and insect killers are other popular chemical compounds. What benefits do they bring? What problems do they cause?

Here is a summary of what you will learn in this section:

- The supply of resources in ecosystems is limited.
- A big change in the supply of resources will disrupt the interactions in an ecosystem.
- A sudden change in resources can threaten the survival of biotic elements in an ecosystem.

Figure 2.13 When a consumer like the lamprey enters an ecosystem, there may be no predators to consume it. Its population can grow rapidly and wipe out other species.

In the Great Lakes and all other ecosystems, the size of the populations of biotic elements is controlled by factors such as available food, predators, climate, and suitable habitat. These factors control or limit the number and health of biotic elements in ecosystems. They are called **limiting factors.**

Ontario's Great Lakes provide a rich habitat for many different species of fish. For years, these fish were a source of food for reptiles, birds, mammals, and people living on and around the lakes. This changed suddenly in the 1960s, when the lamprey, a type of jawless fish, was introduced into the Great Lakes food web via the St. Lawrence Seaway (Figure 2.13).

In the Great Lakes, there was no predator to consume the lamprey. The lamprey had an abundant supply of salmon and lake trout to consume. While the lamprey population increased, the supply of lake trout decreased by almost 90 percent.

A28 *Starting Point*

Skills **I** **C**

Limiting Factors

In the example of the lamprey above, there were no predators, which would normally be a limiting factor. Without this limiting factor, the lamprey population grew out of control. The food web of the Great Lakes changed in many ways after the introduction of the lamprey.

1. Work with a partner and try to predict when the lamprey population would stop growing.

2. What do you think happened to the fish populations the lake trout used to eat?

Why Ecosystems Change

The flow of energy and the cycling of matter are factors that affect the interactions of producers, consumers, and decomposers in ecosystems. The health and size of populations of producers and consumers are directly related to the amount of oxygen, water, food, energy, and suitable habitat available to meet their basic needs. The populations of biotic elements in an ecosystem adjust or regulate themselves so that the supply of these factors matches the needs within the ecosystem.

An ecosystem is constantly affected by a variety of factors that can cause it to change. For example, a lack of rainfall may cause the number of producers to decrease (Figure 2.14). As a result, the populations of consumers in the food web will also decrease. Or if the number of producers increases because of higher rainfall, the populations of consumers may increase. The populations of biotic elements are limited by the supply of abiotic and other biotic elements available to meet their basic needs.

Change is always happening in ecosystems. Ecosystems change because matter is always being cycled. They change because living things grow and die. Ecosystems may change because the supply of biotic or abiotic elements has changed for a short time. Or they may change because the supply of a biotic or abiotic element has changed permanently. Change in ecosystems can also be caused by an event such as bioinvasion or a change in competition for resources.

Bioinvasion

Many of the plants and animals that you may think are common to Canada actually have come from somewhere else. European settlers introduced plants and animals from their home countries. Some well-meaning naturalists introduced foreign species, while other species were introduced accidentally.

Scientists use the term **bioinvasion** to describe the introduction of foreign species into native ecosystems. Many of these new species were stronger than the native species or, like the lamprey, had no natural enemies. They quickly multiplied. Their effects on ecosystems and on other living things have been dramatic.

Figure 2.14 A long-term change in abiotic elements, such as a lack of rainfall, can kill the biotic elements in an ecosystem.

Figure 2.15 The roots of the purple loosestrife plant are so dense that other plants in the area cannot survive.

Figure 2.16 Zebra mussels had no natural predators in the Great Lakes and found habitat that allowed their populations to grow quickly. They clog intake pipes in water treatment facilities and damage the machinery.

The first wild plants of purple loosestrife in North America probably escaped from people's gardens (Figure 2.15). The plants originally came from Europe. The plant has spread so quickly that it has pushed native species out of the ecosystem. This is especially true in wetland and marshy areas.

Zebra mussels were first noticed in the Great Lakes in 1988. By 1994, there were as many as 50 000 mussels/m^2 in some rivers near the Great Lakes (Figure 2.16). They have pushed native mussels out of their spot in the food web and taken over their habitat.

Competition

Changes also occur in the populations of species in ecosystems because of their interactions with other biotic and abiotic factors. One of these interactions is competition.

You probably have been involved in some type of competition. Whether it is running a race or designing a school logo, a human competition involves more than one person trying to reach the same goal. All living things compete with all other living things in their community. They compete for resources like food, water, and habitat. However, the supply of these resources is limited. This means living things are always struggling to get enough of these resources to meet their needs at the expense of other living things.

A29 *During Reading*

Thinking Literacy

Visualizing

Good readers often create pictures in their minds to help them understand what they are reading. What pictures came to your mind as you read about each of the following terms?

- producers

- consumers

- decomposers

- interaction

- energy transfer

- cycling of matter

- competition

- bioinvasion

Draw a summary of this section using these pictures. Create a poster, a computer graphic, or any graphic you wish to link your pictures and to summarize the key points in this section about change in ecosystems. Label your drawings.

Sustainability

An ecosystem is described as being sustainable when it can maintain a balance of needs and resources over time. In the past, the small Aboriginal populations used local resources in ways that did not drain the ecosystem of resources needed by other biotic elements. These practices supported **sustainability** — that is, the ecosystem's ability to continue or sustain itself.

Figure 2.17 Modern communities often destroy natural habitat when they expand.

Aboriginal peoples believe that they are part of local ecosystems. Non-Aboriginal peoples do not tend to think of themselves as part of local ecosystems. As these populations grow, their activities, even in areas far away from natural environments, affect the sustainability of ecosystems. Industry has changed the quality of abiotic elements such as air and water. Development has destroyed habitat, and the quantities of waste have overwhelmed the process of cycling organic matter. (Figure 2.17)

Modern Human Impact

Scientists are questioning whether modern lifestyles will harm ecosystems in ways that could destroy them. Scientists are asking:

- What kinds of changes will happen in ecosystems as a result of our modern way of life?

- Will these changes destroy the sustainability of local ecosystems?

- Can human populations survive without ecosystems to supply their basic needs?

In 1987, the United Nations suggested that human activity must not interfere with the ability of ecosystems to sustain themselves. This means that human activity should use technologies and practices that do not do long-term damage to the biotic and abiotic elements that all organisms need.

Take It Further

Cities in Canada and elsewhere are trying to reduce their impact on the environment. Look at what they are doing and list the effects these changed activities could have on the environment. Begin your research at PearsonScience.

Competition in Ecosystems

Figure 2.18 The plants in this meadow compete for resources.

Question

How does competition affect the number of plant populations in an ecosystem?

Design and Conduct Your Investigation

1. Make a hypothesis to test how the populations of three or more species of plants will be affected when they compete with each other in a small area. (A hypothesis is a possible answer to a question or a possible explanation of a situation.)

2. Decide what materials you will need to test your hypothesis. For example, you might consider the following questions:

   (a) How many populations will you experiment with?

   (b) Will you grow the plants from seeds or work with seedlings?

   (c) How many containers will you need?

   (d) How much soil will you need?

3. Plan your procedure. Ask yourself questions such as:

   (a) What evidence am I looking for to support my hypothesis?

   (b) What steps will I follow to collect the data I need?

   (c) Is the test I am designing fair? How do I know?

   (d) How will I record my results? For example, will I need a data chart? A graph? Both? Neither?

   (e) How long will I run my experiment?

   (f) How long do I have to complete my experiment?

4. Write up your procedure. Be sure to show it to your teacher before going any further.

5. Carry out your experiment.

6. Compare your results with your hypothesis. Did your results support it? If not, what possible reasons might there be?

7. Share and compare your experimental plan and findings with your classmates. Did anyone plan an experiment exactly like yours? Similar to yours? Completely different from yours? How do your results compare with theirs?

Ecosystem in a Jar, Part 2

Question

How does knowledge of the transfer of energy and the cycling of matter explain what has happened in the sealed ecosystem?

Materials & Equipment

- sealed ecosystem created in A16 Ecosystem in a Jar, Part 1

- chart of observations made over the past several weeks

- drawing/photo of the sealed ecosystem made when it was set up

- drawing of what you originally thought the sealed ecosystem would look like after several weeks

---

Figure 2.19

Procedure

1. Review the chart of observations made over the past several weeks.

2. List the interactions you think occurred in the sealed ecosystem.

3. Classify the interactions according to whether they related to the transfer of energy or the cycling of matter.

4. Record the roles of the different biotic elements in the sealed ecosystem.

5. Compare your predictions and drawing of the sealed ecosystem with what it looks like now.

Analyzing and Interpreting

6. For any changes you observe in the ecosystem, suggest reasons that might explain what happened.

7. What organisms were able to meet their basic needs in your sealed ecosystem? How do you know? Which ones did not meet their needs? What could have led to these biotic elements not meeting their needs?

Skill Builder

8. How can you organize your data to report the progress of your sealed ecosystem?

Forming Conclusions

9. In what ways did your prediction match the result? In what ways was it different from your expected result?

10. How does the information you have learned since you created your sealed ecosystem explain your results?

11. How was your ecosystem limited in the number of living things it could support?

Key Concept Review

1. Explain in your own words how populations are limited in ecosystems.

2. How can a new species with no natural predator affect the populations of other species in an ecosystem?

3. (a) What effects would a drier-than-average summer have on a pond ecosystem?

   (b) How is this different from the effects resulting from draining the pond?

4. What is sustainability?

5. What factors affect the populations in an ecosystem?

Connect Your Understanding

6. How might the building of a new highway affect the sustainability of the ecosystem it goes through?

7. Some schools work to reduce the use of paper. Some communities have organic waste treatment programs. Are these examples of sustainable approaches to the environment? Explain your thinking.

Practise Your Skills

8. Design a poster or short multimedia presentation to share ideas on the importance of sustainability.

For more questions, go to PearsonScience.

A32 *Thinking about Science and the Environment*

Revisiting Your Consequences Map

In Chapter 1, you used a consequences map to show a possible chain of consequences resulting from an activity. There are many human activities that can have short- and long-term effects on the environment. As people begin to understand the concept of sustainability, they need to look carefully at the environmental consequences of their activities.

Work with a classmate and make a list of different human activities that can affect the interactions among biotic and abiotic elements, the flow of energy, or the cycling of nutrients in ecosystems. Activities could be related to transportation, entertainment, or lifestyle choices.

What to Do

1. Review the list of activities. Which ones have you done in the past two weeks? Choose one, and create a consequences map for the activity. Be sure to identify the possible chain of consequences.

2. Compare the chain of consequences in your map with a classmate's map. In what ways are they similar? How are they different?

Consider This

3. How does a consequences map help you understand how human actions and decisions can affect the sustainability of ecosystems and the environment?

Foresters

Forests are an important part of Canada's economic resources, providing employment for workers and a variety of products. The trees provide oxygen for Earth, habitat for plants and animals, and fuel and shelter for communities.

Figure 2.20 Foresters spend much of their time out in the field.

Foresters manage and supervise Canada's forest resources. They assess the size and type of trees to determine the value of the wood. When assessing the value of a forest, foresters may decide that it is more valuable if it is left as a habitat, and logging companies will look elsewhere for trees to harvest.

Forest Ecosystems

When making these decisions, foresters consider the ability of diverse and healthy ecosystems to survive logging. Foresters also monitor the impact of cutting trees in animal habitats and work to make sure that there is minimal damage when logging companies proceed with their work.

Trees are a renewable resource, and new trees that belong in the local ecosystem are planted after a harvest to restore the forest. Canada's logging industry can only continue if it follows the United Nations' suggestion and does not harm the ability of forest ecosystems to sustain themselves.

Technology and Forestry

Foresters use a variety of tools, including advanced infrared photography, satellite imagery, aerial photographs and even remote sensing to assess and manage forest resources. They use these technologies to keep an inventory of the number and types of trees in different forests, so proper decisions can be made on whether trees should be harvested for lumber, cut down to stop the spread of disease, or preserved for the wildlife in the area.

Professional foresters work for lumber companies, government monitors, or on their own. They play an important role in supporting a Canadian resource industry as well as preserving ecosystems.

Questions

1. What are some of the factors foresters have to consider before making decisions?

2. How does technology help foresters do their jobs?

3. How do you think the idea of sustainability influences the work of foresters?

Figure 2.21 Infrared photographs can show foresters the amount of living and dead vegetation in an area.

Key Concept Review

1. Energy is a basic need for all living things. How do food webs demonstrate how different living things in an ecosystem get the energy they need to survive? **k c**

2. What role do bacteria and other tiny organisms have in making sure that nutrients are always available in ecosystems? **k**

3. Explain how turning a small forest and the meadow around it into a shopping centre affects the environment. **t c**

4. The zebra mussel arrived in the Great Lakes about 20 years ago. Since then, its population has exploded, and it is found in many lakes and rivers. Prepare an oral news report to explain the rapid growth in the population of zebra mussels. Predict what you think may happen in the future. **c t**

5. What types of activities could make a human community more sustainable? **a**

Connect Your Understanding

6. What mechanisms are in place in a stream ecosystem to make sure that the populations of biotic elements are controlled and interactions are balanced? **t a**

7. Is recycling cans, bottles, and paper a practice that promotes sustainability? Explain your reasoning. **a c**

8. Look at the energy pyramid shown below. Do you think it represents an ecosystem that could survive for a long time? Explain your reasoning. **t c**

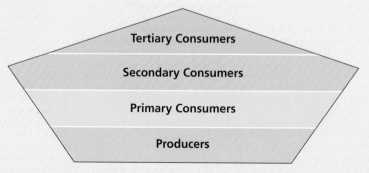

Tertiary Consumers

Secondary Consumers

Primary Consumers

Producers

After Reading *Thinking Literacy*

Reflect and Evaluate

Revisit the preview you did at the beginning of the chapter. Review the main ideas you confirmed or modified as you worked on this chapter. Create a study outline explaining and illustrating each of these main ideas.

ACHIEVEMENT CHART CATEGORIES
k Knowledge and understanding *t* Thinking and investigation *c* Communication *a* Application

Practise Your Skills

9. How could an ecosystem sealed in a jar model a real ecosystem? ⓒ ⓣ

10. Explain why brainstorming a number of options to solve a challenge could improve the final solution. ⓣ ⓒ

11. How can knowing the inquiry process of science help you make decisions in your daily life? ⓐ ⓒ

12. How can establishing criteria for a successful solution help you solve a problem? ⓐ ⓒ

Unit Task Link

The cycling of matter is an important part of all ecosystems. In your science notebook, keep a "trash diary" for a week. Create a table with two columns, Recycled and Not recycled. Classify the things you threw away in one of the two columns.

A33 *Thinking about Science and the Environment*

Impact of Expanding Human Habitats on Other Living Things

When natural ecosystems are undisturbed, the populations of producers, consumers, and decomposers and their interactions tend to be balanced. Through interactions, energy is transferred, and matter and essential nutrients are cycled continuously in habitats on land and in or on water.

Human habitats have made greater and greater use of technology over time. They are likely to feature materials that cannot be cycled quickly. Our demand for energy and other resources is usually more than what is needed to meet basic needs. It is also usually more than we can get from our local area. These resources must be brought in from outside the community.

Our use of technologies has had a big impact on the environment. The expansion of our habitat has often come at the expense of the habitat of other biotic elements.

What to Do

1. Work with a partner and discuss the following statement:

Humans should minimize their impact on the habitat of other organisms when they are planning and building their own habitat.

Do you agree? Why or why not?

Consider This

2. With a classmate or as a whole class, discuss the following questions.

(a) How do human activities affect the interactions and balances in ecosystems?

(b) How does human technology affect the interactions and balances in ecosystems?

(c) How much should humans change their activities so that other habitats and ecosystems can continue to exist? Explain your reasoning.

Modern societies rely on a variety of technologies. Many of these technologies affect ecosystems.

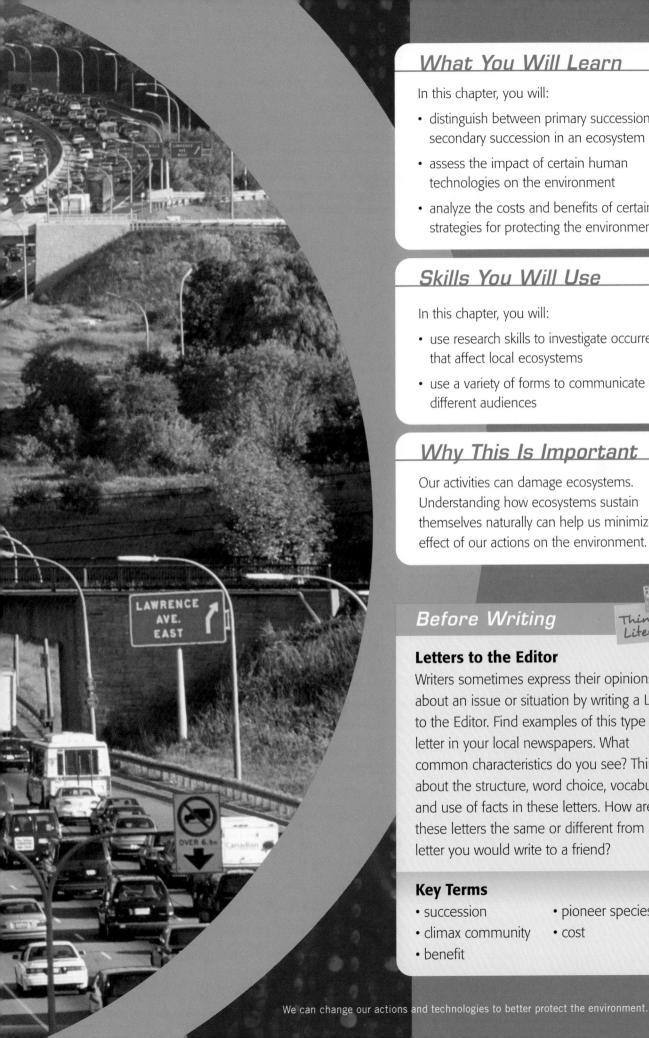

What You Will Learn

In this chapter, you will:

- distinguish between primary succession and secondary succession in an ecosystem
- assess the impact of certain human technologies on the environment
- analyze the costs and benefits of certain strategies for protecting the environment

Skills You Will Use

In this chapter, you will:

- use research skills to investigate occurrences that affect local ecosystems
- use a variety of forms to communicate with different audiences

Why This Is Important

Our activities can damage ecosystems. Understanding how ecosystems sustain themselves naturally can help us minimize the effect of our actions on the environment.

Before Writing

Thinking Literacy

Letters to the Editor
Writers sometimes express their opinions about an issue or situation by writing a Letter to the Editor. Find examples of this type of letter in your local newspapers. What common characteristics do you see? Think about the structure, word choice, vocabulary, and use of facts in these letters. How are these letters the same or different from a letter you would write to a friend?

Key Terms
- succession
- climax community
- benefit
- pioneer species
- cost

Figure 3.1 Forest fires suddenly change the conditions in an ecosystem by destroying plants, animals, and habitat.

In the summer of 2007, an aerial view of the communities of Sandy Lake, Deer Lake, and Keewaywin in northwestern Ontario showed large areas of darkened soil and a variety of shrubs and small bushes. These producers were food for deer, moose, and a number of smaller animals such as squirrels and hares. Eagles soared over the open ground in search of a meal.

Prior to 2006, the aerial view was a very different sight. The area was covered with spruce, pine, and fir trees native to the boreal forest of northern Ontario. The summer of 2006 was very dry, and lightning started forest fires that destroyed thousands of hectares of the boreal forest. Residents of Deer Lake, Sandy Lake, and Keewaywin were evacuated as fire threatened their homes. Animals of the forest fled as their habitat was consumed by flames. As soon as the fire was out, however, a new community of living things began to establish itself.

Ecosystems change constantly, and the interactions between biotic and abiotic elements are balanced over time. Sudden and severe natural events such as a fire or a storm can disrupt these interactions very quickly (Figures 3.1, 3.2). Fires, tornadoes, and landslides destroy habitat, animals, and plants. In the next activity, use your knowledge of how cycling of matter and the transfer of energy work in ecosystems to predict what might happen in a badly damaged ecosystem.

Figure 3.2 The Ice Storm of 1998 destroyed trees and damaged ecosystems.

A34 *Quick Lab*

Dealing With Sudden Natural Events

Purpose

In this activity, you will model how changes in an ecosystem can affect everything in the ecosystem without destroying it.

> ### Materials & Equipment
> - 1 deck of playing cards for every 3-5 students
> - paper, pencil, and markers to record connections

Procedure

1. The different suits in the deck of cards represent the biotic and abiotic components in a meadow ecosystem as follows: spades — water; hearts — air; diamonds — soil; clubs — living things.

2. Place the cards face up on the table and have members of the group take turns choosing one card from each suit. They should place these cards face up in front of their positions.

3. Once all the cards have been selected, students should arrange their cards on their paper to show the connections between the different elements in the ecosystem. They can use a large sheet of paper and a marker to show the connections among the different elements in the ecosystem.

4. Consider the effect of the following events on the ecosystem:

   - a drought reduces the amount of water in the area (remove all spades below 7)

   - a forest fire burns a large part of the meadow (remove all the clubs above 7)

Questions

5. How did the events (the removing of the cards) affect the different connections in the ecosystem? Were there any ecosystems that were wiped out?

6. What other events could affect an ecosystem? Do you think the ecosystem would be able to recover?

3.1 Succession, Recovery, and Renewal in Natural Communities

Here is a summary of what you will learn in this section:

- Ecosystems change in predictable ways known as succession.
- Ecosystems can establish themselves in places where there has never been an ecosystem.
- Ecosystems can recover from catastrophic natural changes.

If people did not cut the grass on their lawns or weed them, the grasses would grow tall and go to seed. They would soon be joined by plants that can outcompete some of the grasses for resources. The newer plants in turn might be replaced by plants that could outcompete *them*.

As the type of plants changed over time, the lawn's animal community would also change. New populations of insects, small animals, and birds would take up residence as suitable habitat became available. After a time, there would be little similarity between the community of biotic elements that used to inhabit the lawn and the community that has moved in.

A35 *Starting Point*

Skills **A** **C**

What happens to a vacant lot?

Figure 3.3

What to Do

With a partner or in a group, study the photograph of plants in a vacant lot in Figure 3.3. Do you think the vacant lot has an ecosystem?

Consider This

1. What do you think is happening in the vacant lot?

2. If the lot is left alone, what do you think it will look like in two years? In five years? Explain your reasoning.

Succession

Succession is the natural replacement of one population of living things by another. The changes take place over a long period of time, and they happen in a predictable way. For example, an untended field of soil will first be inhabited by small plants and insects. Those plants and insects will die, and their nutrients will be added to the soil. The soil will slowly become rich enough to support larger, different plants and the living things that depend on them. In this way, communities are followed, or succeeded, by other communities.

The populations in any succession process will always be suited to the changing habitat. Only organisms that can meet their basic needs will survive. An untended field can become a meadow and, perhaps, later a forest. The plant and animal populations will gradually change as the abiotic conditions change. Any sudden changes to the abiotic elements may have a serious effect on the plants and animals that inhabit the area.

Scientists distinguish between two different types of succession: primary succession and secondary succession.

Primary Succession

Primary succession is the formation of a new ecosystem where no ecosystem has existed. For example, primary succession takes place on newly formed volcanic islands, rocky shores, and sand dunes. The earliest plants to take root must be tough enough to survive in harsh conditions that may not even provide soil for nutrients.

Plants and plant-like species that are part of primary succession are often called **pioneer species.** They could be lichens that can cling to rock surfaces and absorb enough nutrients to survive (Figure 3.4). These tough species are the ones that break down the rock surface and begin the process of forming soil. Pioneer species also include grasses with roots long enough to hold sand dunes in place.

Once tiny amounts of soil appear or sand is anchored, other plants have a place to grow. Their seeds may have been blown to the site by the wind, dropped by a passing bird, or perhaps scraped from the sole of a hiker's boot. The seeds sprout, and a plant sets down roots.

Figure 3.4 Lichen is a pioneer species made up of algae and fungi. It is tough enough to survive in very harsh conditions.

Secondary Succession

Secondary succession occurs when a community has been destroyed or disturbed by natural occurrences or human activities. Secondary succession is different from primary succession because, in secondary succession, these habitats previously supported life. A farmer's field, a vacant lot in the city, a newly forested area, even a strip mine, are examples of where this type of succession occurs. Figure 3.5 shows how untended farmland could change to a meadow, a bush, and then to a forest over 40 years.

Natural communities will change in this way until a fairly stable community forms (Figure 3.5(d)). This community is called a **climax community** and features large plants and animals such as those found in a forest. Climax communities change slowly in small ways over a long period of time. Major changes can occur suddenly because of extreme events, such as fires or storms, or human intervention.

Figure 3.5(a) Year 1 Farm field

Figure 3.5(b) Year 2 Meadow

Figure 3.5(c) Year 10 Bush

Figure 3.5(d) Year 40 A climax community

Change Over Time

Semantic Mapping

After you have read the information on secondary succession, draw a series of boxes in your notebook. Connect the boxes with a series of lines. In each box, write a few words to describe the different stages in a gradual change to a new ecosystem.

Recovery and Renewal

Ecosystems that have suffered catastrophic events such as fires, floods, avalanches or landslides, or even earthquakes can recover. Succession will take place as long as the essential abiotic elements remain to support living things.

An example of the recovery process is the growth of fireweed in a newly burned area (Figure 3.6). This wildflower's seeds travel to open areas on the wind. Fireweed grows best where sunshine is not blocked by tall trees. As the area recovers, bushes and trees will grow taller, and the fireweed will not survive in the shade. However, in the early days, its roots held the soil in place, so those bushes and trees could grow. Decomposers returned nutrients from dead fireweed plants to the soil.

Figure 3.6 Fireweed is one of the first plants to establish itself in an ecosystem after a fire.

Areas that have experienced sudden natural events such as avalanches and landslides, which rearrange the landscape but do not kill all the plants, will also recover as existing plants re-establish themselves. Insects, birds, and animals will return to the habitat to feed and nest.

Catastrophic events caused by human activity may be harder for ecosystems to recover from because they often damage the abiotic elements. For example, human activity may poison the water or the air. After such events, plants will not be able to grow, replenish soil, or support animal life. Instead, the ecosystem may collapse, and nothing will grow on the site for many years.

Take It *Further*

The volcanic island of Surtsey formed off the coast of Iceland in 1963. Find out how scientists have been studying the way abiotic and biotic factors have slowly developed an ecosystem on this island. Begin your research at PearsonScience.

Managing Forests and Forest Fires

Figure 3.7

Issue

Since 1900, Canada's park and forest managers have worked hard to prevent forest fires and quickly extinguish ones that do break out. This policy resulted in a large number of climax communities in the form of mature forests.

In August and September of 2003, a fire in Okanagan Mountain Park in British Columbia burned 25 000 hectares of forest and destroyed 239 homes. 27 000 people were evacuated from the area. This fire, and recent others like it, has led officials to reconsider their policy for managing forest fires. What is the best way to manage and care for the forest ecosystems in Canada's wilderness?

Background Information

- Aboriginal peoples regularly burned areas in the spring. They used fire to create grazing areas and keep travel routes open.

- In areas with cool temperatures, the decomposition process is slow. Decaying wood, leaves, and needles (which are fuel for a fire) accumulate on the forest floor.

- Mature forests are dense, with tall trees that shut out the light. Little else grows in mature forests. This means that there is not much habitat for insects, animals, or birds.

- Grassland ecosystems that burn regularly have a rich supply of young herb and grass plants. They are less likely to be taken over by shrubs and trees.

- Fire quickly turns organic material into ash that is rich in minerals and can be returned to the soil.

- Forests that have burned have openings that allow sunlight to reach the ground. New growth on the forest floor provides habitat for small animals, as well as food in the form of berries and leaves.

- The seeds of trees such as the lodgepole and jack pines are sealed in cones covered with a sticky substance called resin. The cones open to drop the seeds only after fire has melted the coating.

- Lightning has caused fires in forests and grasslands for thousands of years.

- Warmer temperatures and decreased rainfall or snow cover will dry out forests and grasslands and create ideal conditions for fires.

Analyze and Evaluate

1. Use your knowledge of the cycling of matter and succession to explain why fires are a necessary part of healthy forest and grassland ecosystems.

2. If organic matter is piling up on the floor of a mature forest, should a fire be set? Explain your reasoning in an oral report.

Key Concept Review

1. Describe the differences between primary and secondary succession.

2. Write a paragraph to explain to an adult what would happen to a vacant lot in your community if it were left alone for the next 25 years.

3. Make a list of four different events that could change a climax community. For each one, suggest what the area might look like two years after the event.

4. How does your knowledge of ecosystems help you understand the process of succession?

Connect Your Understanding

5. Explain how the following events could be important in the formation of a new community of living things:

   (a) fish-eating birds land on rocky islands

   (b) a coconut is washed up on a beach

   (c) an especially high tide washes seaweed onto a sandy beach

6. In primary succession, do biotic or abiotic elements arrive first? Use examples when explaining your response.

Practise Your Skills

7. Use a series of small diagrams to show how a forest such as the one shown below might recover after a fire. Be sure to include animals in your diagrams.

For more questions, go to PearsonScience.

A38   *Thinking about Science and the Environment*

Declaring War on Weeds

Lawns and grass in neighbourhoods, golf courses, and some public parks require water and fertilizer. They also require care in the form of regular mowing. Many people want a well-kept lawn with no weeds or pests in it. Some people use insecticides to kill unwanted insects and rodents, and herbicides to kill unwanted plants in their lawns. Herbicides are also known as weedkillers. Fertilizer, insecticides, and herbicides often find their way into the soil and local water.

Homeowners also often rake up and take away the grass clippings when they have finished cutting the grass.

Consider This

1. Using what you know about succession, explain why weeds appear.

2. Is it a wise idea to try to keep an ecosystem like a lawn from changing? Explain your reasoning.

Here is a summary of what you will learn in this section:

- Many modern human technologies have affected the quality of air and water for all living things.
- Many human interactions with the environment have affected the habitat of other living things.
- Many of the waste products of human technology cannot be cycled by decomposers.

Human communities benefit from technology. Inventions and human-engineered materials have improved human survival and quality of life. Technology allows us to live comfortably in harsh habitats. It also helps us produce large quantities of food and transport food, goods, and ourselves long distances.

Throughout each day and night, members of human communities consume oxygen, water, and food and produce waste. We use energy for transportation, heating and cooling, and to power businesses and industries. We interact with biotic and abiotic elements for survival, just as other living things do.

When we are developing new technologies to improve our lives, we do not always stop to consider what impact they will have on the other biotic elements in our ecosystem or the abiotic elements in the environment in general.

Figure 3.8 A water pump, whether it is small enough for a family or large enough for a city, is a technology that saves labour and improves the quality of life.

A39 *Starting Point*　　　　　　　　　　Skills Ⓐ Ⓒ

Ecotourism

Untouched ecosystems are becoming rare. One way to maintain them is to close them off and protect them from development and visitors.

Another idea is to show people the complex relationships among the biotic and abiotic elements in these special places by opening them to visitors. Ecotourism is a growing business in areas like Wabakimi Provincial Park near Thunder Bay, where it helps to support the park financially.

These visitors need places to stay and eat, as well as transportation. Roads and buildings must be built. Power sources are required. Opening an unspoiled area to visitors could have some negative costs for the ecosystem.

Consider This

With a partner or in class, debate the following:

Visitors should be kept out of ecosystems that are fragile or unique.

Choose your viewpoint and support your argument.

Assessing Human Impact

While our activities and technologies improve our quality of life, they also affect local ecosystems and Earth's supply of resources. Many of these technologies have damaged ecosystems shared by all. Table 3.1 lists a few of the impacts human activities have on ecosystems.

Table 3.1 Selected Environmental Impacts of Human Activities

Element	Impact
Air	• burning fossil fuels for heating, transportation, and industry pollutes the air
Water	• high water consumption by humans reduces the amount of water available for other organisms • development of human communities can disrupt the flow of water through watersheds • improper or casual disposal of chemicals can damage water quality • chemical spills occasionally poison rivers, lakes, and oceans
Habitat	• destruction of habitats means fewer producers are available to anchor food chains • destruction of habitats removes a basic support to all living things in the ecosystem, possibly leading to extinction of some species

Figure 3.9 New subdivisions of single-family homes are sometimes described as "urban sprawl" because they spread over land formerly occupied by ecosystems.

Figure 3.10 Train accidents like this one often result in poisonous leaks into rivers and lakes.

Housing, Transportation, and Recreation

Outside of Ontario's big cities, communities are building on ecosystems in order to add single-family homes, shopping areas, businesses, and schools (Figure 3.9). These growing communities also need roads so the people who live there can travel to work, get food, and get to other communities. The roads cut through ecosystems, dividing or destroying habitat.

In 2005, it was estimated that Ontario's 8 million vehicles were driven almost 125 billion km. Those trips added carbon dioxide and other pollutants to the air. Shipping goods by train takes cars and trucks off the roads, but accidents can result in chemical and fuel spills that could poison water and soil (Figure 3.10). Ecosystems may take a very long time to recover from the loss of these abiotic elements.

Popular recreational activities such as mountain biking and riding off-road vehicles are other human activities that can cause serious damage to ecosystems (Figure 3.11).

Figure 3.11 Popular outdoor activities with off-road vehicles can tear up the landscape and destroy plants and habitat.

These human activities can damage ecosystems, yet many of these activities are necessary for humans to live. Large farms are needed to provide food. Roads are required to transport food and goods to human consumers. Land is needed for human habitat.

Figure 3.12 Garbage, known as solid waste, is often disposed of in landfill sites.

A growing number of people want to buy organic foods. Find out what organic foods are and why some people may be looking for this type of food. Begin your research at PearsonScience.

Recycling vs. Waste Disposal

Human activities produce large quantities of waste material. You have learned that some waste is organic and can be returned to the soil through organic waste recycling programs. Other waste, such as paper, glass, metal, and some packaging, can be recycled. While these recycling activities remove some materials from the piles of trash, communities in Ontario still produce thousands of tonnes of garbage that must be disposed of. Community garbage is often sent to landfill sites, where the material is buried (Figure 3.12). In 2007, the city of Toronto sent about 441 350 T of solid waste to landfill every day.

Early landfill sites leaked toxic materials and chemicals into the surrounding water and soil, poisoning abiotic elements. Modern landfills are monitored and sealed to prevent toxic leaks from garbage that could include discarded medicines, home and industrial chemicals, and electronic equipment. We need landfill sites to store waste from our activities. No matter how carefully we manage them, landfills cover space once occupied by natural ecosystems.

Taking Out the E-trash

Issue

Modern electronics are very popular. The technologies used in these products are always changing. New features are added. Products get smaller and easier to use, and consumers want to get the newest version. It has been estimated that Canadians throw out 1450 T of cellphones alone in a year. Computers, cameras, game systems, and music players add to the pile.

Electronic products contain plastic and metals such as aluminum, copper, gold, iron, lead, mercury, steel, and zinc. None of these materials can be broken down by decomposers. What should be done with all this waste?

Background Information

1. In order to evaluate the best way to dispose of old electronic products, you need more information. Working in a group of six, each member will choose one of the following options for disposing of unwanted electronics. Not all of the options are available in Canada. Research will need to include options from around the world.

   (a) donating the product to someone else

   (b) sending the product to landfill

   (c) incinerating the product

   (d) recycling in a foreign country

   (e) recycling in Canada for a fee

   (f) requiring the manufacturer to take the old product back

Figure 3.13

2. Use the guidelines below to focus your research. Record the information and sources of your research in notes, charts, or tables. Use your judgement to choose the best methods for recording your data.

   (a) Choose one electronic product you have discarded in the last year. Try to find out the estimated amount of this product that is being discarded every year in Canada.

   (b) Describe how your preferred disposal option works.

   (c) Describe the impact of your preferred option on the environment, if any.

   (d) Describe the impact of your preferred option on human health, if any.

   (e) Estimate whether or not your preferred option could absorb all or most of the electronic waste being generated in Canada.

Analyze and Evaluate

3. As a group, prepare a report recommending the best way or ways to handle electronic waste in Canada. Include the reasons for choosing the options the group is recommending and the reasons for rejecting other options.

A42 *Problem-Solving Activity*

Toolkit 3

SKILLS YOU WILL USE
- Identifying a problem
- Designing, building, and testing

Cleaning Up an Oil Spill

Figure 3.14 Oil spills destroy the insulating qualities of the feathers and fur of many shoreline birds and animals.

Recognize a Need

Oil is shipped long distances in large tankers. From time to time, these tankers run aground and spill their contents along a shoreline. People living nearby must move very quickly to clean up the oil before it damages local ecosystems.

Problem

How can you clean up an oil spill in an ecosystem?

Materials & Equipment

- a square or rectangular shallow container (minimum 1.2 L)
- 1 L of sand
- 4-5 small rocks
- two small plants
- water
- 2 tbsp (30 mL) motor oil
- materials of your choice for use in the clean-up

Criteria for Success

- Oil is completely cleaned out of the water and the other abiotic and biotic materials.

Brainstorm Ideas

1. Research the technologies used to clean up spills from oil tankers. How effective were these technologies?

2. What technologies could you use to clean up your model oil spill?

Build a Model

3. Create a mini–shoreline ecosystem in your container. Use the rocks to protect the sand. Add the water last, using just enough to create a model shoreline.

Test and Evaluate

4. Take 2 tbsp of the oil and add it to the water. Move the container from side to side to model gentle wave action.

5. Use the technology you researched to clean up biotic and abiotic elements in your mini-ecosystem.

6. Share and compare your ideas and findings with your classmates' plans and findings. Did anyone have ideas exactly like yours? Similar to yours? Completely different from yours? How do your results compare with theirs?

Communicate

7. Prepare a report or computer slide show presentation on the success of your clean-up operation. Or present your findings to the class in a form suggested by your teacher.

Key Concept Review

1. Describe two ways in which human activity has had an impact on abiotic elements. How could these impacts affect the environment?

2. How does recycling help solve some of the problems caused by the amount of waste produced by human activities?

3. How could teens discard unwanted electronic equipment without having much or any impact on the environment?

4. Explain why some environmental changes caused by humans cannot be dealt with by the process of succession.

Connect Your Understanding

5. Describe three ways in which your activities affect the environment. Are these effects positive or negative?

Practise Your Skills

6. Why is it important to consider opinions from a variety of perspectives when evaluating information to make a decision?

For more questions, go to PearsonScience.

A43 *Thinking about Science and the Environment*

Limiting Factors and Human Communities

In Chapter 2, you read about limiting factors on populations. These included predators and the supply of resources such as water, food, and suitable habitat.

In 1900, the world's human population was estimated to be 1.7 billion. In 2000, it was estimated to be 6.1 billion.

What to Do

1. Use the Internet to find out what the estimated population of the world is now and what the population is projected to be 10 years from now.

Consider This

With a classmate or as a whole class, discuss the following questions.

1. Do you think limiting factors could affect the world's human population? Explain your reasoning.

2. Which limiting factor do you think is most likely to have an impact on the world's population? Explain your reasoning.

3. What do you think the world's populations could do to protect themselves from the impact of limiting factors?

We can change our actions and technologies to better protect the environment. **73**

Sustainable Human Communities

Here is a summary of what you will learn in this section:

- Decisions to change human activities and technologies to benefit the environment have measurable costs and benefits.
- Human communities can manage their waste products in order to cycle matter.
- Technology and practices to clean the air and water, reduce waste, and reduce energy needs already exist.

Figure 3.15 "Smog warnings" are issued during the summer months when the air quality is poor enough to cause health problems.

On hot, sunny days between May and September, air pollution in Ontario is often visible on the horizon and is sometimes a problem for people with breathing difficulties. Air pollution is most obvious in big cities (Figure 3.15).

People all over Ontario can help reduce the province's "smog days" by driving well-tuned vehicles, driving less or car pooling, taking public transit, or reducing the use of air conditioning. People often make these kinds of choices by comparing the benefits with the costs in terms of money or convenience.

A44 *Starting Point* Skills

Too Much Phosphorus in the Water

In the mid-1960s, North American lakes and rivers were turning green. Algae were so dense that sunlight could not penetrate the water, and, as the increased amounts of algae died, oxygen was consumed by decomposers. This left very little oxygen for the rest of the ecosystem. The problem was caused by phosphates in laundry detergent. They remained in treated waste water being cycled back to freshwater ecosystems and acted as a fertilizer, fuelling growth.

While the soap industry spent millions on research for another chemical and asked for more time, consumers demanded phosphate-reduced detergent be made available immediately. They got their wish, and the popular environmental movement got its start.

Consider This

1. If you knew you were using a product that was destroying a local ecosystem, would you stop using it? Why or why not?

2. If the replacement for the product cost more than the original one, would you pay the extra money? Explain your reasoning.

Choosing Sustainable Communities

A sustainable human community is one that more closely models an ecosystem. Energy comes from renewable resources, and waste products are broken down into elements that can be re-used. Changing the way communities work in order to become more sustainable benefits the health of people as well as ecosystems. Adopting sustainable practices such as recycling may involve spending money or perhaps making a personal effort to do some things in a less convenient way.

Can communities change? Before 2004, residents of the town of Markham, Ontario were putting 35 percent of their solid waste into blue boxes or leaf and yard waste composting. The other 65 percent was going to landfill. In 2004, the town announced that 70 percent of Markham's solid waste would be diverted from landfill through recycling by 2007. More recycling programs, including a green bin organic waste program, were set up, and by the end of 2007, the town had achieved its goal (Figure 3.16).

Figure 3.16 Materials to be recycled are picked up from homes and businesses.

The Costs and Benefits of Recycling

Millions of dollars are spent building recycling plants, organizing the collection and sorting of materials, and educating citizens on their role. It can be a very costly process, and the benefits may not be visible immediately.

For example, in the early days of recycling, recycled paper was much more expensive than new paper. Now the recycling process is more efficient, and recycled paper products are affordable. The benefits of recycling paper include more than saving trees. When compared to the processing of wood pulp, less total energy and water are required in the manufacturing process, and fewer chemicals such as bleach are used. Paper recycling also reduces the amount of solid waste that goes into landfill (Figure 3.17).

Individuals must compare those benefits to the costs to themselves in terms of the amount of time they spend sorting materials for recycling and the taxes they pay to build and support recycling programs.

Figure 3.17 Recycling programs for paper are now common in many schools and offices.

We can change our actions and technologies to better protect the environment. **75**

Figure 3.18 Disposable products may seem convenient, but their disposal costs money. Improper disposal affects the environment.

Figure 3.19 People choosing to walk or bike to their destinations are helping to reduce air pollution.

Beyond Recycling: Re-use and Reduce

"Re-use" and "reduce" are the other two ways to solve the challenge of modern waste disposal. Using containers, tools, and materials again rather than disposing of them and buying new ones saves money and reduces solid waste. Although it may be less convenient and cost time and personal energy, these options are better for the environment. For example, it takes time to rinse and re-use a water bottle made for repeated use instead of having a fresh "disposable" one available each day, but there is a benefit to the environment of not manufacturing and then disposing of millions of plastic water bottles in landfill (Figure 3.18).

The processes and technology to recycle products such as electronics are not as advanced as they are for paper, glass, and metal. Using products for longer periods means continuing to use older models. Is that a cost consumers will accept to get the benefits of a healthy environment?

Reducing use of technologies that pollute or destroy ecosystems is another way to protect them. This may mean walking to school or riding a bike instead of being driven in a car (Figure 3.19). It may mean choosing products that do not require batteries. These are personal decisions that individuals can make after they compare the benefits of the technology to the cost of the impact on the health of the environment.

A45 *During Writing*

Thinking Literacy

Considering Other Opinions

Talking about an issue with others gives you a chance to explain your opinions and to think about other opinions.

People depend on technology every day, but many activities using technology harm the environment. Who should be responsible for the negative effects on the environment, and what should they do about it? In your classroom, mark each corner to represent one of the following: technology users, technology makers, people who sell technology, and the government.

Take a few minutes to consider who you think is responsible for protecting the environment, and move to the corner that represents your choice. Discuss your ideas with the other people in your corner. Your group will then summarize and present the groups' opinion to the class.

As you listen to the other opinions, do they affect your thoughts in any way? Add any new ideas to your organizer. You are now ready to write a draft copy of your Letter to the Editor.

Choosing Sustainable Technologies

The technologies that can reduce the need for fossil fuels for transportation, heating, and powering industry exist and are being introduced into Ontario communities. There are many examples of the possibilities.

- In the hot summer months, some buildings in downtown Toronto are cooled by circulating cold water from Lake Ontario through their systems. This reduces energy consumption and carbon dioxide emissions.
- A wind farm near Shelburne, Ontario generates enough electricity to power 20 000 homes (Figure 3.20).
- Electric cars are being built in Canada and elsewhere.
- Electronic equipment can be powered without batteries.
- New buildings are being designed with "green" roofs and solar panels, and older buildings are being remodelled to use more sustainable practices (Figure 3.21).

Evaluating Costs and Benefits

The development of new technologies costs money, and the financial costs of these changes can be calculated. But there are other **costs** — social and environmental costs — that are not as visible or easy to calculate. An example of a social cost of air pollution is an increase in respiratory illnesses.

Benefits can also be financial, social, or environmental. A financial benefit of reducing air pollution would be a reduction in healthcare costs. A social benefit would be fewer people whose lives are disrupted by illness.

The environmental costs of development or pollution — loss of habitat, fresh water, and clean air — are not paid directly by humans. However, the connections among all living things are becoming more clear. You have learned that all living things, including humans, depend on each other for survival. The benefits of a healthy environment are benefits for all living things. Can these benefits be calculated?

Assessing both costs and benefits of new technologies and ways of doing things is an important part of looking at the impact of human activity and technology on the environment. Your use of sustainable technologies will help improve and maintain a healthy environment for all.

Figure 3.20 Wind farms can contribute to the supply of electricity in Ontario.

Figure 3.21 A "green" roof includes soil and plants that absorb water as well as heat in the summer to keep the building cooler.

Suggested Activity • · · · · · · · ·
A46 Decision-Making Analysis on page 78

Take It *Further*

There are many groups of ordinary people working together to build sustainable communities and preserve the environment. Choose one and find out what their objective is and what their members are doing. Begin your research at PearsonScience.

What kind of car will you be driving?

The Issue

The supply of oil to make the gasoline that powers conventional car engines is large but limited. Populations in India and China are becoming rich enough to buy their own cars, and the demand for this oil-based fuel will continue to increase. In addition, the exhaust from these engines is damaging the air quality in communities around the world.

All of these factors suggest that alternatives to conventional vehicles and car engines must be developed and on the road in the coming years.

Background Information

- In order to find out how cars of the future might be powered, you need more information. Working in groups of three, identify three alternatives to a conventional car engine that uses gasoline for fuel.

- Have each group member choose one of the alternatives, and use the guidelines below to focus your research. Record the process, results, and sources of your research with notes, diagrams, or tables. Use your judgement to choose the best methods for recording your data and information.

  - What mechanism powers the vehicle?

  - What kind of fuel does the vehicle use?

  - What are the by-products or emissions from the vehicle's operation?

  - How well does the vehicle perform?

  - What is the potential cost of the vehicle and its fuel?

  - How easy will it be to refuel the vehicle?

- What social changes (if any) might be necessary in order to make the vehicle successful? For example, gas stations are a feature of all communities. If the alternative vehicles do not use gasoline, what will happen to the gas stations?

- What would be the benefit of using this new kind of car? Include financial benefits as well as any environmental benefits.

- Share your information with other members of your group. Consult with other groups as well. You may have gathered information that they can benefit from, and they may have done the same for you.

Analyze and Evaluate

1. What criteria will you use when you evaluate the cars of the future?

2. Which alternative do you think is most likely to be accepted? Explain your reasoning using a comparison of the costs and benefits of making the change.

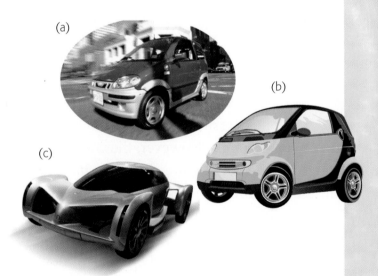

(a)

(b)

(c)

Figure 3.22(a) ZENN (zero emissions, no noise) car
Figure 3.22(b) Smart car
Figure 3.22(c) Energy-efficient design

What do you want to do today?

Issue

Human activities and technologies have an effect on the environment. Often there are choices available that will have a limited impact on the environment and can help protect ecosystems.

Background Information

Consumers are found in every ecosystem on Earth. In addition, human consumers are often found in malls and shopping centres in North America, as well as online.

Shopping for and buying items is an important part of the economy. Human consumption includes getting the weekly groceries, buying the latest fashion, getting a haircut, or going to a restaurant for a quick snack. Packaging, plastic bags, emissions from cars driving to the mall, throw-away dishes, and basements full of objects that are not used anymore are all results of these human activities.

The products we buy are made from resources that come from Earth. Energy is used to manufacture, package, and transport them to markets. More energy is used to light and power stores and malls. Considerable waste is generated after products have been used. What impact do these activities have on the environment? As we begin to understand about the environmental impact of our consumption, what are we willing to do to change that impact?

Analyze and Evaluate

1. Consider one of the activities listed below and how it affects the environment:

   (a) visiting a fast food restaurant for a meal with your friends

   (b) the family's grocery shopping

   (c) going to the mall to pick up something new to wear or play with

   (d) another activity that you participate in that has an impact on the environment (check with your teacher to ensure it is applicable)

2. Use the chart below to analyze the impact of your chosen activity on the environment.

Benefit to you (+)	Cost to the environment (-)	Options

   In this activity, benefits (+) are things that are good for you, the consumer. Costs (-) are things that are not good for the environment. In the Options column, list ways you could reduce the negative impact of the costs but still get the benefit of the activity.

3. Once you have filled in information on the activity you chose, find two classmates and compare the Benefits, Costs, and Options you each listed.

4. Discuss with your small group any other questions, concerns, or related information you have about your activity. Record these on the back of your chart.

5. Work as a group to develop a creative way to share your findings with the rest of the class, (speech, computer slide show, editorial, or video report) or suggest ways to balance the Benefits and Costs of some common activities at an Environmental Action Fair. Your teacher will tell you the date by which you must be ready to present.

Key Concept Review

1. Describe how financial costs can influence choices people make about actions that affect ecosystems.

2. Describe how wind farms can help protect the environment. Are there any potential negative impacts?

3. Describe two examples of new technology and ways of thinking that can make a positive difference to the environment.

Connect Your Understanding

4. Give an example of a social cost and a social benefit of preserving a meadow instead of building a new arena.

5. How are social and environmental costs different from financial costs? Are they similar in any way?

6. Design a poster to promote one of the following:
   (a) walking to school
   (b) having a "no waste" lunch
   (c) not leaving a car running

Practise Your Skills

7. Use a chart to show the financial, social, and environmental costs associated with building a new shopping centre.

For more questions, go to PearsonScience.

A48 *Thinking about Science and the Environment*

Positive Actions for the Environment

Residents of Brighton, a town of about 5000 people near Lake Ontario, built a marsh in an old cornfield. It is for treating waste from the town's sewage treatment facilities. The plan is to construct wetlands that treat waste water, while re-establishing a diverse ecosystem.

In northern Quebec, a protected area that includes the areas drained by the rivière du Vieux Comptoir, the mouth of the river, and the James Bay area where the river flows into is being created. The local Cree people will share their knowledge of the land and the bay and assist in managing the area.

What to Do

1. Discuss with a classmate how the two projects each combine human activity and protection of ecosystems.

2. Look in the newspapers and online for other examples of human activities that preserve or maintain a healthy environment.

Consider This

In what other ways do human communities maintain the health of ecosystems while they are growing and expanding?

Making Connections

Jay Ingram

Jay Ingram is an experienced science journalist and is the host of Daily Planet on Discovery Channel Canada.

Rewilding

Imagine driving through western Canada and the United States and taking time out to see the wild elephants, lions, camels, and cheetahs there. How could this be? The idea is called rewilding, and people are talking about it.

Some scientists argue that most of the large mammals living in Africa and Asia face extinction. Rather than just letting them die, why not introduce some of these species to the wide-open spaces of North America? There, free from human population pressure and habitat destruction, they could survive and prosper.

It may not be as crazy as it sounds. For one thing, twenty thousand years ago North America was home to a variety of similar animals. There were camel, lion, cheetah, the elephant-like mammoth, and the mastodon. Where there's a history, there's at least the likelihood of a suitable habitat.

There's enough land available to make such a project at least thinkable. In fact, the North American habitat could benefit: camels and elephants, by grazing on woody plants, would help restore the American grasslands to their former glory. The now-extinct American cheetah likely preyed on the pronghorn, prompting its evolution as one of the fastest animals on earth. Maybe African cheetahs would resume the hunt that has been suspended for many thousands of years.

One of the prime motivations for rewilding is that large animals, whether carnivores or herbivores, exert a disproportionately large influence on their habitats. Predators like lions cull their herbivore prey, leave carcasses for scavengers and are host to a variety of ticks, lice, and other invertebrates that in turn are fed on by others.

Obviously there are huge political and biological problems with the idea. Even if the American west is relatively under-populated, most of the land is still in private hands. And who in Africa would want to allow this program, a tacit admission that their conservation efforts have failed? And we are living in a different time, a different climate, a different world: replacement species might not be so well-suited to the habitat into which they are being introduced. Sure there were cheetahs in North America ten thousand years ago, but we have no idea how modern cheetahs would do.

Maybe in the end the value of this idea would be to encourage more adventurous thinking about conservation and biodiversity and to concentrate on those endangered species we already have.

Key Concept Review

1. Explain how ecosystems change naturally. Use specific examples. k c

2. How do catastrophic events in nature affect the balance of biotic and abiotic elements in an ecosystem? k

3. List three impacts human activities have on water. k

4. Explain the strategies your community uses to divert waste from landfills. t c

5. Write a poem or a rap verse to explain how reducing, re-using, and recycling materials can benefit the environment. t a

6. Describe how you would decide which of the drink containers shown in the photos is better for the environment. t a

Connect Your Understanding

7. Draw an 8-panel cartoon that would explain why it is important to reduce the use of resources that come from Earth. t c

8. Design a poster to promote an alternative energy source. Be sure to share the benefits of this new technology. t c

9. What are the benefits of a forest fire in a forest ecosystem? k

10. Ancient civilizations in Egypt were based on the Nile River. Each year the Nile would flood its banks and add fertile sediment to the local soil. How would this help the farmers who lived near the river? k a

After Writing — Thinking Literacy

Reflect and Evaluate

Review your Letter to the Editor, and then discuss with a partner the ideas presented in each of your letters. Have facts and opinions been clearly expressed? Have the concepts of change in ecosystems and our role as stewards of the environment been communicated? At the beginning of this chapter you examined several examples of Letters to the Editor. Do your letters include the characteristics you saw in these examples?

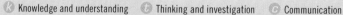

ACHIEVEMENT CHART CATEGORIES
k Knowledge and understanding t Thinking and investigation c Communication a Application

11. Write a letter to the local council describing how recreational development may alter the environment shown in the photo below. Make it clear whether you support or oppose the development and explain why. ⓣ ⓒ

Practise Your Skills

12. Explain the steps you would follow to analyze the impact of a particular human activity on the environment. ⓐ ⓒ

13. Design a computer slide-show presentation to teach primary students about reducing, re-using, and recycling materials. ⓣ ⓒ

Unit Task Link

Some human activities in the developed world must change in order to preserve ecosystems. Make a list of the top five activities that you believe must change in order to protect the environment. Indicate whether the change is related to reducing, re-using, or recycling.

A49 *Thinking about Science and the Environment*

Stewardship

You have been learning about how biotic and abiotic elements in ecosystems depend on each other for survival, and how ecosystems, when left alone, can sustain themselves.

This chapter has looked at how human activities can harm the ability of ecosystems to sustain themselves. It has raised questions about how human activities could be changed to protect the environment. You have read examples of how some communities have changed their activities.

This unit began with a discussion of the term "steward." When we plan our daily activities, should we consider our role as stewards of the environment? Why or why not?

Consider This

With a classmate or as a whole class, discuss the following:

1. Is protecting ecosystems an effective way to be a good steward of the environment?

2. How have some of the practices of Aboriginal peoples been good examples of stewardship of the environment?

3. How are sustainable activities related to being a good steward of the environment?

4. Make a list of five things you can do to be a good steward of the environment.

1.0   Ecosystems are communities where biotic and abiotic elements interact.

KEY CONCEPTS

- Interaction of biotic and abiotic elements
- Role of producers
- Interactions of producers and consumers

CHAPTER SUMMARY

- Biotic elements (living things) have five basic needs: oxygen, water, food, energy, and habitat.
- Biotic elements interact with both living things and non-living (abiotic) elements to meet their basic needs.
- Plants are the only organisms that can use the Sun's energy to make food. All ecosystems include plants.
- All other organisms must consume other living things to get food.

2.0   Interactions in ecosystems support the transfer of energy and the cycling of matter.

KEY CONCEPTS

- Energy transfer in ecosystems
- Cycling matter
- Interactions and changes in ecosystems

CHAPTER SUMMARY

- Food chains and food webs show how the Sun's energy is transferred in ecosystems.
- At each step in a food chain, less energy is available to the next consumer.
- Matter moves continuously from non-living things to living things and back to non-living things in a cycle of constant change in ecosystems.
- The supply of resources in ecosystems is limited.
- A big change in the supply of resources disrupts interactions. Sometimes a big change threatens the survival of living things in an ecosystem.

3.0   We can change our actions and technologies to better protect the environment.

KEY CONCEPTS

- Succession, recovery, and renewal in ecosystems
- Human technologies and activities and their environmental impact
- Human communities and sustainability

CHAPTER SUMMARY

- Ecosystems change naturally in predictable ways known as succession.
- Ecosystems can recover from catastrophic natural changes.
- Many modern human activities and technologies have damaged abiotic and biotic elements in ecosystems. Ecosystems may take a very long time to recover.
- Human communities have the knowledge and technology to reduce the environmental impact of their activities.

Reduce the Size of Your Ecological Footprint

Getting Started

Earth, our habitat, has a total area of just over 50 billion hectares, but less than one-quarter of that area produces food and other resources. This means that just 12 billion hectares are available to provide the basic needs of all producers and consumers (including humans) on Earth. For six billion humans, this works out to two hectares each, which we must share with other living things.

You have learned that all living things must meet five basic needs in order to survive. You have also learned that there is a limited amount of resources available for living things to meet those basic needs. By assessing your lifestyle choices, you can find out whether you use resources equal to more or less than "your" two hectares of land. The amount of Earth required to support you is known as your "ecological footprint."

Your Goal

You will score your activities to assess the size of your ecological footprint. Then you will review your lifestyle and find ways to make your footprint smaller.

What You Need to Know

You can calculate your Ecological Footprint using an Ecological Footprint Calculator (EFC). Your teacher will provide this. You will be scoring your activities in six categories: food, water, energy, transportation, shelter, and lifestyle.

Steps to Success

1. Use the EFC to calculate your ecological footprint. Which categories were high? Were any categories low? How did you compare with the rest of your classmates?

2. In pairs, examine your scores in each of the six categories. Identify changes (a minimum of two per category) you could make that would reduce your score.

3. As a class, share ideas on how everyone can reduce their ecological footprints. Include ideas for reducing activities and re-using or recycling items. How many of these changes are you willing to make? Why or why not?

4. Create an ecological footprint contract that will commit you to making at least one change in each category that will reduce your ecological footprint. Choose changes that are realistic and achievable.

How Did It Go?

5. Use the EFC to recalculate your impact on the environment, assuming that you have made the changes described in your contract. How big is your footprint now? What would you have to do to reduce it to two hectares?

6. Do you think you can change your lifestyle to one that uses less of Earth's resources? Write out each change in activities that will be necessary and how you could make it.

7. Create a poster, calendar, or diary to help you track your progress in reducing your ecological footprint. Challenge your classmates to find out who has been able to make the changes.

Key Terms Review

1. Create a mind map that shows your understanding of the terms listed below. You may want to add some words of your own to show how the terms are connected. Ⓚ Ⓐ

- abiotic
- biotic
- climax community
- decomposers
- consumers
- food chains
- energy
- human impact
- habitat
- organic matter
- interactions
- sustainability
- producers
- succession

2. Use the words listed below in a paragraph that explains how the Sun's energy is transferred through an ecosystem. Ⓚ Ⓒ carnivore, consumer, decomposer, herbivore, omnivore, producer

3. *Sustain* is the root word in *sustainability*. How does the meaning of *sustain* help you understand what the word *sustainability* means? Ⓚ Ⓣ

Key Concept Review

1.0

4. Describe an ecosystem in your own words. Apply your definition to the following statements, and explain why each one is true or false. Ⓚ Ⓒ

(a) A schoolyard is an ecosystem.

(b) A puddle on the road is an ecosystem.

5. Explain why abiotic factors are essential to ecosystems everywhere. Ⓚ Ⓒ

6. Describe three types of interactions that could take place in an ecosystem, and give an example of each. Ⓚ Ⓒ

7. Ecosystems change both naturally and as a result of human activity. Give an example of each type of change, and explain how it could affect the ecosystem where the change is occurring. Ⓣ Ⓒ

8. How can looking at the costs and benefits of an activity help evaluate the effect the activity has on the environment? Ⓐ Ⓒ

9. Select an area near your school that has both biotic and abiotic elements. List three of each. Draw lines to show possible connections among the different elements. Ⓚ

10. List three of the basic needs of living things, and explain their importance. Ⓚ

11. How are producers and consumers similar? How are they different? Explain why producers are at the beginning of every food chain. Ⓚ Ⓒ

12. Plants make their own food through photosynthesis. This is how they obtain the matter and energy they need to survive. Ⓚ Ⓒ

(a) What are the raw materials for photosynthesis?

(b) What are the products of photosynthesis?

(c) Give three reasons why plants are important for ecosystems.

ACHIEVEMENT CHART CATEGORIES
Ⓚ Knowledge and understanding   Ⓣ Thinking and investigation   Ⓒ Communication   Ⓐ Application

13. Look at the picture shown below. Identify four biotic elements that could be living in this location. Ⓚ Ⓒ

(a) Explain how these biotic elements might be connected to one another.

(b) Explain how the biotic elements might be connected to the abiotic elements in the location.

(c) Would you expect to find scavengers and decomposers in an ecosystem like this? Why or why not?

2.0

14. In terms of the flow of energy through an ecosystem, what is the correct order for each of the following elements? Ⓚ

(a) earthworm, rabbit, rose, Sun, wolf

(b) bacteria, otter, sea urchin, seaweed, Sun

15. Study the diagram below.

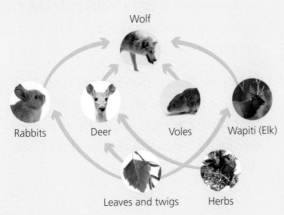

Wolf

Rabbits   Deer   Voles   Wapiti (Elk)

Leaves and twigs   Herbs

(a) Identify at least three food chains. List them in the correct order. Ⓚ Ⓐ

(b) Does a food web give a better picture of interactions in an ecosystem? Explain why or why not. Ⓚ Ⓐ

16. What would happen if the matter in the abiotic environment was not recycled? How do you know? Ⓣ

17. Compare the number of producers in an ecosystem to the number of herbivores. How do you think the number of carnivores compares with the number of herbivores? Give reasons to support your answer. Ⓣ Ⓒ

18. Explain the term *sustainability*. Give two examples of how an ecosystem in a natural setting is sustainable. Ⓚ Ⓐ

19. How might the introduction of a non-native plant or animal species affect an ecosystem? Ⓣ Ⓒ

3.0

20. Over the years following a forest fire, the plants and animals listed below appear in the area. In what order do you think they appear? Explain your answer. Ⓚ Ⓐ

bear, birch tree, fireweed, grass, mouse

21. How have humans affected a natural area in your community? Were these effects positive or negative? Explain your answer. Ⓐ Ⓒ

22. Use examples to demonstrate your understanding of the terms listed below. ⓣ ⓒ

environmental benefit, environmental cost, financial benefit, financial cost, social benefit, social cost

23. Explain how the following activities affect the balance of interactions in an ecosystem. ⓚ ⓐ

(a) cutting all the trees in a forest

(b) running motorcycles and ATVs (all-terrain vehicles) through a wetland

(c) spraying a pesticide to control insects on a lawn

24. Look at the photo below and explain how the shore ecosystem will be affected by the oil spill. Use a series of diagrams to show how the area might change over the next 20 years. ⓐ ⓒ

Connect Your Understanding

25. Your school wants to start a recycling program. What information would you need in order to determine if this is a good idea? Design a survey as a first step in investigating the issue. ⓐ ⓒ

26. Whether they are started naturally or by people, forest fires change the ecosystem of a forest.

(a) Name at least three other natural changes that can affect ecosystems. ⓚ ⓣ

(b) Choose one of the above natural changes. Describe how it might affect an ecosystem. ⓚ ⓒ

27. Look at this photo. Suggest three effects the event could have on the environment. For each effect, suggest ways the environment could recover. ⓣ ⓐ

28. Now that you have completed this unit, do you think you will make different decisions when choosing activities that will affect the environment? Why or why not? ⓚ ⓐ

Practise Your Skills

29. What human needs and environmental concerns should be considered when designing a plan to use a piece of undeveloped land in a city? Would these needs and concerns be any different in the countryside? ⓣ ⓐ

30. Describe an environmental issue in your community. Design a poster or picture that illustrates the issue. Be sure your poster includes the causes and effects of the issue. ⓐ ⓒ

ACHIEVEMENT CHART CATEGORIES
ⓚ Knowledge and understanding   ⓣ Thinking and investigation   ⓒ Communication   ⓐ Application

31. Design an action plan to help the community deal with the issue you described in question 31. List the factors you would take into consideration. 🅰🄒

32. Create a chart to demonstrate the costs and benefits that need to be considered when making informed decisions about human impact on the environment. If you wish, use the issue from question 31. 🅰🄒

Revisit the Big Ideas

33. Identify which of the following statements are false. Reword the false statements to make them true. 🄚

    (a) Ecosystems can only be large.

    (b) Ecosystems contain both biotic and abiotic elements.

    (c) Only the stones and sand in a puddle are needed to make up an ecosystem.

34. Use the following examples to demonstrate how people can affect energy transfer and the cycling of matter in an ecosystem. 🄣🄒

    (a) A developer fills in a wetland to build houses.

    (b) A farmer ploughs up a grassland to plant a crop.

    (c) A town changes the drainage system in an ecosystem to reduce flooding.

35. Identify one example of human impact on an ecosystem that you could help to reduce. Describe what you could do to reduce this impact. 🄚🄣

A50 *Thinking about Science, Technology, Society, and the Environment*

Can you go "carbon neutral"?

Going "carbon neutral" is a way of balancing an activity that omits carbon dioxide with one that removes carbon dioxide from the atmosphere. The amount of carbon dioxide emissions caused by one activity is calculated. Then activities that remove (or offset) the same amount of carbon emissions from the environment are undertaken or funded. Supporting renewable energy products or planting trees can all be carbon offsets.

Consider This

With a small group of your classmates, discuss the following statement:

Going carbon neutral will give people an excuse to not change their attitudes and actions toward the environment.

Structures:
Form and Function

Unit Overview

Fundamental Concepts

In Grade 7 Science and Technology, six fundamental concepts occur throughout. This unit addresses the following two:

- Structure and Function
- Energy

Big Ideas

As you work through this unit, you will develop a deeper understanding of the following big ideas:

- Structures have a purpose.
- The form of a structure is dependent on its function.
- The interactions between structures and forces is predictable.

Overall Expectations

By the end of this unit, you will be expected to:

1. analyse personal, social, economic, and environmental factors that need to be considered in designing and building structures and devices

2. design and construct a variety of structures, and investigate the relationship between the design and function of these structures and the forces that act on them

3. demonstrate an understanding of the relationship between structural forms and the forces that act on them and within them

These homes were designed and built to conserve energy.

Exploring

The Garden City Skyway Bridge (in the background) is high enough for ships to sail underneath. The ship has just sailed between the two halves of a lift bridge.

Almost everything you can see and touch is a structure: the chair you sit on, the pen you use, the book you are reading, the boulder in the park, the tree you climbed. Even you are a structure, made up of several other structures: skeleton, heart, brain, and so on.

Every structure has a form and a function. The **form** is the basic shape of the structure; the **function** is the job that the structure does.

Some structures are natural (trees, rocks, flowers, you), and some are manufactured (airplanes, vases, picture frames, bridges). Manufactured structures are designed with their forms and functions in mind. Designers choose the materials to make each structure and decide how to construct it.

In this unit, you will study the forms and functions of many different structures. You will also study the forces that can act on structures, and learn how different structures react to these forces. You will learn how to predict the action of forces on structures. Forces and structures are constantly interacting. When we understand these interactions, we can build better structures.

Many products that you buy can have an impact on the environment. It is important to consider these impacts when you make buying decisions. Making good decisions will ensure the sustainability of life on Earth.

Ergonomic Design

Some structures are designed to be "ergonomic." This means that the designers understand scientific information about the human body. Ergonomic design can help prevent people from getting hurt while performing repetitive tasks. Many ergonomic designs assist people who have physical challenges. Choosing ergonomically designed structures can improve quality of life.

Compare the form and function of this chair compared with the one you are sitting on right now.

Think about how you interact with structures when you are doing your schoolwork. You probably sit on a chair with your papers on a desk. Many office workers spend long periods of time working at desks. All of this sitting can be very hard on the human body if it is not supported properly.

As you know, chairs come in a wide variety of forms, but they all perform similar functions. Think of the differences between a stool in the science lab and the chair you sit on to watch television. Several furniture manufacturers make chairs that are ergonomically designed with the office worker in mind.

Before designing these chairs, the manufacturers observed how people sat in chairs when they went about their daily tasks, such as working on a computer, talking on the phone, reaching for work materials, and working at their desks. This research helped the designers.

...MORE TO EXPLORE

Design a Better Desk

As you read this, you are probably sitting on a chair at a desk. Think about the jobs (functions) your desk needs to do. How does its form help it perform its functions? Could you improve its form in order to improve its functions?

Purpose

To suggest improvements to the form of a school desk so it can perform its functions better

---

Materials & Equipment

- paper
- pen

Procedure

1. List the functions of your school desk.

2. Consider how well it performs each function the way it is now.

3. Make suggestions that you think will improve the way it performs each function.

4. Compare your list with that of a classmate.

Questions

5. What do you consider the most important function of your desk? Why?

6. If you could make one of the changes you suggested, which one would it be? Why?

Considering Form and Function

Think about the structures in your classroom: chairs, desks, shelves, pens, containers, and many other large and small structures. Each structure has a form and performs a function.

What to Do

1. Use a chart like the one below to list at least six structures you see in your classroom.

Structure	Description of Form	Description of Function

2. Describe each structure's form.

3. Describe each structure's function.

Consider This

With a classmate or as a whole class, discuss the following questions.

4. What structures have the most complex forms?

5. What structures serve more than one function?

6. How might form and function influence each other?

Contents

Unit Task

In your life, you will use many structures that others design. You might also modify an existing structure, and you may design your own structures. For your unit task, you will design something to improve the energy efficiency of an existing structure.

Essential Question

Think of a structure that you modified from its original form. Why didn't you use as it was or build something new?

Getting Ready to Read

Thinking Literacy

Open Word Sort

Before you begin this unit, work with a partner to write each of the key terms from each chapter on a card. Look for possible ways to categorize the words. Arrange the cards in groups with category labels. Share your categories with the class.

4.0

Designers consider the form and
the function of a structure and
the forces that act on it.

A tent is a structure you can sleep in.

What You Will Learn

In this chapter, you will:

- explore structures and their functions
- classify structures as solid, frame, or shell
- describe the forces that can affect structures

Skills You Will Use

In this chapter, you will:

- use scientific language when describing structures
- investigate how structures are designed for safety

Why This Is Important

Every object you encounter is a structure. Each structure has specific purposes, called functions. All structures must be designed and built to withstand the forces they will face. By classifying structures and seeing how they are affected by different forces, you will begin to understand what makes a good structure.

Before Reading

Thinking Literacy

Structure Mind Map

You can use a mind map to record what you learn about structures. Take a blank sheet of paper and write the word "Structure" in the centre. When you discover ways to classify structures, add them to your mind map using words and/or pictures. Draw connecting lines to show relationships. Continue with other information you learn about structures.

Key Terms

- structure
- solid
- load
- shear
- function
- frame
- tension
- torsion
- form
- shell
- compression

Figure 4.1 People live in a wide variety of structures.

Just about everything you see is a structure: buildings, cars, trees, bicycles, baskets, your skeleton, your pop can, and so on. And each of those structures has at least one function. A house or an apartment building is a structure that provides shelter, keeps us warm, and gives us a place to keep our other structures (Figure 4.1). Some animals build structures—nests, lodges, and honey combs—also to provide shelter (Figure 4.2).

The various forces in the world affect structures. For example, when a strong wind blows, the trees sway. If you step on a marshmallow, it squashes. The wind and the weight of your foot are forces affecting the trees and the marshmallow, respectively.

Sometimes, you can predict the interactions between forces and structures. You know that the marshmallow has no chance of staying fluffy under your foot. However, it is harder to predict when a branch will snap instead of sway.

Figure 4.2 Animals live in a wide variety of structures too.

Throughout your life, you will make choices when you buy structures such as clothing, electronic items, cars, and homes. In order to make good choices, you need to understand key ideas about structures. In this chapter, you will study several types of structures, looking at their forms and functions (Figure 4.3). You will find out what forces, such as the wind, can act on them. You will also see how structures are designed to sense and withstand those forces.

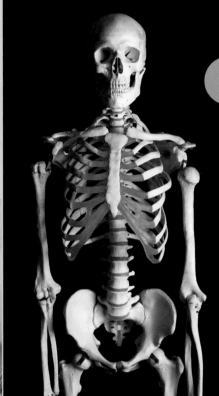

Figure 4.3 All of these things are structures.

Wind Effects

Depending on where they grow, some plants are stronger than others. In this investigation, you will investigate how the wind can affect different plants.

Purpose

To observe the effects of wind on various structures

Materials & Equipment
■ cardboard to wave as a fan
■ 3 or 4 different potted plants

Procedure

1. Examine the structure of each plant.

2. Predict what might happen if wind blew on each plant.

3. Wave the cardboard like a fan in front of each plant, first gently and then more forcefully. Record your observations.

Questions

4. Describe how the wind affected each plant.

5. Which plants behaved similarly? Why?

6. What might happen in each case if the wind were even stronger?

Here is a summary of what you will learn in this section:

- A structure can be classified by its function.
- A structure can be classified by its construction.
- A structure can be classified as a solid, frame, or shell structure.

When people think about structures, they often think about towers and bridges. While these structures are impressive, the truth is that every object you encounter is a structure. If you pack snow to make a snowball, you have made a structure. If you combine ingredients and bake a loaf of bread, you have also made a structure.

If you look carefully at a wide variety of structures, you will notice that many of them have similarities. Different structures might serve the same function, like the structures in Figures 4.4 and 4.5. In this section, you will explore ways to classify structures.

Figure 4.4 A rock can serve as a seat.

Figure 4.5 A car seat has a specific function.

B4 *Starting Point*

Skills **A** **C**

Have a Seat

Think about at least six different structures that you can use as a seat. Make a list of them. Some can be indoors, some can be outdoors.

What are the advantages and disadvantages of each one in its function as a seat? Share your ideas with a classmate.

Making Connections

Good readers activate their prior knowledge by making connections between what they read and themselves, the world, and/or other texts. As you read about classifying structures in this section, think about connections you can make to the information presented.

Classifying Structures

We often classify structures by looking at their functions. Some structures are made to contain something, some structures support something on top, and some span a space. For example, if you notice soil running out of your school garden when it rains, you may decide to build a retaining wall to hold the soil in. If you have trouble reaching a high shelf, you may use a step or stool to lift yourself up. If workers are building a wall, they build scaffolding first, and walk around safely (see Figure 4.6).

A bridge is a structure designed to span a gap. Sometimes the gap is a stream or river (see Figures 4.7 and 4.8). Other bridges span another roadway; if so, we call the bridge an overpass. Early bridges consisted of a log felled over a stream; modern bridges are designed in many different forms. Look at the bridges in your community. No matter how simple or complicated the form of each bridge, its function is still to span a gap safely.

Another way to sort structures is to examine how they are built and what they are built from. We will look at this in Chapter 5. A third way to classify structures is to divide them by their forms, into solid structures, frame structures, and shell structures.

Figure 4.6 Construction workers erect a scaffold so that they can work on high walls.

Figure 4.7 Three bridges in Vancouver. The modern bridge in front is the Skytrain Bridge, the middle one is a road bridge, and the lowest is a railway bridge. The railway bridge has a "swing" section that opens to let ships through.

Figure 4.8 Covered bridges were designed and built many years ago. The roof allowed the snow to slide off so that its weight would not damage the bridge. This covered bridge in Guelph was built recently by volunteers.

Classifying Structures

Draw a table with four columns and six rows. In the first column, write the names of six structures you can see in your classroom. As you work through the chapter, write the function of each structure in Column 2. If you are unsure of the function, put a question mark. In Column 3, list the materials each is made of.

In Column 4, write whether you think it is a solid structure, a frame structure, or a shell structure.

Compare your table with that of a classmate. Discuss the items you put question marks beside. Compile a class list for discussion. What types of structures come up the most often?

Solid Structures

Do you know what mountains, dams, sand castles, wax candles, and apples have in common? All are considered **solid** structures (Figure 4.9). Most solid structures are solid all the way through, although a mountain might contain caves, a dam might have rooms to hold electrical generators, and an apple may have a worm hole. A solid structure weighs more than a hollow structure of the same size and made of the same material.

Suggested Activity • · · · · · · · ·
B7 Quick Lab, page 105

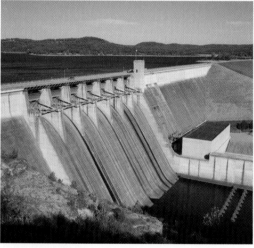

Figure 4.9 Packing the material together is important when constructing solid structures.

Frame Structures

Frame structures are made of parts fastened together. The parts are often called structural components. For example, your skeleton is a frame structure. Its structural components—your bones, ligaments, and tendons—are joined together. A bicycle frame is another example of a frame structure (see Figure 4.10).

Frame structures can exist as just the frame or as a frame covered by a coating. For example, a tennis racket, dish-drying rack, and spider's web are structures that are only frames. Umbrellas, cars, or bats' wings consist of a frame covered by some sort of material.

Figure 4.10 A delicate spider's web and a sturdy car frame are both frame structures because they are built like a skeleton.

Shell Structures

Most strong, hollow structures are **shell** structures. Have you ever been inside an igloo or looked up into a domed roof? Have you poured milk out of a carton into a glass or blown up a balloon? If so, you have seen a shell structure (Figure 4.11).

Since shell structures have space inside them, they often make good containers. They also use very little material in their construction. This means that they are quite light for their size. Clothing can even be considered shell structures.

*Take It **Further***

Some very famous structures from around the world include the Eiffel Tower, the Great Wall of China, and Mount Everest. Can you think of a famous solid structure, shell structure, and frame structure? Begin your search at PearsonScience.

Figure 4.11 The igloo, the egg carton, and the egg shells themselves are shell structures.

Combination Structures

Many structures are combinations of shell, frame, and solid structures. For example, Figure 4.12 shows how a house is built from solid structures—bricks, nails, and pieces of wood called boards. The boards are nailed together into a frame that gives the building strength. Both the walls and the roof are now frame structures.

When the frame is finished, the wall and roof frames are covered with plywood. Windows and doors are placed into holes cut in the plywood.

The builder now covers the outside wall with bricks or siding, and the roof with shingles. These keep the house dry when it rains.

Figure 4.12 A house is built from solid structures that are put together to form a frame. The walls and the roof form a covering around the frame.

Building Solid, Frame, and Shell Structures

Structures that have the same function may have very different forms. For example, all chairs are designed to support the weight of a person sitting on it (Figures 4.13, 4.14, and 4.15). In this lab, you will build different forms of chairs and test their strength.

Purpose

To build structures to illustrate solid, frame, and shell structures

Figure 4.13

Materials & Equipment

- toothpicks
- modelling clay

Procedure

1. Sketch three chairs: one that can be classified as a solid structure, one as a frame structure, and one as a shell structure.

2. Build a model of each chair with toothpicks and modelling clay. Try to build the chairs approximately the same size.

3. Think of a different structure and repeat steps 1 and 2 for the structure of your choice.

4. As a class, design a way to test the ability of each chair to support weight.

Questions

5. What did you notice about the use of materials when you built solid structures, frame structures, and shell structures?

6. Which type of structure was best able to support weight?

7. What generalizations can you make about solid, frame, and shell structures?

Figure 4.14

Figure 4.15

Unpacking the Packaging

Packaging is a structure that you encounter every day. It is used to protect other structures during transport. Packaging also displays the product in the store. Something as simple as a bar of soap (a solid structure) may come in a cardboard box (shell structure) that might be wrapped in plastic (another shell structure).

In this activity, you will study packaging as structures. When choosing your packaging, select a wide variety of products, such as food, school supplies, and electronics.

Purpose

To study the structures involved in packaging

Materials & Equipment

- all of the packaging associated with several recent purchases
- pencil and paper
- kitchen or bathroom scale

Procedure

1. You will look at all of the packaging that came with several different products. Keep the sets of packaging separate.

2. Take one set of packaging. What did it contain? Examine the packaging material. Describe the packaging qualitatively, in a chart like the one in Table 4.1.

3. Describe the amount of packaging quantitatively by weighing it or finding its volume.

Table 4.1 Unpacking the Packaging Recording Chart

Product	Qualitative Description	Amount of Material	Type(s) of Material

4. Repeat the process for three more different items.

Questions

5. Compare your chart with those of your classmates. Do you agree with the way your classmates described the various packages?

6. What structures came with the most packaging? What structures came with the least? What structures do you buy that have no packaging?

7. Compare the weight or volume of each structure with the weight or volume of the packaging it came in. Do you notice any trends?

8. Do you think the packaging did its job?

9. Do you think each piece of packaging was necessary?

Key Concept Review

1. Define "structure" in your own words. Describe three ways in which you can classify structures.

2. Classify the following structures as a solid structure, a frame structure, or a shell structure.

   (a) three-ring binder   (d) basketball net

   (b) a tent   (e) an ice skate

   (c) a backpack   (f) a sand castle

Connect Your Understanding

3. Make a chart with four columns. In the first column, list five structures used in either a soccer or a basketball game.

   (a) In Column 2, classify each structure as solid, frame, or shell.

   (b) In Column 3, describe the form of each structure.

   (c) In Column 4, state the function of each structure.

4. Sometimes transporting structures exposes them to forces that they would not encounter during normal use.

   (a) List different ways that you have seen structures protected for shipping.

   (b) Describe one way that you feel is effective.

   (c) Describe one way that you feel is not.

   (d) What do you do with packaging materials once your structure arrives at its destination?

5. Do you think a designer should begin work with form in mind or with function in mind? Give reasons for your thinking.

Practise Your Skills

6. Think of a structure that can be classified as both a frame structure and a shell structure. Explain why you think the structure can be classified in both ways.

For more questions, go to PearsonScience.

B9   *Thinking about Science and Technology*

Structures in Your Lunchbox

What to Do

1. Think about a packed lunch and the structures used to hold each item. What types of structure are they?

Consider This

With a classmate or as a whole class, discuss the following questions.

2. Are structures used to hold food usually shell structures, frame structures, or solid structures? Why do you think that is?

3. What materials are the structures that hold your lunch made from? Can they be reused or are they disposable?

4. How might the choices of structures we use to hold food affect the environment?

5. Which is more of a challenge to transport: solid or liquid food? Why?

Forces That Can Act on Structures

Here is a summary of what you will learn in this section:

- A force is any push or pull.
- Forces act on structures.
- Forces can be classified as external (wind, gravity) or internal.
- The magnitude of forces, their direction, and their point and plane of application influence how they affect structures.
- Shear, tension, compression, and torsion are types of internal forces that can affect structures.

Figure 4.16 It is hard to believe that this barn was once strong and useful.

You may hear news stories about a buckled road, homes destroyed by tornadoes, or the collapse of an old building (Figure 4.16). What do these things have in common? They are the result of forces that acted on a structure but the structure could not resist the force.

A **force** is any push or pull. Forces act on all structures. Whether the structure is small or large, it must be designed and built to withstand the forces it will face. If the structure is not strong enough, it may experience structural failure. If it is too strong, time and resources might be wasted. Understanding forces helps you to design and build better structures.

All structures experience forces at all times. Sometimes the effects of those forces are not apparent until time has passed. That it why it is important to design a structure carefully, build it skillfully, and monitor it diligently throughout its useful life.

B10 *Starting Point*　　　　　　　Skills

Gravity Is a Force

When you were younger, building towers of blocks and knocking them down may have fascinated you. You were experimenting with gravity. Use some things from your pencil case and around your desk to make a tall and stable structure on your desk. Keep going until your structure fails. What caused your structure to fail?

Build another structure and wave a piece of paper at it to simulate wind, or build it on a desk and then jiggle the desk to simulate an earthquake.

Describe what happens.

Discuss with a classmate why your structures failed. What do you think you could have done to delay the failure of your structures?

Note Taking

Scan through this chapter looking for the topic headings. As you find each one, re-write each topic heading in the form of a How? What? or Why? sentence. Write the questions in a chart like the one in Table 4.2. As you read the chapter, record your notes in the appropriate column. When you record your notes, remember that you are trying to record the main ideas. Instead of using sentences, use key words and phrases.

Table 4.2 Chart for Note Taking

Topic Heading in the Form of a Question	Point-form Notes

Internal and External Forces

Structures should be designed to withstand the forces that can act on them. Some of those forces come from outside the structure. Gravity is an external force that acts on all structures all the time. Gravity constantly pulls structures toward Earth's centre. As well, you have probably seen wind blow papers and plastics around. Figure 4.17 shows that wind can even blow people around! Everyday use of a structure can also involve external forces. For example, a ladder is designed to support the weight of the person climbing it. When you pull out a drawer, you are exerting an external force on the drawer.

Figure 4.17 The wind is an external force acting on these girls and their umbrella.

Other forces are caused by one part of a structure acting on other parts of the structure. This type of force is called an internal force. Examples include the tension in a stretched elastic and the compression caused by the weight of a roof pressing down on the walls of a building.

Describing Forces

Think about the last time you went out in a windstorm. You could feel the strength of the wind, and you noticed when the windspeed increased. You may have noticed the direction in which it was blowing. Sometimes, the wind may have acted on your whole body; at other times, you may have felt it only on your legs.

To describe how any force is acting on a structure, engineers talk about three main things: the force's magnitude, its direction, and the point and plane of its application (see Table 4.3). The point of application is the exact location where the force meets the structure. The plane of application is the side of the structure affected by the force.

Table 4.3 Describing Forces

Factors Used to Describe a Force	Question to Consider	Example
Magnitude	How big is the force compared to the size and weight of the object?	A gentle breeze causes a flag to flutter. In a very strong wind, the flag appears stiff.
Direction	Where is the force coming from?	If the wind is blowing into your face, it is difficult to walk. If the wind is blowing on your back, you can walk faster, but you might find it difficult to keep your balance.
Point and Plane of Application	Where does the force meet the structure?	Is the wind affecting the entire structure or just a part of it? A strong gust of wind at your feet might be enough to knock you over.

External Forces and Loads

Every structure needs to support a load. The total **load** is the sum of the static and dynamic loads. The static load is the effect of gravity on a structure itself. The dynamic load is the forces that move or change while acting on the structure. It is called "dynamic" because these forces change their magnitude, direction, and point and plane of application over time. Figure 4.18 shows the dynamic forces of the truck moving over the bridge and the wind on the bridge.

Think about a bookcase. Its static load consists of the materials that the bookcase is made from. Gravity acts on these materials whether there are books in the bookcase or not. All structures must be able to support their own weight.

WORDS MATTER

"Dynamic" means changing, and "static" means not changing.

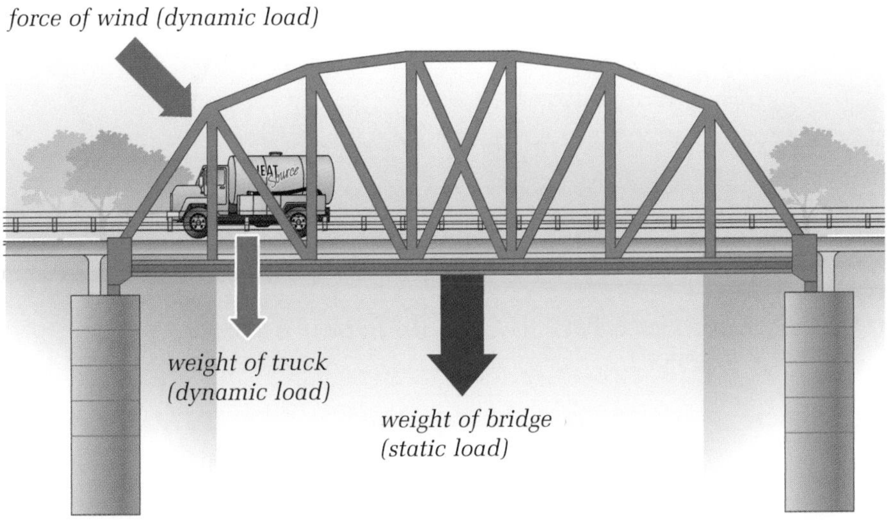

force of wind (dynamic load)

weight of truck (dynamic load)

weight of bridge (static load)

Figure 4.18 Forces acting on this bridge include the weight of the bridge (static load), as well as two dynamic loads: the weight of the truck and the force of the wind.

The dynamic load on the bookcase includes the weight of the books on the shelf. The size of this load changes with the number of books. The effect of this load also depends on where they are placed on the shelf (Figure 4.19).

When you design a structure, you want it to be able to support both its static and dynamic loads. If it is not strong enough, it may fail. If the structure is too strong, it may waste resources.

*Take It **Further***

Athletes' bodies experience these forces in many ways. Think of your favourite sport. Investigate the forces experienced by the athletes playing this sport, because of their own movements or because of the equipment they use. Begin your search at PearsonScience.

(a)   (b)   (c)

Figure 4.19 When the books are placed in the middle of the shelf (a), the shelf may sag from the unsupported dynamic load. If you place the books nearer the supports ((b) and (c)), the shelf does not sag.

Internal Forces

Reach one of your palms up toward the ceiling while reaching the other palm down toward the floor. Does it feel like your body (also a structure) wants to move in two different directions? You have just generated an internal force. This internal force is caused by one part of your body acting on another part. Other structures also experience internal forces.

Suggested Activity • • • • • • • •
B12 Quick Lab, page 113

Figure 4.20 Internal forces

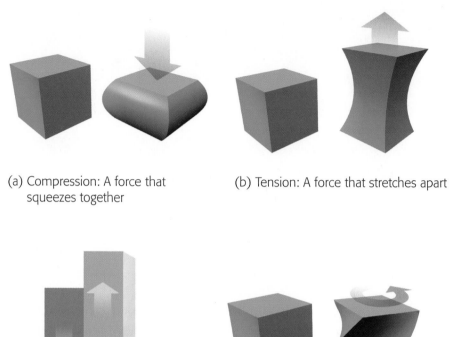

(a) Compression: A force that squeezes together

(b) Tension: A force that stretches apart

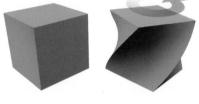

(c) Shear: A force that pushes in opposite directions

(d) Torsion: A force that twists

Depending on the direction in which they act, internal forces can be classified as compression, tension, shear, or torsion (see Figure 4.20). The twisting motion of the skater in Figure 4.21 causes torsion inside the skater's body. During other parts of the routine, the skater will experience other internal forces. During a lift, the skater doing the lifting experiences compression. Stretching of the arms to perform gestures may cause tension or shear, depending on the direction of the arms.

Designing for Forces

When engineers design structures such as bridges and large buildings, they consider all the forces that could affect it over its lifespan. For example, a bridge in winter has to support snow as well as the cars and trucks. Buildings in areas with a lot of earthquakes must be able to withstand the shaking without losing their windows or falling down.

The engineers often design large structures to withstand what they call a "100-year storm." This is an event that is likely to happen only once in 100 years. Storm damage you see on the television news is often from storms of this size.

Figure 4.21 The twisting motion causes torsion inside this skater.

What It Feels Like to Be a Structure

Figure 4.22 This person is experiencing compression of the neck muscles. This is similar to what a column might experience in a building.

It can be difficult to imagine how internal forces act on a structure. By using your body to act them out, you will learn more about the different types of forces.

Purpose

To experience compression, tension, shear, and torsion by using your body

Materials & Equipment

- space to move around
- a small textbook

Procedure

1. With a partner, determine how you can act out each of the forces using your bodies. Write down your ideas. For example, to experience compression, you might put the book on your head, as in Figure 4.22.

2. With your teacher's permission, carry out your ideas and record your observations in a chart like the one in Table 4.4.

Table 4.4 What It Feels Like to Be a Structure

Force	Action	Observations
Compression		
Tension		
Shear		
Torsion		

Questions

3. Discuss this activity with your partner. Talk about each action and how it felt. How might structures experience and react to this type of force?

4. Think of an everyday situation in which you experience each type of force (for example, when you reach for something on a high shelf or pitch a baseball). How does your body react to each of these forces?

5. Choose a structure. Suggest ways to minimize compression, tension, shear, and torsion on that structure.

Raise the Flag

Earlier, you observed the effect of wind on various plants. In this activity, you will study in more detail how wind affects structures.

Figure 4.23

Purpose

To investigate the effects of wind on a model flag

Materials & Equipment

- pencil
- piece of tissue paper
- string
- tape
- scissors
- plastic drinking straw
- sheet of note paper

Procedure

1. With a partner, make a model of a flag and flagpole out of the tissue paper, pencil, string, and tape, simulating the dimensions and the connections (see Figure 4.23).

2. Use the sheet of paper to make a fan. Wave the fan to create a wind effect on the flag. Record your observations.

3. Blow through the straw at different parts of the flag. Record your observations.

Questions

4. Describe how the flag moves when you use the fan. How does it change when you wave the fan at different parts of the structure (bottom, middle, and top of the pencil)?

5. Describe how the flag moves when you blow through the straw. How does it change when you blow through the straw at different parts of the structure (bottom, middle, and top of the pencil)?

6. How does using the paper fan demonstrate "plane of application" of a force?

7. How does using the straw demonstrate "point of application" of a force?

Key Concept Review

1. Define "force" in your own words.

2. What types of forces can act on structures? Give examples of each of these types of forces.

3. Categorize each of the following forces as internal or external.

   (a) gravity

   (b) compression

   (c) a strong wind

   (d) tension

4. A family of beavers builds a dam across a stream. Describe the forces that would act on this dam. Describe the magnitude, direction, and point and plane of application of each force.

Connect Your Understanding

5. Some roads have signs that specify a maximum load for the vehicles that travel on them. Why might this be?

6. Which forces are easier to anticipate and design for, internal or external? Why do you think this is so?

7. Describe the most common types of injuries sustained by players in your favourite sport. What does this tell you about the types of internal forces that affect the players' bodies?

Practise Your Skills

8. Consider a structure in your schoolyard. Describe the structure and its function, and classify it as frame, solid, or shell. Explain what internal and external forces it might be subjected to.

For more questions, go to PearsonScience.

B14   *Thinking about Science and Technology*

Damaged Structures

Every day, structures bear the brunt of external forces. Some are damaged by those forces; others are not.

What to Do

1. Describe a structure that you think was subjected to a large external force. What evidence causes you to think that it was subjected to this force?

2. What steps could have been taken to protect that structure from the force?

3. How might technology be used to prevent further damage to the structure?

4. Share your thoughts with a classmate or the whole class.

Here is a summary of what you will learn in this section:

• The function of a structure dictates how strong it must be.

• A good design takes into account the function of the structure.

• Symmetry is an important design consideration.

• Engineers ensure structural safety by using various design features.

Figure 4.24 Potholes are caused by freezing and thawing of the water in cracks in the road.

Figure 4.25 These trees were damaged by ice in Eastern Ontario in 1998.

Every day, you walk along sidewalks and are driven along roads. You may have seen and felt potholes in the roads (Figure 4.24). Occasionally, someone is injured when a roof collapses. Roofs are designed to withstand a certain "snowload." A large amount of snow can collapse a roof if it isn't shovelled off. A bridge spanning the Mississippi River collapsed in Minneapolis, Minnesota, in the U.S.A., killing several people. Natural structures also fail when forces are too strong for them (Figure 4.25).

Sometimes, the failure of a structure is tragic. But no one ever reports about the millions of bridges, buildings, and airplanes that do their jobs! These structures are inspected regularly. Occasionally, however, something fails. Whether the failure is a pothole or a bridge collapse, engineers learn from it and improve their designs to ensure safety.

In this section, you will learn about some of the ways in which designers plan safety into structures and the factors they consider when designing and monitoring them.

B15 *Starting Point*   Skills

Everyday Failures

Think about your everyday life. Perhaps your pencil broke just as you were finishing a math problem. The wind may have blown over your bicycle and bent a pedal.

As a class, brainstorm a list of structural failures that can happen at any time.

With a partner, pick three of the failures from the class list. Discuss each situation and write at least one possible cause for each failure.

Making Connections

Making connections to a topic helps readers keep their focus while reading, remember better what they read, and understand the topic more completely. As you read this section, think about the connections you can make to the topic of designing safe structures. Add any new information you learn to your structure mind map.

Preventing Failure

No one can design a structure to be 100% failure proof. The materials it is made from wear down over time. A person may use it incorrectly and break it. Unexpected forces might come into play.

Engineers use the techniques of risk management to reduce the risk of failure as much as possible. They deal with known risks in one of three ways: ignore the risk, avoid the risk, or design for the risk.

Some things that could happen to a structure are highly unlikely. For example, an elephant may walk into your room, sit on your chair, and break it. This is a highly unlikely event, so chairs are not designed with this in mind. This risk is ignored.

Most bridges are designed with supports that can withstand the impact of a ship. However, if a bridge is designed with no supports in the water (Figure 4.26), the risk of a ship collision has been avoided.

Designing for risk requires a thorough understanding of the structure and the forces that may affect it. Designers often over-compensate for the various risks, making the structure stronger than it really needs to be. They also build in safety features, such as backup systems and warning systems that may use sensors.

Figure 4.26 Boats cannot collide with the supports of this bridge, because they are not in the water!

Designing for Risks

Pencils are designed to withstand "normal use"—the force of day-to-day writing. They were not designed to withstand the force of a hammer! That risk was ignored by early pencil designers. As well, people do not use pencils underwater, so that risk could be avoided by designers.

Pretend you are the designer of another structure (your choice). What risks would you consider? What risks would you ignore or avoid? Share your ideas with a partner. Then, join with another pair and continue the conversation.

Write a summary of your ideas.

Figure 4.27 Have you ever seen the "maximum load" notice on an elevator?

Suggested Activity • • • • • • • •
B19 Inquiry Activity, page 121

Designing for Loads

When designing a structure, the designers must calculate the load it will need to support. A chair, for example, must be able to support itself. If the chair is designed for normal use, designers consider the range of people who might use the chair. Occasionally, more than one person might sit on the chair at one time. Thus, they design the chair to support more than itself plus the biggest occasional load. Some structures have warning notices about the maximum load they are designed to support (Figure 4.27).

Designing for Safety

In Ontario, all builders must follow the regulations set out in the Ontario Building Code. The code gives minimum standards for all aspects of a building, including load-bearing design and materials. The Ontario Building Code assures the public of a certain level of safety.

The Ontario Fire Code is a law that states that every home in Ontario must have working smoke alarms on every floor and outside all sleeping areas. A smoke alarm is a device that can detect smoke. Properly installed and working smoke alarms can warn people to get out of a burning building. This reduces the number of fire-related injuries and deaths.

Designing for Efficiency

Something described as "efficient" operates well without a waste of time, effort, or expense. For example, if two students build bridges that can support the same load, the bridge that uses the lesser amount of materials (usually by weight) is considered more efficient.

Sensors

A **sensor** is any device that can detect or measure real-world conditions. Different sensors can detect heat, light, pressure, or sound, as well as changes in the amounts of these things.

Sensors in a home include smoke detectors, carbon monoxide detectors, and thermostats. A thermostat (Figure 4.28) monitors ("senses") the temperature. Different thermostats control the heating and cooling in your home, and the temperature in your oven and your refrigerator. Thermostats respond to temperature changes by activating other equipment. When the furnace thermostat detects that the temperature in the house has gone down, it signals the furnace to turn on.

If a smoke alarm (Figure 4.29) detects smoke, it sounds a loud horn. Carbon monoxide detectors sound when they detect a build-up of deadly carbon monoxide gas.

Sensors are also used in entertainment. Perhaps you have played a computer game with a floor pad (Figure 4.30). Sensors in the pad send information to the computer about your dance steps. This results in a score for your performance, which motivates you to try to improve.

You may also have come into contact with motion detectors. In some buildings, lights turn on when someone enters a room. When you hold your hands under the tap in some restaurant washrooms, the water runs. Doors in many stores open as you walk toward them. These types of sensors all detect a change and activate equipment to respond accordingly.

Engineers use many types of sensors to ensure public safety. Sensors that can detect vibrations are frequently installed throughout new commercial buildings. Day-to-day vibrations from traffic are monitored by a computer. After a tornado or an earthquake, the computer can determine if the structure has been damaged and tell if it is safe to go back inside.

Figure 4.28 A thermostat. You set the temperature you want at the top, and the thermometer at the bottom reads the current temperature in the room.

Figure 4.29 Sensors can perform their functions properly only when they are in good working order.

Figure 4.30 Sensors are found in many devices from the practical to entertainment.

Take It *Further*

One type of sensor has been given the nickname "smart sensor." This simply means that the information collected by the sensor is processed by a built-in computer. Begin your search for smart sensors at PearsonScience.

Be an Inspector

One method used to ensure the safety of structures is visual inspection. Inspectors examine an existing structure for signs of weakness. These signs include cracks, warping, and rusting or corrosion of metal. Many everyday structures show these signs of weakness long before they fail, so the defects can be repaired. Structures are often modelled, and simulated forces are applied to the structures to test their limitations.

Purpose

To study everyday structures for signs of weakness

Materials & Equipment

- two identical, disposable food containers with lids

Procedure

1. Examine the disposable food containers and think about how they are used. Write down how you think the structure might show signs of weakness when it is used over and over again.

2. Put one of your containers aside. With the other container, simulate how you might use it. For example, you might wash it or put items into it. You might put the lid on and take the lid off and pour items out. Continue the simulation for 10 cycles. Record your observations in a chart like the one in Table 4.5.

Table 4.5 Signs of Weakness

Cycle #	Observations	Inferences

3. Compare the unused container with the one you used in the simulation. Record any signs of weakness.

4. Repeat the simulation for another 10 cycles and record observations again.

Questions

5. Did the structure show the signs of weakness you predicted?

6. How might you design the structure so that it lasts longer?

7. This activity simulates what would happen over a period of time. Suggest another situation in which simulations could be used to test a structure.

8. How would you design a sensor that could tell the owner when the food container was going to fail?

Loads to Measure

Figure 4.31

Bridges have to support huge dynamic loads throughout their length. In this investigation, you will simulate the load at different parts of a bridge by using a spring scale (see Figure 4.31).

Question

What is the effect of the location and the direction of a force acting on a structure?

Materials & Equipment
- straws
- tape
- spring scale

Procedure

1. Using straws and tape, construct a simple bridge to cross a gap of 50 cm. Place the bridge between two desks and tape the ends to the desks.

2. Simulate the load on the bridge by using a spring scale to pull down on the bridge in each of the following ways until the bridge just begins to bend. At that point, read the force on the spring scale, then release the scale.

   (a) Pull straight down from the centre of the bridge.

   (b) Pull straight down from one end of the bridge, close to the support.

   (c) Pull down at a 45° angle from the centre.

   (d) Pull down at a 45° angle from one end.

3. Record your measurement for each situation.

Analyzing and Interpreting

4. What was the difference between pulling straight down from the centre and from one end of the bridge?

5. What was the difference between pulling straight down and pulling at a 45° angle at the centre of the bridge? Was this result the same at the end of the bridge?

Skill Builder

6. How might you modify the procedure to increase the accuracy of your measuring?

Forming Conclusions

7. What do you conclude about the importance of knowing where a force will act on a structure?

8. Determine the weakest point on your bridge. If you were a bridge designer, where would you test your bridges for the maximum dynamic load it can support?

Key Concept Review

1. Describe some ways in which structures can fail. Why is it important to try to prevent these failures?

2. (a) Pick one structure that has to support a large load. Describe how it was designed for this load with safety in mind.

   (b) Repeat for a structure that has to contain something.

   (c) Were sensors incorporated into the design to increase safety?

3. In your own words, distinguish between "dynamic load" and "static load." Include an example to support your answer.

Connect Your Understanding

4. When engineers consider the forces that can act on a structure, they must think about all parts of the structure. Describe three different places on a bridge that would experience very different forces.

5. Make a list of all of the sensors you can think of in your school building. Describe the function of each sensor.

Practise Your Skills

6. You have been asked to design a desk to use for a laptop. What factors should you determine so that you can decide on the maximum load the desk can support?

7. Some structures show signs of stress long before they actually fail. Pick a structure in your classroom and describe any signs of stress you can see. Decide whether the structure needs to be repaired or replaced.

For more questions, go to PearsonScience.

B20 *Thinking about Science and Technology*

Safe Activities

What to Do

1. Make a T-chart. On the left side of the chart, list some of the activities you participate in, such as skating, bike riding, etc. Write a title for this column.

2. On the right side of the chart, list some of the structures that keep you safe while you do these activities.

Consider This

With a classmate or as a whole class, discuss the following questions.

1. How do each of the structures keep you safe?

2. What improvements could you make to any of the structures to keep you safer?

3. Why are you required by law to use some structures (such as a helmet when riding a bicycle) that prevent injury? Why is using other structures (such as elbow pads while riding a bicycle) optional?

Confederation Bridge

Figure 4.32 During winter, ice poses a threat to the Confederation Bridge.

Before May 1997, people took a ferry to get to Prince Edward Island. The ferry journey was long and you had to wait in line at each end. The Canadian and P.E.I. governments wanted a better way to make the journey. However, this solution had to be environmentally friendly, safe, and financially sound. A company called Strait Crossing Development Inc. won the privilege of designing, building, financing, and operating a bridge. This 12.9-km-long bridge would have to span waters that are ice covered in winter, as shown in Figure 4.32.

Many safety features were incorporated into the design, construction, and monitoring of the Confederation Bridge. For example, the "design life" of the bridge was 100 years. This is more than twice the design life of most other buildings and bridges. The bridge features over 750 sensors that monitor deformities in the bridge's concrete, changes in temperature, and vibrations caused by traffic or natural disasters such as earthquakes. Universities, the government, and private companies do the monitoring.

The Confederation Bridge has a 24-hour-per-day bridge patrol and visual monitoring. In addition, the maximum speed allowed on the bridge is changed according to weather conditions. In good weather, the maximum speed is 80 km per hour, and it takes about 10 minutes to cross the bridge.

In 1994, the Canadian Construction Association awarded the Environmental Achievement Award to Strait Crossing Development Inc. This award was given even before the bridge opened because the construction company took special care to ensure the safety of wildlife in both the water and the land affected by the construction of the bridge.

 A live web cam lets you see the Confederation Bridge in real time. This is especially interesting in rough weather. Go to PearsonScience for a link to the web cam.

Questions

1. Why was the bridge built?

2. What were some of the challenges of building this particular bridge?

3. What are some of the safety features incorporated into the bridge's design?

Key Concept Review

1. Review three ways in which structures can be classified. When might each classification system be best used? *K*

2. Classify the following list into three columns, titled Solid, Frame, and Shell: comb, candle, bridge, apple, ladder, egg, igloo, tent, car, book, house, and eraser. *K*

3. Define "form" in your own words. Sometimes designers design for form but sacrifice function. Describe a structure you have used that seems to fit this description. *C*

4. Define "function" in your own words. Sometimes designers design for function but sacrifice form. Describe a structure you have used that seems to fit this description. *C*

5. Describe three different structures that are useful for carrying school supplies. How are they similar in form and function? How are they different? What forces are these structures designed to withstand? *a*

6. For each of the structures below, describe its form, its function, and the forces that act on it. *K*

    (a) banana

    (b) laptop computer

    (c) elastic band

    (d) ice skates

    (e) shopping cart

7. For each of the following structures, describe the static and dynamic loads it must support. *a*

    (a) a road

    (b) a book

    (c) a CD jewel case

    (d) a wall of a house

8. For each structure in question 7, describe the magnitude, direction, and point and plane of application of an external

After Reading Thinking Literacy

Summarizing

Revisit your mind map to help you summarize what you have learned in the form of a 5-4-3-2-1-organizer. To do this, list:

- 5 key ideas you learned in this chapter
- 4 internal forces acting on structures
- 3 ways to classify structures
- 2 ways to prevent the failure of a structure
- 1 question you still have

ACHIEVEMENT CHART CATEGORIES
K Knowledge and understanding   *C* Thinking and investigation   *C* Communication   *a* Application

force that acts on it. Describe how each structure might experience at least one internal force. ⓐ

Connect Your Understanding

9. Suggest another way to classify structures that is not described in this chapter. What are the advantages and disadvantages of your method? ⓒ

10. Many structures are designed to be stronger than they need to be. Give an example of this and explain why. ⓐ

11. Think about the route you take between home and school. Briefly describe an example of each of the following that you pass: a shell structure, a frame structure, a solid structure, and the structure that supports the biggest load. ⓚ

12. Why do governments pass legislation to ensure minimum levels of safety in the design of structures? ⓚ

13. After some fires, firefighters have found that smoke alarms were either missing or not working properly. How can firefighters encourage people to make better use of these safety devices? ⓣ

Practise Your Skills

14. The human body and a house are both structures. Compare these two structures by explaining their similarities and differences. ⓐ

Unit Task Link

As you plan for your unit task, consider the form and function of different structures that use energy in your home. What forces affect them, and what safety features do they include? Think about how you could incorporate newer technology into one of these structures in order to improve the energy efficiency of your home.

B21 *Thinking about Science and Technology*

Structures and Technology

What to Do

1. Think about one activity that you do each day. What structures do you use in this activity? Do they put any stresses on your body?

Consider This

With a classmate, discuss the following questions.

2. Are the structures you use for that activity comfortable to use?

3. Are the structures ergonomically designed?

4. How could you improve the structures you use for that one activity?

Good design, materials, and construction make structures stable and strong.

Inuit people built this inukshuk to help travellers find their way.
"Inukshuk" means "something that performs the function of a person."

Figure 5.1 Your classroom has many structures that are made of different materials and held together by different fasteners.

Figure 5.2 The desk leg is welded to the horizontal bar and the length of the leg can be adjusted with a bolt.

Your classroom contains many different structures. Each structure has a form and a function. If you examine some of the structures, you will notice that the structures in your classroom are made up of many types of materials.

If you examine each structure even more closely, you will see that those materials are held together by different types of fasteners, such as bolts and welds (Figure 5.2), wire (Figure 5.3), and thread and glue (Figure 5.4).

The combinations of materials and fasteners used to build or manufacture structures can affect their stability and strength. Look at several different bookcases. You may notice that some of them sag in the middle and others do not. This may be due to the material they are made from. A shelf that does not bend may have been built using stronger or thicker material. On the other hand, the shelf may be supported with another structural component, for example, an extra piece of material.

Structures must be strong enough for their intended functions and to be able to withstand the forces that might affect them. This might mean adjusting the design, choosing different materials or altering construction techniques. Time and effort are needed in order to design effective structures.

In this chapter you will learn how structures are designed for strength, stability, function, and form.

Figure 5.4 Book pages are sewn together with thread, then glued into the binding.

Figure 5.3 These beads are strung together with wire.

B22 *Quick Lab*

Materials and Fasteners Hunt

Purpose

To generate a list of as many materials and fasteners as possible in 1 min.

Materials & Equipment

- stopwatch or watch with a second hand
- paper and pencil

Procedure

1. Write "Materials" on your sheet of paper.

2. When your teacher gives you the signal, start writing a list of all of the different types of materials you see around your classroom. Stop when the teacher gives you the signal that 1 min is up.

3. Turn your paper over and write "Fasteners" on your sheet of paper.

4. When your teacher gives you the signal, start making a list of all of the different types of fasteners you see in your classroom. Stop when the teacher gives you the signal that 1 min is up.

Questions

5. Look at your list of materials and your list of fasteners. How do the lists compare?

6. What do you notice about materials and their effect on form and/or function?

7. What do you notice about fasteners and their effect on form and/or function?

8. Choose a structure in your classroom. Imagine that it was made from a different material and put together with different fasteners. Would it have the same form or function? Would you be able to use it in the same way you do now?

Here is a summary of what you will learn in this section:

• A structure is stable if forces are balanced.

• Unbalanced forces can cause stress and fatigue in structures.

• Proper materials can be used to stabilize structures.

• Building techniques can be used to stabilize structures.

Figure 5.5 When the shelf looks bent like this one, it is under stress.

Most of us have sat on a wobbly seat at some time in our lives. Every time you shift in your seat, you get a little wobble. You could fold up some paper or cardboard and put it under one of the legs of the chair. Why does this stop the wobbling? Because you have balanced the chair.

You might have seen a bookcase shelf that sags in the middle (Figure 5.5). The sag shows that the structure is having trouble withstanding the weight of the books. What you can do to fix the sag depends on your situation. You could take some of the books off. However, if you have no other place to put the books, you might have to strengthen the bookcase itself.

In this section, you will look at what happens when structures are unstable and explore ways of stabilizing them.

B23   *Starting Point*   Skills Ⓐ Ⓒ

The Tipping Point

Hold your arms out in front of you at chest level, palms up, making a platform with your arms. Have a classmate put one textbook on your arms near your palms. Do you feel a slight urge to put your arms down? Have the classmate put another textbook on top of the first. Is the urge stronger? How many textbooks do you think you could support like this? In the end, would adding just one book cause you to drop all of the books? What if your classmate stopped at two textbooks? How long do you think you could hold your arms up?

Structural Strength

Some structures seem to stand the test of time. You may have seen the Colosseum in Rome or the pyramids of Egypt on television. These structures were built thousands of years ago and are still standing. On the other hand, some buildings may have to be demolished less than a century after they were built, because they have become unsafe (Figure 5.6).

Structural Shapes

Some of the strength of a structure lies in the shapes used in its design. You may have heard that the triangle is a very strong shape and is found in many structures. Squares and rectangles are not as strong as triangles. Three-dimensional triangular prisms and pyramid shapes are also stronger than three-dimensional rectangular prisms.

Figure 5.6 Some structures last thousands of years while others do not.

B24 *Learning Checkpoint*

Triangular Strength

Triangles are stronger than squares. Test this out for yourself using a few straws and some tape.

Bend one straw into a square (Figure 5.7a), one into a rectangle (b), and one into a triangle (c). Tape the ends of each straw together.

Rest each structure upright on the table. Gently push in the same plane as the shape on an upper corner of the structure. Which is the strongest?

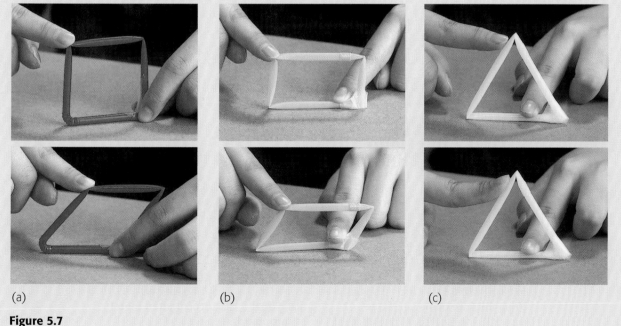

(a)   (b)   (c)

Figure 5.7

Good design, materials, and construction make structures stable and strong.   **131**

Structural Components

Suggested Activity • ·········
B27 Inquiry Activity on page 138

When you look at buildings, try to see that many of the same features appear in many different buildings. Arches, beams, and columns are used over and over again in building design because these **structural components** can add strength. Also, many people find them aesthetically pleasing. Several different structural components are shown in Figure 5.8.

Figure 5.8 Structural components

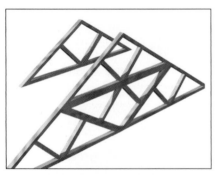

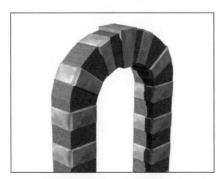

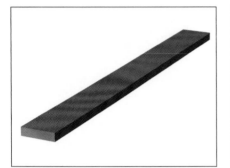

A beam is a flat structure that is supported at each end. If too much weight is put on a beam, it will bend in a u-shape or even break in the middle.

An **I-beam**'s shape gives it strength. I-beams have less weight than solid beams of the same length. Because they have less of their own weight to support, I-beams can support larger loads.

A **column** is a solid structure that can stand by itself. Columns can be used to support beams and I-beams.

A **truss** is a framework of beams joined together. Trusses are usually in the form of interlocking triangles.

A **cantilever** is a beam that is supported only at one end. When weight is placed on the other end of the beam, the beam bends in an n-shape to resist the load.

Girders, or **box beams**, are long beams in the shape of hollow rectangular prisms.

An **arch** can support a lot of weight. The force of weight on an arch is carried along the sides of the arch to its supports. This spreads out the effect of any load.

When a sheet of metal or cardboard is shaped into a series of pleats, or triangles, it is called **corrugated metal** or **cardboard**. A corrugated sheet is stronger than a flat sheet.

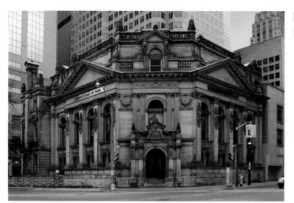

Figure 5.9 The Hockey Hall of Fame in Toronto

Structural components can be used alone or in combination. For example, the windows and door of the Hockey Hall of Fame building (Figure 5.9) are in the shape of an arch. The arch shape spreads the force of the load through both sides of the arch and into the foundation. The columns between the windows support beams on top. The triangle above the beam is similar to a truss.

Structural Materials

Imagine a bookcase made out of tissue paper. Imagine one made out of concrete. Both options seem silly, but for different reasons. A tissue paper bookcase is impractical because the material is too flimsy to withstand the load of the books. A concrete bookcase would be strong but extremely heavy and difficult to move into place. It is important to choose appropriate materials when designing and building structures.

Take It Further

Wood is an important building material. It is renewable if managed properly and can be used for many different structures. Recently, bamboo, a type of grass, has become a popular building material. Find out more about its advantages and disadvantages. Begin your search at PearsonScience.

Centre of Gravity

Can you balance a ruler on one finger? The only point that this can happen is at the exact middle of the ruler. Each half of the ruler is exactly the same, or symmetrical. This point is called the **centre of gravity**.

Every structure has a centre of gravity. This is the point that gravity seems to act on. The location of the centre of gravity in a structure helps to determine how stable the structure is. How would you determine the centre of gravity of something like a chair (see Figure 5.10)? When you sit on the chair, the centre of gravity of the chair plus the human is different from those of the chair and the human by themselves. That is why some stools tend to tip over only when someone sits down on them.

Suggested Activity • · · · · · · · · ·
B26 Quick Lab on page 137

Figure 5.10 The legs of the highchair are more splayed than those of an ordinary chair because its centre of gravity is higher. The splayed legs make the highchair more stable.

Figure 5.11 The clown falls over when you punch it, but returns to its upright position quickly. The clown did not really knock the person down!

Stability

Stability depends on materials and construction techniques as well as the centre of gravity. A table has a high centre of gravity but is usually stable if it has four legs relatively far apart. The closer together the legs are, the less stable it becomes. Stability is also determined by whether the structure is solid, frame, or shell—a solid structure with a high centre of gravity can be less stable than a frame table is.

Some structures are designed to be unstable (for example, a clown punching bag, Figure 5.11) or weak (for example, the front ends of cars and the water-filled plastic barrels at highway off-ramps that absorb a lot of energy, Figures 5.12 and 5.13).

Figure 5.12 A car would lose a lot of its energy hitting the barrels. It would be a lot less damaged than if it hit the pillar directly.

Figure 5.13 Many race tracks use bales of straw to protect the drivers and the audience from accidents.

When Things Go Wrong

Structural Stress and Fatigue

When a structure is poorly designed or built, it may not be able to withstand all of the forces it has to face. When a structure has to face large combinations of internal and external forces over a long period of time, the structure might weaken. This may result in structural **stress**. At first, signs of structural stress may disappear when the internal and external forces are reduced.

Figure 5.14 This old house shows structural fatigue. However, it may take several more wind storms before it fails completely.

For example, if you place an abnormally large book on the middle of a bookshelf, the shelf might bend. The bend in the shelf is a sign of stress. When the book is removed, the shelf may go back to its original shape. However, if the shelf cannot withstand the stress, it might crack. Permanent changes, like the bookshelf cracking, are signs of structural **fatigue**.

Structural Failure

If you ignored the structural fatigue and placed more large books in the middle of the shelf, the shelf may collapse. This is called structural **failure**. However, in this case, the failure would not be a surprise. The structure had already shown structural stress by bending, structural fatigue by cracking, and finally structural failure by collapsing.

As a structure ages, its materials may become brittle and break. Constant wind, rain, and snow can "weather" houses and barns until they look like the house in Figure 5.14.

WORDS MATTER

"Fatigue" means extreme tiredness. Both people and structures can be fatigued or tired out.

Take It *Further*

Demolition companies use several methods to demolish structures. Small buildings are bulldozed, very large buildings are imploded. Find out about these businesses, the equipment and procedures they use, and their safety records. Start your search at PearsonScience.

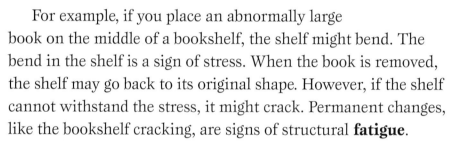

B25 *During Reading*

Thinking Literacy

Inferring

Sometimes the answer to a question can't be found in the text. Readers often have to draw conclusions using what they already know and new information or clues from the text to answer a question. This is called inferring or making an inference.

Have you ever heard the expression "It was the straw that broke the camel's back"? How could something as light and as small as a straw break a strong animal's back? Think about this and relate it to the activity you did with the textbooks on your arms. Share your inference with a partner.

Product Recalls

Despite all of the planning that goes into new structures, sometimes flaws are not discovered until the product is sold to the public. When the flaws are serious, manufacturers use a **product recall**. The manufacturers contact the media, who broadcast the recall on the news. They may also use their own advertising to alert the public. Consumers can take the affected product back to the store for a refund, for exchange for another model, or to have the affected structure fixed.

Sometimes, it is an issue with the materials used. For example, some children's toys have been recalled because it was discovered that the paint had high levels of lead. Lead can cause brain damage (Figure 5.15).

Sometimes, parts of a larger structure break off too easily. This is also a concern with toys because small parts can be choking hazards.

Child and baby car seats have been recalled when harnesses have been found to be faulty. A large video game company re-issued the safety straps on their popular controllers because the original ones broke under regular use. And thousands of owners of laptop computers got new batteries when the batteries in some of the computers overheated or burst into flames.

Cars are often the subjects of recalls. In this case, the owners take their cars back to the dealership for the necessary repairs at no charge to them.

Several years ago, a car was recalled because of a poor design: its gas tank was too close to the rear end. If these cars were rear-ended, they often burst into flames. The bad design cost several people their lives. The manufacturer had to replace vehicles with the flaw and pay compensation to the injured and the families of the deceased. As well, the news reports were very bad publicity for the company. As you can see, it is better to design well in the first place than to pay for bad design later on.

Figure 5.15 Because children often chew on their toys, the paint must not contain lead.

Stability

Figure 5.16 Candles come in many shapes. Some are less stable than others.

When you balance something like a ruler, it is simple to find the centre of gravity. Usually, however, the centre of gravity is not as obvious. It is not always easy to determine the centre of gravity of an object, but generally speaking, the lower the centre of gravity is on an object, the more stable the object is.

Some of the candles in Figure 5.16 have a small base and a high centre of gravity. They are more likely to tip than shorter, fatter candles are.

Purpose

To investigate centre of gravity of a variety of structures

> **CAUTION:** Handle sharp objects like scissors very carefully.

Materials & Equipment

- pencil and paper for recording
- ruler
- scissors
- paper for constructing
- tape

Procedure

1. Roll one piece of paper into the shape of a fat cone and tape it closed.

2. Roll another piece of paper into a thinner cone the same height and tape it closed.

3. Roll a third piece of paper into an even thinner cone, also the same height, and tape it closed.

4. Cut the bottom of each cone so that it can stand on the table with the pointed side up.

5. Test to see which cone is the most stable by trying to tip each one over.

6. Record your results.

7. Make three cylinders with different widths but the same height as your cones. Repeat steps 5 and 6.

Questions

8. Which cone was the hardest to tip over? Why? Compare your results with those of the class.

9. Which cylinder was the hardest to tip over? Why? Compare your results with those of the class.

10. Which shape was harder to tip over, cones or cylinders? Why?

11. What can you conclude about the location of the centre of gravity of each cone and each cylinder?

12. How can you use this information to build more stable structures?

B27 *Inquiry Activity*

Toolkit 2

SKILLS YOU WILL USE
- Designing a fair test
- Recording and organizing data

Structural Components and Materials

When designing and constructing a structure, you need to know about structural components and materials. In this lab, you will experiment with components and materials to learn more about their properties.

Questions

1. What are the properties of some structural components?

2. What is the effect of using different materials when building structural components?

Materials & Equipment
- various types of paper
- masking tape
- scissors
- a roll of coins for testing

CAUTION: Handle sharp objects like scissors very carefully.

Procedure

Part 1 The Components

1. Look at some of the structural components in Figure 5.8 on page 132. Choose three to build using photocopy paper and tape.

2. Build your components using as little tape as possible in each case.

3. Determine how strong each component is by using your coins.

4. Record your findings on a chart like the one in Table 5.1.

Table 5.1 Results of Components Test

Name of Component	Sketch	Results

Part 2 The Materials

5. Choose one of the components you tested above.

6. Build the componenet three times using a different type of paper each time. Try to use the same amount of tape and paper for each one.

7. Determine how strong each sample is by using your coins.

8. Record your findings in a table.

Analyzing and Interpreting

9. What did you find out about components in Part 1? Compare your results with those of another group.

10. What did you find out about materials in Part 2? Compare your results with those of another group.

11. Which component resisted the forces the best?

12. Which material resisted the forces the best?

Skill Builder

13. Could any parts of this test be made fairer? Explain how.

Forming Conclusions

14. What are some of the properties of the structural components you tested? Where would this component be useful?

15. What are some properties of the materials you tested? Where would these materials be useful?

Key Concept Review

1. Define "structural strength" and "stability" in your own words.

2. Briefly describe how each of the following contributes to structural strength.
   (a) structural shapes
   (b) structural components
   (c) structural materials

3. Use the words "structural stress," "fatigue," or "failure" to describe each situation below.
   (a) a bend in a plastic cup
   (b) a melted plastic cup
   (c) a hole in a plastic cup
   (d) a crack in a glass
   (e) a chip in a glass
   (f) pieces of shattered glass on the floor

Connect Your Understanding

4. Think of an ancient structure that exhibits one of the structural components. Compare it to a modern structure that uses the same structural components.

5. Think about a crumpled-up takeout paper cup. What factors could have contributed to that structure's failure?

6. Explain why a triangular shape is stronger than a rectangular shape.

Practise Your Skills

7. Think of the form and function of an inukshuk (Chapter 5 opener), an igloo (Figure 4.11), and a kayak (Figure 5.17). Choose one of these structures and do the following.
   (a) Draw a diagram to show its form.
   (b) Label any structural components present in the structure.
   (c) Describe the materials that are used to build it.
   (d) Repeat (a) to (c) for a structure of your choice.

Figure 5.17

8. Use commercial building materials such as interlocking blocks to build the tallest stable structure you can. Measure its height. Dismantle the structure. Using the same pieces, try to make the structure even taller. Is the second structure as stable as the first?

For more questions, go to PearsonScience.

B28 *Thinking about Science and Technology*

News Flash

Think about a recent product recall you heard about on the news. Determine the issue that prompted the recall. With a group of classmates, discuss the product recall. Use scientific terms from this chapter in your explanation.

5.2 Elements of Design

Here is a summary of what you will learn in this section:

- A good design takes into account the function of the structure.
- Good design considers the strength and stability needed by a structure.
- Symmetry is often used in good design.
- Ergonomic design of objects makes them easier to use.

Many structures, such as bicycles and ladders, are built to be strong and sturdy. If you use them properly, they will last a long time. Proper use includes not overloading them. For example, tricycles are not built to withstand the weight of a full-grown adult. The axle of a toy wagon is not designed to be as strong as the axle on a truck. Even stepladders meant for everyday use may come with warnings about the maximum load and against standing on the top rung (Figure 5.18).

Well-designed structures are safe, easy, and comfortable to use, and are strong enough for the job they are designed for. In this section, you will learn some of the elements of good design.

Figure 5.18 It is not safe to stand on the top rung of a stepladder.

B29 *Starting Point* Skills Ⓐ Ⓒ

Bicycles Built for Two

Work with a partner to identify structural differences in the two cycles in Figure 5.19. Suggest reasons for differences in the design and construction of these two structures. Communicate your results to another pair.

Figure 5.19 These two structures have the same function, but they were built to withstand different forces.

Elements of Good Design

All structures are designed and built for specific functions. How do you know if your structure has a good design? To find out, ask yourself these questions as you are designing and building.

Does my design link the structure to its function?

Sometimes this question is not as easy to answer as it might seem. Designing a simple structure for a simple function is quite easy. For example, a coffee table is a small structure designed to support small loads and add to the décor of a home. Designing a structure to fit a more complex function, such as a machine to pick peaches without bruising them, is much more complicated.

Can my design withstand the forces that the structure will encounter?

Good designers consider both the static and the dynamic loads that might affect the structure. Structures with similar forms may serve different functions. A coffee table made from pressed wood might withstand the forces in a home with a small child. A delicate glass coffee table may not survive in the same circumstances.

Is my design easy to build with the materials I want to use?

If you were asked to build a coffee table out of wood, another out of glass, and a third out of metal, would that affect your designs? Of course it would. Some materials are easier to cut and join together than others. Some materials can be bent while others cannot.

Is my design ergonomic?

An ergonomic structure minimizes stress on the user's body. The design and layout of office furniture and supplies often involves ergonomics. People who do repetitive jobs may suffer from repetitive strain injury if they are not using proper equipment and techniques to reduce the stress on their bodies. Figure 5.20 shows a wrist support that can help prevent repetitive strain injury to the wrists.

Suggested Activity • · · · · · · · ·
B33 Problem-Solving Activity on page 145

Take It Further

After a designer or an inventor designs a new structure, he or she applies for a patent. The patent is a legal document that says that the inventor owns the idea and can sell it. Find out about patents. Start your search at PearsonScience.

Figure 5.20 This keyboard has an ergonomically designed wrist support.

Figure 5.21 This boy controls his computer by moving his head from side to side.

Figure 5.22 What is aesthetically pleasing to one person may not be to another.

Ergonomics can be thought of as the science of people-structure relationships. An ergonomically designed structure is easy to use. It might be adjustable for different sizes of bodies. It might also support the body while the structure is in use. For example, some chairs offer extra back support so that the user avoids back pain if sitting for long periods of time.

Ergonomic designers also design special structures for people with disabilities. For example, someone with a broken arm might use a fork that has a cutting edge. Wheelchairs are often designed specifically for their riders, so they ride in comfort and can work the controls easily. And controls have been designed that can be operated by fingers, toes, eye movements, or even puffs of air (Figure 5.21).

Is my design aesthetically pleasing?

If you could choose any coffee table for your home, which would you choose? You might like either of the two shown in Figure 5.22, or you might hate both! All coffee tables have the same function, so why are there so many different forms? The main reason is that different people find different forms and shapes more aesthetically appealing than others. Some people find symmetry appealing. Others may enjoy something a little more unusual. Some may find a particular material more appealing because of its texture or colour. No matter what the structure, it will not be equally appealing to all people because aesthetic appeal is highly personal.

B30 *During Reading*

Thinking Literacy

Inferring

Readers can make inferences based on written or visual information. By connecting to their prior knowledge and experiences, readers can draw conclusions as to what is happening, why, what came before, or what will come next. Use your inferring skills to suggest why someone might buy either of the coffee tables in Figure 5.22.

Do I want my design to be symmetrical?

You may have noticed that many structures seem to have equal halves. This means that they are designed symmetrically. There are a number of reasons for this. Humans tend to like things to look symmetrical. It is aesthetically pleasing. Symmetrical things are usually also stable. Think about the wobbly chair. The wobble is caused because one of the chair legs is not the same length as the others. Symmetrical structures can spread the load more evenly. Humans and many other animals are also symmetrical in form (Figure 5.23).

Prototypes

When you are happy with the answers to all of these questions, you may have a good design. However, this does not mean that it is the best design possible. Something that looks fine on paper may not be as practical when you are using it. You often cannot know everything you need to know until you test your design. This is why manufacturers often make prototypes of a structure before they commit to a design.

A **prototype** is a model used to test and evaluate a design. If you are designing something really big, test a smaller prototype as much as possible before building the full-scale version. You should also test prototypes if you are designing something that you want to produce in large quantities. It would be awful to manufacture a million new pens and then find out that they are uncomfortable to hold!

Figure 5.23 The line of symmetry divides the object into two equal halves.

WORDS MATTER

"Proto" in the word "prototype" means first in time, earliest, or original. So a prototype is the first of its type ever made.

B31 *Learning Checkpoint*

Design and Function

In the last chapter, you learned about solid, frame, and shell structures. This was a way of thinking about structures based on how they were designed and constructed. You also considered packaging as a structure. This was a way of thinking about structures based on their function. How do you think design and function influence each other? Jot down a few ideas and share them with a partner. Then, join with another pair and continue the conversation.

Supporting a Load

Figure 5.24 Students use several different containers to carry their books to school.

Every day, you use your body as a structure to support a load when you carry things. Many students use a backpack or other type of bag to carry their material for school (Figure 5.24).

Purpose

To explore ways to carry a load

Materials & Equipment

- a backpack with adjustable straps
- a school bag (not a backpack)
- a shopping bag
- a typical load of books and school materials

Procedure

1. Put the schoolbooks and materials in the backpack.

2. Carry the backpack on one shoulder and record your observations of the internal forces you feel in your body.

3. Carry the backpack on both shoulders and record your observations.

4. Adjust the shoulder straps a little at a time to try to minimize the stress on your body. Record your observations.

5. Repeat the procedure with the school bag and with the shopping bag.

Questions

6. What is the best way for you to support the load of your schoolbooks and materials? Compare your choices with those of your classmates.

7. How does the best position relate to the centre of gravity of your body plus the bag?

8. What features of different bags are important when supporting a load?

9. What features would you put in the ideal bag for yourself?

SKILLS YOU WILL USE
- identifying possible solutions
- carrying out a plan

Newspaper Bookcase

Recognize a Need

You have been asked to design and build a bookcase using only newspaper and masking tape.

Problem

Can a bookcase be made from newspaper and masking tape that will support a textbook?

CAUTION: Handle sharp objects like scissors very carefully.

Materials & Equipment
- newspapers
- masking tape
- textbook
- scissors
- ruler

Criteria for Success
- The bookcase must stand up by itself.
- The bookcase must be constructed of newspaper and masking tape only.
- The bookcase must support at least one textbook for one minute.
- The best bookcase must pass criterion 3 and be built with the least amount of material.

Brainstorm Ideas

1. What shape should the bookcase have?

2. How big should the bookcase be?

3. What structural components should be incorporated into the design?

Build a Prototype

4. Draw sketches of a few different designs for your bookcase. Discuss the pros and cons of each design with your group.

5. Decide on the design you would like to build and check your design with your teacher.

6. Gather the materials you will need and build your bookcase.

Test and Evaluate

7. Place the books on the bookcase. Check the time to see if your bookcase meets the design criteria. Keep working until you have a design that works.

8. When you have a design that works, study it to decide how you can improve it. Could you use less material? Could you make it stronger? Could you make it more aesthetically pleasing?

9. Modify your design and build another model.

Communicate

10. Create a chart with a diagram of your finished bookcase. Highlight the structural components and the materials you used that made your design a good one.

Key Concept Review

1. Why must a good design take into account the function of the structure?

2. What is symmetry and how might it affect the design of structures?

3. What might be the consequences of ignoring the strength and stability needs of a structure?

4. List the elements of design and describe how each might have been considered by the designer of the desk you are sitting at.

Connect Your Understanding

5. Think about the structures you use every day. Which structure do you think is an example of good design? Which structure is an example of poor design? What design question(s) do you think the designer could have answered better?

6. Prototypes are often expensive to build because each component must be made specifically for the prototype. Why would manufacturers invest in the development of a prototype?

Practise Your Skills

7. In this section, you built a newspaper bookcase to support one book. Rebuild your bookcase using different shapes, different components, or different materials in order to improve its form and function.

8. If you could choose to build any type of bookcase, what would you choose? Outline the design features that you think would be the most important in your decision.

For more questions, go to PearsonScience.

B34 *Thinking about Science and Technology*

An Aging Population

As consumers age, they look for structures that are easier to use. People with arthritis in their fingers may find it easier to use kitchen utensils with larger, more ergonomically designed handles.

What to Do

1. Gather several examples of one type of kitchen utensil.

2. Hold and pretend to use each kitchen utensil. In one sentence, describe how easy it is to use each one.

Consider This

3. Share your findings with a classmate or the whole class

4. Identify trends in the findings.

5. How does each utensil exhibit the elements of good design? Do well-designed utensils function more effectively than poorly designed utensils do?

6. What role does aesthetics play in kitchen utensil design?

Beth Anne Currie,
Children's Environment and Health Consultant

Figure 5.25 Beth Anne Currie

Beth Anne Currie works for Canadian Partnership for Children's Health and the Environment (Figure 5.25). In her role as a children's environment and health consultant, she works to protect children from exposure to environmental contaminants. Her specialty is the design and marketing of green roofs and living walls. These elements can improve the environmental conditions for people who live in cities.

This is a long way from—but connected to—Currie's start as an emergency room nurse. She helped people then and still does. After working through a water-borne disease outbreak, she decided to go back to university to study the environment.

Green Roof Design

Green roofs are made from different materials and need to be stronger than traditional roofs. They can reduce the volume of storm water run-off, improve air quality, and reduce the roof surface temperature. This makes the building cooler.

While Currie designs the roofs, it takes a team of people to build and maintain them. The tradespeople and horticulturalists must understand green roof construction. Informational technology experts regulate the irrigation system through the use of sensors and specialized computer programs.

Currie's advice to people interested in a job like hers is to get advanced training in health care or the environment. An interest in ecology is essential. Asked what keeps her motivated, she replied, "When you're committed to ensuring we protect our environment, there's usually so much happening on the opposite side of that issue that you can't help but be fired up about how you can help, or who you can write a letter to, or where you can get funding to support something good!" Learn more at PearsonScience.

Questions

1. How might knowledge of structures help in the design of green roofs?

2. Why would an interest in ecology be an asset to someone interested in this type of work?

3. In the future, if you consider building a green roof, what other information would you need in order to help you make the decision?

Key Concept Review

1. Describe several factors that contribute to a structure's stability. ⓚ

2. What is the role of symmetry in the design of structures? ⓚ

3. (a) Explain why knowledge about the centre of gravity of structures is important to designers. ⓚ

   (b) How does changing the location of the centre of gravity of a structure affect it? ⓚ

4. Name three structural components and explain how they contribute to a structure's strength and stability. ⓐ

5. Explain how each of the following affects the strength and stability of a bicycle. ⓐ

   (a) choice of materials

   (b) structural shapes

   (c) structural components

Connect Your Understanding

6. Why might a designer choose a material that is not the strongest available? ⓣ

7. Describe a structure in your home that makes use of several different structural components. Include a sketch and label the components. ⓐ

8. Many structures, such as clothes, furniture, and cars, change as fashion changes. Why do you think this is? ⓒ

9. Most consumers do not design, construct, and test their own bookcases. Some buy ready-to-assemble furniture; others buy furniture already assembled. What are the advantages and disadvantages of these two types of furniture? ⓣ

After Reading *Thinking Literacy*

K-W-L Review

At the beginning of this chapter, you created a K-W-L chart. Now that you have completed the chapter, take a few minutes to record information in the "What I Learned" column. You probably have more questions too. Write at least three more things you would like to learn more about. Make a plan on how you could find out more about each of these things.

ACHIEVEMENT CHART CATEGORIES
ⓚ Knowledge and understanding   ⓣ Thinking and investigation   ⓒ Communication   ⓐ Application

10. Describe one local structure that is a good example of the effective use of structural components. Explain why you think the components are used well. (a)

11. Using the Elements of Good Design as a guide, describe what you feel to be the best-designed structure in your classroom and in your school. (a)

Practise Your Skills

12. Using straws and tape, build a structure that stands by itself and shows at least two structural components at work. (t)

13. Estimate the maximum load that your desk was designed for. How could you test this? (a)

Unit Project Link

As you think about what you would like to design to improve your home's energy efficiency, consider the role of stability in your structure. Review the elements of good design as you consider each of your ideas. Can you make use of other designers' ideas to help you with your decisions?

B35 Thinking about Science and Technology

Car Sales

Once consumers decide to buy a car, they have to choose which car to purchase.

What to Do

1. List three car models that you know.

2. Access consumer information about these cars either on the Internet or from another source.

3. Prepare a chart comparing the three cars based on the factors of cost, fuel efficiency, and safety rating.

Consider This

With a classmate or as a whole class, discuss the following questions.

4. What might prompt a consumer to decide to purchase a car?

5. How might each of the factors listed in your chart influence a buyer's decision?

6. Relate the car's safety rating to the terms "structural stress" and "structural failure."

7. What product recalls, if any, have affected the cars you researched?

8. If you were asked to design a new and improved car, discuss a change you would make to improve safety and one you would make to increase aesthetics.

6.0

The lifespans of structures need to be considered to make responsible decisions.

People buy things, use them for awhile, then discard them. Scrap metal (shown here), aluminum, paper, glass, and plastic are separated from each other and recycled.

What You Will Learn

In this chapter, you will:

- describe factors that make a structure aesthetically appealing
- recognize and describe the lifespan of familiar structures

Skills You Will Use

In this chapter, you will:

- analyze the role of consumers in the manufacture of structures
- make a personal plan of action with respect to lessening your impact on the environment

Why This Is Important

Every decision you make about purchasing something can affect Earth. Many purchases come in some kind of packaging. Sometimes we purchase things we do not really need. Most of our purchases end up as waste. Understanding these issues will help you make responsible decisions.

Before Writing

Thinking Literacy

Question and Answer Pattern

Writers of non-fiction use a variety of organizational patterns to communicate information and ideas. They try to choose a pattern that will give readers what they want or need to know about a topic. Sometimes writers use the pattern of asking and answering questions. Scan Unit B for headings that appear as questions. Do answers directly follow the questions? Why might the writer have chosen this pattern for organizing this topic? Where else have you seen this pattern used?

Key Terms

- consumer
- manufacturer
- market research
- lifespan

Figure 6.1 Technology allows people to communicate in a wide variety of places and situations.

It's difficult to imagine a time without telephones! In the 1870s, Elisha Gray and Alexander Graham Bell experimented with devices that could transmit speech electronically. Bell was the first to patent the invention. Back then, no one could walk around outside while talking on the phone (Figure 6.1). Early phones were large, and were bolted to the wall (Figure 6.2).

These days, many families have more than one telephone. There may be an extension in every room. Some families have a cellphone for each member. What happens to all of the old phones? Landfill sites contain many old phones, along with the television sets, computers, clothes, and plastic toys (Figure 6.3).

Figure 6.2 The design of telephones has changed over the years. Early in the 20th century, you paid for each call. Your calls would be shorter and mainly to give information. Now, calls are much longer, as people use the phone to "keep in touch."

Many of these products still worked when they were discarded. Perhaps they were replaced by newer models. Perhaps they outgrew their usefulness to their owner but could have been useful to someone else.

What makes someone buy a new phone? For some people, it is because the old phone broke. For other people, it is because a newer model came along. In this section, you will consider some of these issues.

Some of the ideas in this chapter will generate different points of view. It is important to think about each idea. Discussing ideas openly and respectfully, especially with people who may not agree with you, is a good way to gain insight.

Figure 6.3 Old cellphones end up in landfill sites.

B36 *Quick Lab*

How Many Phones?

Purpose

To examine the impact of one technology on the environment

> **Materials & Equipment**
> - an old telephone
> - paper and pencil

Procedure

1. Examine the phone and make a list of the materials you observe in its construction.

2. Write how you think phones are disposed of when they are no longer useful.

3. Estimate the number of phones your family owns at the present time.

Questions

4. How might you estimate the number of phones owned by the families in your class? How might you do this for your entire school?

5. Estimate the number of telephones that are owned by families in Canada.

6. How do you think you could estimate the number of business phones in Canada? Should it be half, the same, double, or more? Imagine a pile of all the phones in Canada. What would it look like?

7. Find out if phones can be recycled when no longer useful.

Here is a summary of what you will learn in this section:

- Manufacturers try to determine consumer need in order to make good decisions about products.
- Consumers make purchases based on needs and wants.
- Ergonomics may be a consideration in some purchases
- Consumers can influence manufacturers to make good products.

You are a **consumer**, a buyer of things (Figure 6.4). Each time you buy something, you have made a decision. Sometimes the decision is small, such as the type of drink you would like with your lunch. At other times your decision might be bigger, such as an item of clothing or a bicycle. Some day, you may make a decision to buy (or not buy) a car. You may purchase a home. How do people make these decisions, and why are manufacturers so interested in your decision making?

In this section, you will answer these questions and learn about the relationship between manufacturers and consumers.

Figure 6.4 A shopping mall is one place where consumers make decisions about purchases.

B37 *Starting Point*

Skills

Reading Advertisements

Collect advertisements for jeans from magazines, newspapers, and flyers. If you could pick any one of the pairs of jeans to have for your own, which one would you pick? Why? Discuss the reasons for your choice with a partner.

Manufacturers

Manufacturers are interested in what you think. They want to produce products that you will want to buy. They hope that even if you are not in charge of buying a particular product, your family will be influenced by what you think.

Figure 6.5 Some manufacturers store products in warehouses like this one.

Manufacturers have to sell their products in order to remain in business (Figure 6.5). However, there are many manufacturers, and each one wants you to choose their product. You, as the consumer, have to make the decisions about how you will spend your money. Manufacturers know that each consumer has a limited amount of money to make their purchases, so they compete for "the consumer dollar" through advertising campaigns.

Market Research

Before manufacturers design a new product, they need to be reasonably sure that someone will want to buy it. They do not want to commit a lot of time and resources to manufacturing the product just to find that no one wants it. Shoes are an example. Before designing yet another brand of running shoes, the manufacturer has to gather and evaluate some data. This is called **market research** (Figure 6.6).

Figure 6.6 Market researchers often survey shoppers in malls.

You may have been asked to answer questions for a survey at a mall, on the telephone, or on the Internet. Market researchers ask people to give an opinion so that they understand what consumers are thinking. The researchers report to the manufacturer on whether they think that people will buy those shoes.

These days, technology is an important part of gathering market research. Each time a consumer uses a credit, debit, or point collection card, information is entered into an enormous database. This information reveals important trends, such as the popularity of certain brands or colours.

Suggested Activity • · · · · · · · ·
B39 Design a Lab on page 159

Consumers are becoming increasingly concerned about the environment, so many manufacturers have designed products to meet this demand. Your favourite stores may have switched to resusable shopping bags instead of thin, disposable plastic bags. You can also find clothing made from materials such as seaweed and bamboo.

Advertising

Manufacturers use many different ways to convince you that their product is best. Some advertise on radio or television, in magazines, and on the Internet (Figure 6.7). Some provide incentives such as mail-in rebates to try to convince consumers that they are getting a good deal. Some hire famous people to endorse their products. They think that consumers will feel that products endorsed by celebrities have more status.

Figure 6.7 Internet use has brought new forms of advertising: pop-up ads, banner ads, and hover ads.

B38 *During Writing*

Anticipating Readers' Questions

Throughout this chapter you will consider the impact of choosing "greener options" in your everyday life. Researchers in science and technology have developed many ways to recycle used and discarded products into new, useful materials and products.

Work with a partner to create a list of possible questions and answers you think readers may have about recycled materials and products. You will need to make some decisions about audience and format before you begin. Will your audience be the other students in your class, parents in the community, or someone else? Will you use a poster, brochure, or other format? The choices you make will help you decide on the questions you will ask. Develop an outline or graphic organizer to record possible questions. As you read more of this chapter, use this organizer to keep track of information and ideas that will help you answer your questions.

Being a Wise Consumer

When consumers are faced with decisions about what to buy, they need to use certain skills in order to make good choices. If you were interested in buying a car, you would probably take the car for a test drive. If the car will be used by your whole family, you may take everyone with you to make sure the car has enough space for car seats or pets.

Even with small purchases, you should take the item for a "test drive." If you were buying a cellphone, you may hold different phones in your hands to see how they feel. You may dial a few numbers to see if the keypad is easy to use (Figure 6.8). You might call a friend to test the sound quality. All of these tests give you more information so that you can make a wise decision.

WORDS MATTER

"Wise" is an adjective that is related to the noun "wisdom." Some people say that wisdom is a combination of knowledge plus experience.

Figure 6.8 Some people prefer a large keypad while others prefer a smaller one.

Another part of being a wise consumer is to let manufacturers know if you are unhappy with a purchase. Most manufacturers are eager to improve products if people have problems with them. Perhaps the running shoes you bought came with weak laces that broke the third time you tied them. Maybe you accidentally turn your cellphone off every time you put it into your pocket. You could let the manufacturer know about these issues by phoning, e-mailing, or writing them.

Needs and Wants

Have you ever asked for something by saying, "Please, please, I really need it"? Your mom or dad may have disagreed with you about whether you actually "needed" the expensive running shoes or just "wanted" them (Figure 6.9). Sometimes you have to decide whether you need something or just want it.

It is easy to become confused about whether something is a need or a want. People need certain things to stay alive. The basic needs are food, water, oxygen, energy, and a suitable habitat. Where do fancy shoes fit in?

Take It Further

Organizations such as Industry Canada or Consumers Union try to make it easier for consumers to make decisions about buying products. They often test products to see if they live up to their claims or prepare questions for consumers to consider when they are deciding to buy certain items. Find out what one of these organizations (or a similar one) says about cellphones. Begin your search at PearsonScience.

Suggested Activity • • • • • • • • •
B40 Quick Lab on page 160.

Figure 6.9 Often, it is difficult to tell one brand of shoe from another.

Aesthetics

Sometimes it is not the strength or stability of a structure that makes a consumer decide to buy it. Sometimes it is "just something about the way it looks." You might like the colour. You might like the shape. You might pick it because it has an aesthetic quality that appeals to you. Antique cars, like the one shown in Figure 6.10, appeal to some people, while other people just want a car that will get them from one place to another.

Figure 6.10 Some people like antique cars because of their aesthetic quality.

Ergonomics

A well-designed product is a pleasure to use. When scientific research is used in the design of the product, manufacturers often add the label "ergonomically designed" to the packaging. Some consumers consider this very important, especially for products that are used over and over again. Items from pens to seats can be designed to minimize stress on the human body when they are used.

Universal Design

Designers have become much more conscious of the concept of universal design. The term "universal design" refers to structures that can be useful to many different users. For example, in the past, people thought that ramps and doors that open at the push of a button were just for people in wheelchairs (Figure 6.11). However, these features are equally useful to older people, people pushing strollers, and people carrying large loads.

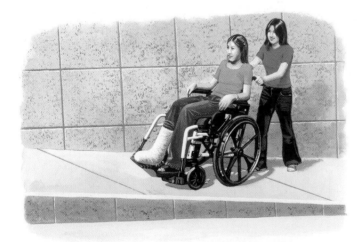

Figure 6.11 Many buildings have ramps leading to the doorways.

Surveying the Market

Surveys. You may get them in the mail. Your school might send them home to gather information. You might be sent one by e-mail after visiting a retailer. Manufacturers often survey the general public to find out if a new product will sell.

Purpose

To develop a survey to collect information that would be useful to a manufacturer who is developing a product to meet a societal need

---

Materials & Equipment

- pencil
- paper
- access to computer
- examples of surveys

Procedure

1. Look over examples of surveys to see how other people write them.

2. Work with a partner to think of a societal need, such as the need to increase home composting, the need to reduce the use of electricity, the need to prevent injury when using electronic devices, or something else that interests you.

3. Design a survey form that you could use to gather information about whether this need concerns your peers, and what product they would require to meet this need.

4. Make a draft of your survey questions, paying attention to the following:

   (a) Does your form protect people's privacy and encourage honest reflection?

   (b) Will your questions provide data that you can analyze and graph?

   (c) Is there a way for people to give you "comments"?

   (d) Will people be able to complete the survey quickly and accurately?

   (e) Will you leave the survey with people for them to complete on their own, or will you ask each individual the questions and record the answers yourself?

   (f) Will you provide an incentive for people to respond to your survey?

   (g) Can you use a method that does not involve pencil and paper to collect the information?

5. Design a one-page form in an attractive, easy-to-use format. You may use a computer and word processing software.

6. Decide with your teacher who you will ask to fill out your survey. Conduct the research.

Questions

7. Examine your completed surveys. Decide on a method to organize your data so it can be analyzed.

8. Complete the data analysis.

9. Write a paragraph that summarizes your findings.

10. Based on your findings, what course of action would you follow in the development of your product?

Wise Choices

Figure 6.12 Advertisements are designed to convince consumers to buy that particular product.

Before you buy a product, you have to decide which brand you want at which price. Picking the right one takes some research.

Purpose

To create a checklist of considerations for purchasing a cellphone

Materials & Equipment

- pencil
- paper
- highlighter

Procedure

1. On a piece of paper, make a list of all of the things you would like your ideal cellphone to do (Figure 6.12). For example, you may want your phone to act as a camera too.

2. On the same piece of paper, make a list of all the physical features you would like your ideal phone to have. For example, you may want your phone to have a durable shell because you may drop it.

3. Highlight each item on your list that is a "need." For example, you need to be able to make reliable phone calls. However, a cellphone's ability to play music may not be a need. Although it is a nice feature, it is not essential to the functioning of the phone. Usually, extra features add to the overall cost of an item. However, they may make a product seem more appealing.

Questions

4. Consider your list with a classmate. Do you have similar needs and wants? Why do you think this is?

5. Some cellphones have many features. Could some of these features be neither a need nor a want?

6. Based on your research, would it be better to buy a telephone plan that includes a free phone, or to buy a cellphone and pay a monthly fee? Are there any other things you should consider?

Key Concept Review

1. Explain the concepts of "ergonomics" and "universal design." How might they affect buying decisions?

2. Describe how each of the following factors relates to being a wise consumer.
   (a) advertising
   (b) needs and wants
   (c) aesthetics

3. What do you think it means when an object is described as "aesthetically pleasing"? Give three examples of objects you find aesthetically pleasing.

Connect Your Understanding

4. In order for them to be wise consumers, why should people be aware of how manufacturers think?

5. Imagine that you have been hired to do market research for a manufacturer of sun hats. Prepare three questions you would include in your survey.

6. When you read advertisements, it is sometimes useful to maintain "healthy scepticism." Why might this be the case?

Practise Your Skills

7. Think of an item your family uses every day, like tissue paper, soap, or bread. Make a list of the items and list the brands your family usually buys next to each item. If you do not always stick to the same brand, note that too. Why does your family make those purchasing decisions?

For more questions, go to PearsonScience.

B41 *Thinking about Science and Technology*

Science and Advertising

Advertisers often use so-called "scientific" claims in order to promote their products.

What to Do

1. Recall three advertisements that use scientific claims.

2. Make a three-column chart to summarize these ads. Use the headings Product, Scientific Claim, and Expert Cited.

Consider This

As a class, discuss the following questions.

3. Why might manufacturers use these types of claims in their advertising?

4. When do you think these types of claims are the most effective?

5. When do these claims make you doubtful?

6. How do scientific claims affect your buying decisions?

Here is a summary of what you will learn in this section:

- Every structure has a lifespan.
- Structures are designed with the lifespan in mind.
- Responsible manufacturers and consumers consider the safe disposal of structures in their decision-making.
- Disposal of structures can affect the environment.

Figure 6.13 You often find baby items at a rummage sale.

When you were born, your parents likely purchased a crib, a highchair, a car seat, and several other things. When you grew older, what became of these items? Perhaps your younger brothers and sisters are using them. Maybe the items were sold or given away when they were not needed anymore.

Some items, such as the highchair, serve a function for a set amount of time. Young children need highchairs from the time they can sit up until they can sit at the table on a regular chair. With other items, the decisions are not as easy.

People have several ways of disposing of unwanted products. They can sell them at a garage sale, give them to a friend, or give them to a charity rummage sale (Figure 6.13). They can re-use boxes, jars, and other containers. They can compost organic waste or put it in a green bin. They can recycle glass, paper, plastic, and metal. On the other hand, they can just throw everything out with the garbage.

In this section, you will learn about the lifespans of different structures. You will find out how people decide when and how to dispose of those structures when they no longer need them.

B42 *Starting Point*

Skills Ⓐ Ⓒ

Where Did It Go?

Think back to your favourite thing when you were young. Did you have a special stuffed animal or a special blanket? You may have photographs of you with your favourite thing, or you may still have it. Write down as much about your favourite thing as you can. When did you get it? How did you use it? Has it changed since you first got it? If you do not have it any more, why not? Share your memories with a partner.

Everything Has a Lifespan

You may be familiar with the term "lifespan." Perhaps you learned about lifespans when you studied living things in the past. You understand that every living thing is born, lives, and dies. Did you know that structures have lifespans too?

Think about the lifespan of a pencil or your school building. How are they alike? How are they different? Discuss your ideas with a partner. Be prepared to share your thoughts with the class.

The Lifespan of a Product

Every product has a lifespan. This lifespan starts as an idea and goes through several steps before it is even available to consumers. More steps in the life cycle take the product through its use to its disposal. Not all products go through every step in the life cycle, however, as illustrated by the windshield wiper example in Table 6.1 on the next page.

Suggested Activity •·········
B45 Decision-Making Analysis on page 167.

How Long Should a Product Last?

When manufacturers plan a product, they have to answer this question. If a shoe manufacturer made shoes that wore out quickly, consumers would feel that they did not get their money's worth. If it made shoes that never wore out, the shoes might cost too much and people would not buy them. If people did buy them, the manufacturer might never sell any more shoes!

WORDS MATTER

The noun "obsolescence" comes from the adjective "obsolete," which means "discarded" or "out of date."

When a manufacturer deliberately designs a product with a limited lifespan, it is called **planned obsolescence**. The materials and technology used guarantee that the product will not last as long as the consumer might want. Also, fashion often dictates how long a product will be used. Many people have unfashionable clothing in their closets that they don't wear any more.

Figure 6.14 These windshield wipers are over 50 years old.

Figure 6.15 Modern windshield wipers are stronger than the old ones.

Table 6.1 From Idea to Disposal

Step in the Process	Description of Process	Example
Idea	The inventor thinks of a new idea for a product or a modification to an existing product.	In 1902, Mary Anderson was riding a streetcar in New York City during a snowstorm. She watched the streetcar driver try to see by leaving the windshield open and letting the cold weather into the car.
A model	The inventor creates designs to try out to decide which one is best.	Mary Anderson made sketches for a windshield wiper that showed a lever on the inside that was attached to a wiping mechanism on the outside.
Choosing materials	Materials are chosen for the components of the product.	She hired a company to make a model out of wood and rubber strips.
Research	The inventor may need to learn more about materials or how to improve the design of the product.	In 1903, Mary Anderson was awarded a patent for the windshield wiper design.
Improving the design	After research, it might be necessary to change the design so that it lasts longer, is easier or cheaper to make, or uses different materials.	After Anderson's patent expired in 1920, car manufacturers improved the design. Figure 6.14 shows an old car with its windshield wipers.
The prototype	With some products, designers make working models instead of a full-scale version of the final product. This prototype is made to ensure that everything works as planned and that the final product will be easy to manufacture.	There is no record of Anderson's prototypes.
Market research	Information is gathered to find out how much of the item should be produced. Researchers also find out how much people are willing to pay for the item	Anderson wrote to a large company to sell them her design but they were not interested.
Production	The manufacturer decides where and how the product will be made and starts making them.	Anderson was discouraged and did not develop the idea herself. However, some car companies did use it, and she received royalties for her invention until the patent expired. Today, windshield wipers are installed on every automobile manufactured.
Advertising	The public is informed that there is a new product for them to buy. Sometimes, this step happens months before the product is even available to the public.	Since the windshield wipers come on automobiles, there is not much direct advertising. However, replacement wiper blades are heavily advertised.
Distribution	The product is sent to retailers or directly to the consumer. Figure 6.15 shows windshield wipers on a new car.	Most windshield wipers are manufactured for automobile manufacturers. Replacement wipers and blades are sold to car dealerships and automotive stores.
Consumer's choice	For each product they buy, consumers often have to choose among several different brands.	Some companies advertise specialty wipers for different seasons so that consumers can change them to suit local weather conditions.
Disposal	When the product breaks, wears out, or is no longer needed, it is discarded. It may be composted, re-used, recycled, or sent to a landfill.	When wipers wear out, they are generally sent to landfill.

Something like a game system might be designed to last a few years (Figure 6.16). Manufacturers know that the technology used in the games is always changing. In a few years, the consumer may be ready to buy something new.

Even buildings are not designed to last forever. Home-owners and building maintenance people know that their buildings must be cleaned, maintained, and occasionally renovated to keep them in good shape. The eavestroughs have to be cleaned regularly. The shingles and siding might have to be replaced every 20 years.

Figure 6.16 When new game systems come out, people stop using the old ones.

Product Disposal

When people make purchasing decisions, they do not always think about what will eventually happen to the product when it breaks or they don't want it anymore.

Many people think that the lifespan of a product ends when the garbage truck picks it up. However, it doesn't actually end until the product breaks down. This can take years, even at a landfill. Recycling, re-using, and composting are often better than a landfill site is.

If you know that a product is recyclable after use, would you choose to buy it instead of a similar item that is not recyclable? Some items can be sold to another owner. Cars, clothing, and toys often get resold instead of thrown out (Figure 6.17). Eventually, however, items wear out and become unusable. Then they end up in landfills or recycled.

Figure 6.17 People often sell bicycles or cars privately.

Take It *Further*

"Manufacturing" means to organize the way something is made. Usually, this is done to make a large number of the same item. Manufacturing might involve the use of machinery or it might involve breaking down the steps of making something into parts that different people can do. Some manufacturing practices are better for the environment than others. Investigate two ways in which a familiar item might be manufactured and report your findings in the form of a T-chart. Begin your search at PearsonScience.

Research a Lifespan

In this section, you have read about the lifespan of windshield wipers. Find out about the lifespan of a product you are interested in. Figure 6.18 might give you some ideas.

Purpose

To research the lifespan of a familiar product

Materials & Equipment

- paper and pencil
- access to the library and/or Internet

Procedure

1. Pick a product from the photographs here or choose your own.

2. Write down the steps in a product's lifespan. (See Table 6.1 for the steps.)

3. Fill in the steps you already know. Do some research to fill in the steps you do not know.

Questions

4. Did anything surprise you about the lifespan of your product?

5. Can you think of ways in which the lifespan might be lengthened or shortened?

6. Suggest some ways to lessen the environmental impact of making, using, and disposing of this product.

Figure 6.18 Each of these products has a lifespan.

Altering a Product Lifespan

Issue

Many things affect the lifespan of a structure. One factor you can control is how you care for the structure. Sometimes it is possible to repair a structure rather than purchase a new one.

Background Information

Buildings are designed to have a long lifespan. When a home, school, or factory is built, it is designed to last from many decades to centuries. However, ideas and materials change over time. Many buildings across the country are abandoned; they are no longer being used. Perhaps there is an abandoned building in your neighbourhood. What should be done with these buildings when people want to use the land that they sit on?

Consider these two viewpoints on the issue (Figure 6.19).

- Some people feel that old buildings have historical and architectural value. They feel that the old building should be saved if possible, and perhaps incorporated into a new structure.

- Other people feel that it is better to demolish the old building because newer materials are available and safety standards are now higher. It is often quicker and less expensive to demolish a building and start over with new materials than to restore an old building.

Your task is to choose one side of the argument and research the issue. You will present your findings as either a debate or a class presentation. Your teacher will provide more details about how to present your information.

Analyze and Evaluate

Begin your research using the following resources.

1. Go to PearsonScience to begin your search for information.

2. Look in print materials such as magazines, newspapers, and books for information on historical buildings in your neighbourhood.

3. Summarize the information you find in a short report for presentation to your class or for use in a debate. Be sure to include only information that supports your viewpoint and refutes the opposite view.

Figure 6.19 Some people would preserve the old school while others would tear it down and build a modern school.

Key Concept Review

1. Write a paragraph to describe the steps in planning a product from idea to disposal.

2. Describe the concept of planned obsolescence. How might this affect the planning and design of a product?

3. Think of a three-ring binder. Describe each of these stages in the product-planning process.

   (a) choosing materials

   (b) improving the design

   (c) advertising

   (d) disposal

4. Why should product disposal be considered when you make buying decsisions?

Connect Your Understanding

5. Compare the design of a product whose lifespan is purposely short (for example, a paper cup) with the design of a similar structure with a longer lifespan (for example, a china mug). What decisions would the designers of each item make?

6. Think about the oldest thing your family owns, perhaps a memento from an ancestor or something that travelled with your family from another country. Describe the item. What steps does your family take to extend the lifespan of this item?

Practise Your Skills

7. Think of a product your family uses every day, such as shoes, a car, or a television. How do you think the concept of planned obsolescence applies?

For more questions, go to PearsonScience.

B46   *Thinking about Science and Technology*

Product Disposal

When you discard a product, you decide whether to put it into a compost collector, a recycling container, or a garbage can. However, not all of these containers are always available.

Consider This

With a classmate or as a whole class, discuss the following questions.

1. Where are the waste containers in your school?

2. How do the waste containers vary in form when their function is different?

3. Are all three types of containers present at each waste collection site?

4. What happens to people's waste when one or more of the containers are missing?

Here is a summary of what you will learn in this section:

- Minimizing impact on the environment should be a key consideration in purchasing decisions.
- Buying products that are locally made and need less energy to produce can help the environment.
- Recycling or composting products that are no longer useful means less garbage in the landfill.
- Consumer demand has encouraged manufacturers to explore greener options.

When you decide to buy a scoop of ice cream, you still have a few other decisions to make. You decide on the flavour, then the server asks, "Is that in a cone or a cup?"

This simple decision can have an impact on the environment. Ice cream in a cone is completely edible (Figure 6.20). If you choose a cup, you get a disposable container and a plastic disposable spoon that often cannot be recycled. Even though it is just one little container and one little spoon, think of the number of people who each get a container and a spoon. The amount of garbage produced in this way has started to concern many consumers. This has encouraged some manufacturers to design biodegradable containers and utensils.

In this section, you will look at how the structures we purchase and dispose of affect the environment. Writing a personal action plan will help you make some important decisions.

Figure 6.20 Canadians do like their ice cream!

Suggested Activity • • • • • • • •
B49 Quick Lab on page 172.

B47 *Starting Point*   Skills Ⓐ Ⓒ

Take Stock

Think about your family's fast food habits and the types of fast food your family eats.

1. What is your family's favourite fast food? How is it packaged?

2. How might this type of packaging affect the environment?

3. Can you do something to lessen its impact on the environment? Discuss your ideas with a classmate.

How Structures Affect the Environment

Humans will always need and want things. However, the things we need and want can have an impact on the environment. As responsible citizens, we need to examine our decisions and try to lessen our impact on Earth and its resources.

Every product you buy requires raw materials and energy to manufacture. Fuel is needed when the product is transported. And the product will need to be disposed of when you no longer need it.

If you choose products made from renewable materials, and then recycle or compost them, you are lessening your impact on Earth. Using renewable resources, such as the plants shown in Figure 6.21, means that others in the future will be able to enjoy the same things you have now. By recycling or composting, you send fewer items to the landfill.

If you choose products that need less energy to manufacture, you are lessening your impact on Earth. Generating energy (electricity, heat, etc.) is expensive and can release pollutants. If the products you choose need less energy to manufacture, you reduce the cost and the amount of pollution produced.

If you purchase structures that operate on less energy than similar structures, you are lessening your impact on Earth. Figure 6.22 shows two flashlights. One uses batteries, which are an expensive and wasteful source of energy. The other uses a hand crank, which is a renewable source of energy as long as you eat your meals!

If you buy locally produced items, you are lessening your impact on Earth. Since locally produced items don't have to be transported long distances, this saves on energy and minimizes pollutants. Many people eat locally produced food, and some purchase that food at roadside stands (Figure 6.23)

Figure 6.21 Clothing made from cotton or bamboo is recyclable. Nylon and rayon are not recyclable.

Figure 6.22 Both of these flashlights use energy to produce light. One uses batteries for energy. The other uses your energy when you turn the crank.

Figure 6.23 When you buy food from the farmers, it has not travelled very far.

If you modify your behaviour in order to conserve energy, you are lessening your impact as well. For example, you could turn the heat down a degree or two in your home in winter. If you put on warmer clothing, your family will save money and help reduce the total amount of energy it uses.

Consumers are also growing more conscious of the need to think about how raw materials are managed, the working conditions of people who manufacture the products and the consequences of buying goods intended to last only a short time. As consumers make these concerns known to manufacturers, changes are being made. Have you noticed labels like "organic," "fair trade," or "produced from materials in a sustainable way"? What do you think these labels mean? Sometimes products that bear these labels cost more than products that do not. Would you be willing to pay more for something, like a T-shirt, made in an environmentally responsible way?

Suggested Activity •·········
B50 Decision-Making Analysis on page 173.

Take It Further

You may live in an apartment or a house. Your home is most likely made out of wood, concrete, and/or brick. These are traditional building materials for homes in Canada.

However, some interesting housing materials may have less impact on the environment. Some people are building houses out of old cans and tires. Others are using straw bales. Investigate an alternative housing method and report back to your class. Begin your search at PearsonScience.

B48 *During Writing*

Thinking Literacy

Reorganizing Ideas: ARMS

Writers revisit their work to add, change, or delete ideas and information. One strategy they use to help reorganize is called "ARMS" (add, remove, move, substitute).

Revisit your "Question and Answer" organizer on recycled materials and products and think about changes you want to make. Is there a question you would like to add or remove? Are there better words you can substitute in a question or answer? Now, write your draft.

The lifespans of structures need to be considered to make responsible decisions. **171**

Personal Action Plan

Throughout this unit, you have learned about structures, their classification, and the forces that act upon them. You have thought about consumer needs and wants. You understand that every purchasing decision has an impact on Earth. It is time for you to put what you have learned into action in your own life (Figure 6.24). You may not make all of the decisions about what to buy for your family, but you do have influence. You also make choices for your own purchases.

Purpose

To prepare a personal plan of action for making wiser consumer decisions

Materials & Equipment

- pencil and paper

Procedure

1. Make a list of the purchasing decisions you make for yourself or have influence over. You may pick your own clothes. You may have a say in what your family buys at the grocery store. You might buy your own batteries for your electronic gear.

Figure 6.24 Each person's decisions make an impact.

2. Consider products and practices. What are the different ways to lessen your impact on Earth? For each item on your list, propose a way to make it more environmentally responsible. You might organize your list in a chart like the one in Table 6.2.

Table 6.2 Personal Action Plan

Purchasing Decision	Proposed Change	Change Immediately, Discuss, Find out More?

3. For each decision, decide whether it is something you can change immediately or discuss with your family, friends, and classmates, or whether you need more information.

Questions

4. Look over your list and make sure there is at least one change you can make immediately. Why will this action lessen your impact on Earth?

5. Consider the items you need to discuss with your family. What information do you think your family will want to consider before they make a decision?

6. Consider all of the items you want to find out more about. How will you get your information?

7. Write a letter to yourself outlining your personal action plan. This personal action plan is a commitment you are making to yourself and Earth.

How Green Can We Be?

Figure 6.25 It's lunch time!

Issue

Every school also makes an impact on the environment. Students and staff spend a lot of time at schools and need the school to be safe and comfortable. The issue is: what changes can be made at school to lessen its impact on the environment?

Background Information

Energy is used to heat, cool, and light a school. Many school activities generate waste products. In order to reduce the school's impact on the environment, some of these activities and some of the energy use can be changed.

Some changes can be made with little or no cost. For example, asking students to bring litterless lunches, such as the lunch shown in Figure 6.25, costs no money but reduces the amount of waste produced at the school. Other changes, such as installing energy-efficient windows or switching to solar-powered water heating, will cost money.

Consider these two viewpoints on this issue.

- Some people feel that it is enough to make inexpensive changes to lessen the impact on the environment. Changes in behaviours such as turning off the lights when not needed and keeping the building at a moderate temperature do not cost much money.

- Others feel that changes in behaviour are just the start. Changes in infrastructure, such as increased insulation and the use of low-wattage light bulbs, must be made in order to be more environmentally responsible.

Your task is to choose one side of the argument and research the issue. You will present your findings as either a debate or a class presentation. Your teacher will provide more details about how to present your information.

Analyze and Evaluate

Begin your research using the following resources.

1. Go to PearsonScience to begin your search for information.

2. Look in print materials, such as magazines, newspapers, and books, for information on reducing your impact on the environment.

3. Summarize the information you find in a short report for presentation to your class or for use in a debate. Be sure to include only information that supports your viewpoint and/or refutes the opposite view.

Key Concept Review

1. Describe how every buying decision can affect the environment.

2. Describe how modifying your buying decisions can lessen your impact on Earth.

3. For each of the items below, describe the buying decisions that would have the least impact on the environment.

   (a) cleaning supplies

   (b) fresh fruit and vegetables

   (c) clothing

Connect Your Understanding

4. Describe why it is important to consider greener options every day, even when making "small" decisions such as buying ice-cream.

5. Why is it considered better to reduce or re-use than to recycle?

6. Noted environmentalist David Suzuki has warned against "green-washing," a trend that businesses have adopted to convince consumers that their practices are more environmentally responsible than their competitors' practices. Why do you think he might be concerned?

Practise Your Skills

7. Think of one thing you will buy, use, or dispose of today. Can you think of a way to make that decision greener?

8. Describe one way you think your family could make less of an impact on the environment with respect to its purchasing decisions. Write a paragraph that you think will convince your family to try your suggestion.

For more questions, go to PearsonScience.

B51 *Thinking about Science and Technology*

Re-structures

Science and technology have discovered many ways to use recycled items. For example, polyester fleece is made from recycled plastic bottles. Think of the future of one recycled material, such as aluminum, paper, plastic, or glass.

   Within a group, choose one recycled material and answer the following questions.

1. What products is that recycled material made into?

2. What are the benefits of choosing those products?

3. What are the drawbacks of choosing those products?

Making Connections

Jay Ingram

Jay Ingram is an experienced science journalist and is the host of Daily Planet on Discovery Channel Canada.

A Changing Centre of Gravity

Where is your centre of gravity? In this unit, you learned that it is the point within a structure that gravity seems to act on. So if you are balanced on the tip of one toe, your centre of gravity is directly over that toe. Otherwise you would fall over, pulled to one side or the other by gravity. But how high up is it? Probably just about in the middle, where there's as much of you above it as there is below.

The thing is, your centre of gravity can move, sometimes even outside your body! When you crouch down and wrap your arms around your knees, your centre of gravity drops down with you. It may actually leave your body to float somewhere in the space between your arms, legs, and head.

In the 1960s, an Olympic high jumper named Dick Fosbury became famous for shifting his centre of gravity. Up to that time, high jumpers ran parallel to the bar, then kicked one leg up, and rolled over the bar (trying not to touch it), dragging the other leg behind. Some people were really good at this, and could clear a bar that was well over 2 m high.

Fosbury used a completely different technique that became known as the "Fosbury Flop." He ran at the bar, then at the last minute turned his back and jumped head first and backward over the bar. At the last minute, he kicked both legs up and over. Fosbury won the high jump at the 1968 Olympics in Mexico City in this way. He jumped 2.24 m.

Today almost every high jumper uses the Fosbury Flop because it is so effective. With other techniques, jumpers have to get their centre of gravity over the bar. But Fosbury was able to sneak his centre of gravity under the bar, even though he was going over it. Picture him flopping: at first, only his head was over the bar, then only his torso (with his arms and legs under) and finally, only his legs were over. At no time was most of his body over the bar; his centre of gravity stayed under the whole time.

Figure 6.26 Dick Fosbury changing his centre of gravity

Key Concept Review

1. Describe the relationship between manufacturers and consumers. **(k)**

2. Use the basic steps in the lifespan of a product to trace the development of your own idea for a new type of water bottle. **(a)**

3. Why do manufacturers take consumer preferences seriously? **(c)**

4. Write a short paragraph that shows how these words relate to one another: consumer, market research, advertising. **(c)**

5. Which of the following statements are true and which are false? Rewrite the false statements to make them true. **(k)**

   (a) Many products are sent to the landfill, even when they are in usable condition.

   (b) Technology is never used when gathering market research.

   (c) A well-designed product is unpleasant to use.

   (d) Eventually, all products end up in landfills or are recycled into other products.

   (e) If you choose products that need less energy to manufacture, you are increasing your impact on Earth.

Connect Your Understanding

6. The lifespan of similar products can vary greatly. Some items, such as a special piece of furniture or china, have been handed down for generations, while similar items last only a short time. Why might this be? **(t)**

7. If you could modify a pen to be sold to students your age, what modifications would you make, and why? What key points would you emphasize in an advertisement? **(a)**

8. Why should consumers consider the lifespan of structures in order to make responsible decisions? Give an example of a time you have considered (or would consider) the lifespan of a structure before making a purchasing decision. **(c)**

After Writing — Thinking Literacy

Reflect and Evaluate

Exchange your "Question and Answer" writing piece with another pair. Read their work carefully. Provide each other with some feedback, for example: What two things did they do well? Is there another question you would have liked answered? Did you learn something new about recycled materials? Finally, share tips for writing a good "Question and Answer" writing piece with the class.

ACHIEVEMENT CHART CATEGORIES
(k) Knowledge and understanding   **(t)** Thinking and investigation   **(c)** Communication   **(a)** Application

9. How can the desire to minimize the impact on the environment influence buying decisions? 🅣

10. What role(s) can consumers play in ensuring that green choices are available? 🅣

11. Sometimes the "greener option" is not always obvious. What would you need to think about when deciding if it is better to: 🅐

    (a) use cloth or disposable diapers?

    (b) buy plastic or cardboard containers for storing items?

    (c) use a product that lasts several years and then has to be sent to the landfill or a similar product that lasts half the time but can be composted or recycled?

12. (a) What do you think consumers can do to encourage manufacturers to produce "greener" products? 🅣

    (b) Some would say that this is only part of the solution and that consumers need to learn to live less materialistically. What do you think? 🅣

Practise Your Skills

13. A family you know is thinking about buying a new washing machine. Suggest three questions they should ask to ensure that they make a wise choice. 🅐

Unit Project Link

When you want to improve the energy efficiency of an everyday task, you may have difficult choices to make. Sometimes, replacing an existing structure with one that is more energy efficient can be costly. For example, front-loading washing machines use less electricity, water, and detergent to do the same job as conventional washing machines. Thus, they cost less money per load. However, a front-loading washing machine can cost more to purchase than a conventional washing machine. Which would you buy? Discuss the thinking you would use to make this decision.

B52 *Thinking about Science and Technology*

What's in a Bag?

These days, many purchases are carried home in plastic bags. However, plastic bags take a big toll on the environment. They take a long time to break down and can also harm animals that try to eat them.

What to Do

1. Estimate the number of plastic bags your family takes home in a week.

Consider This

With a classmate or as a whole class, discuss the following questions.

2. When you are shopping, when do you need to use a plastic bag? When could you make do without one?

3. What alternatives to plastic bags are being offered? Who is offering these alternatives?

4. What are the drawbacks to using plastic bag alternatives? Suggest solutions to these drawbacks.

5. Challenge your family to reduce the number of plastic bags it uses by considering other alternatives.

UNIT B Summary

4.0 Designers consider the form and the function of a structure and the forces that act on it.

KEY CONCEPTS

- Every structure can be described and classified.
- Forces act on structures.
- Structures need to be designed with safety in mind.

CHAPTER SUMMARY

- Structures can be classified by their function.
- Structures can be classified by their form as solid, frame, and shell structures.
- Internal and external forces act on structures.
- Designing a structure requires an understanding of the forces and loads that act on it.

5.0 Good design, materials, and construction make structures stable and strong.

KEY CONCEPTS

- Structural strength is affected by many factors.
- Good design involves many elements.

CHAPTER SUMMARY

- Structural shapes, structural components, and structural materials are the main things to consider for structural strength.
- The centre of gravity of a structure affects its stability.
- Structural stress, fatigue, and failure affect structures.
- Designers must ask themselves questions about the elements of design throughout the design process.
- Some of the questions have definite answers. Others are a matter of personal taste.

6.0 The lifespans of structures need to be considered in order to make responsible decisions.

KEY CONCEPTS

- Manufacturers and consumers have responsibilities.
- The lifespan of a product can be traced.
- Decisions made about structures can affect the environment.

CHAPTER SUMMARY

- Manufacturers determine consumer need by using market research, and try to influence consumer thinking with advertising.
- Being a wise consumer involves identifying personal needs and wants.
- The lifespan of a product might include planned obsolescence.
- Product disposal should be a factor in buying decisions.
- Conserving energy in each phase of the lifespan of a product, from idea to disposal, affects Earth positively.
- Modifying their personal behaviour to reduce their impact on Earth is the responsibility of every citizen.

Everything Old Can Be New Again

Getting Started

Many of our buildings—our homes, schools, and offices—are getting older. When they were constructed, the cost of energy was not a concern. Designers chose the technology and materials based upon how the building should look, not how it should conserve energy. Many older buildings are poorly insulated or have inefficient electrical systems.

However, in today's world, energy conservation is crucial. Can we make our older buildings more energy efficient? Creative ways to renovate aging buildings will lessen their impact upon the environment.

Your Goal

You will design and build a prototype (or a model) of a structure that could lessen the environmental impact of your home or school. Choose one of the following three options.

- Modify an existing structure to make it work more efficiently.

- Invent the next great "green" invention!

- Do research and build a model of a recent innovation that is not yet used widely.

What You Need to Know

Consider your own home, apartment building, or school. Think of how you could lessen its environmental impact. Think of some things you might design and build, or some things you might modify, to achieve your goal of greener living.

Steps to Sucess

1. With a small group, tour a home or your school. Outside, examine the architecture, the materials, and the surrounding property. Inside, look in the rooms, hallways, and other features. Make a list of any ideas you have to improve the energy efficiency of the building. This is the brainstorming stage, so the more ideas, the better!

2. With your group, pick one idea that you think would efficiently lessen the environmental impact of the building.

3. Talk about the materials you will choose. Will you build a model or a working prototype?

4. Construct your prototype or model. Follow the safety rules you have learned in this unit.

5. Test and evaluate your final product.

How Did It Go?

6. Are there any safety concerns related to either the construction or the testing of your structure?

7. How could you improve upon your model or prototype? What materials would you use if money were not an issue?

8. If you were designing for an actual structure, who might be opposed to the use of your idea? Why might they be concerned?

9. How environmentally friendly are the building materials?

10. Consider the lifespan of your product. Will this be a long-term investment?

11. In your whole class, combine all ideas that are best suited to homes. Form a committee to write a report that lists and explains each structure. Include digital pictures of each structure. Predict what the total energy savings might be if all of the innovations were installed in a single home.

12. Form a second committee to write a report related to the structures that are best suited to your school. Present this report to the principal and custodian of your school. Have all of the structures available for viewing. Record their feedback in a report response.

Key Terms Review

1. Create a word web that illustrates your understanding of the following terms. ⓚ

- structure
- function
- solid
- frame
- shell
- magnitude
- force
- load
- structural components
- stress
- fatigue
- failure
- symmetry
- centre of gravity
- product recall
- prototype
- consumer
- manufacturer
- market research
- lifespan

Key Concept Review

4.0

2. Explain how you find structures all around you by making a list of eight indoor structures and eight outdoor structures. Describe the form and function of each. ⓚ

3. Describe the types of forces that can affect structures. Explain how designers consider these effects in their designs. ⓚ

4. Describe how designers minimize the risk of failure in structures. ⓐ

5. Some structures are designed to support small loads, and other structures are designed to support large loads. How are these types of structures similar, and how are they different? ⓚ

6. Why might structures that serve the same function have very different forms? ⓒ

Question 7

7. Sketch the illustration in your notebook and label the dynamic load(s) and the static load(s). ⓚ

8. Using mainly diagrams, describe three different types of internal forces. ⓚ

9. No structure can be designed to be 100% failure proof. How might a designer decide that a structure is "safe enough"? ⓒ

5.0

10. Describe and then relate the terms "centre of gravity" and "stability." ⓚ ⓒ

11. Why do manufacturers issue product recalls, even when they know that they can cost their business millions of dollars? ⓣ

Question 12

12. List the structural components that you see in the photograph. ⓚ

13. Describe three structures that include triangular shapes in their design. Why did the designers use triangles rather than rectangles? ⓐ

14. Explain how each of the following contributes to structural strength. Describe how all of these factors relate to the design and construction of a bridge. ⓚ

(a) structural shapes

(b) structural components

(c) structural materials

ACHIEVEMENT CHART CATEGORIES
ⓚ Knowledge and understanding   ⓣ Thinking and investigation   ⓒ Communication   ⓐ Application

15. Which of the following statements are true and which are false? Rewrite the false statements to make them true. ⓚ

(a) The design for a structure is related to its function.

(b) Good structures consider the dynamic loads only.

(c) All materials are the same when it comes to cutting and joining them.

(d) Ergonomics can be thought of as the science of people–structure relationships.

(e) A prototype is the last product to be manufactured.

16. Describe why the concept of aesthetics in design is a personal one. ⓣ

17. Symmetry can add to structural stability. Explain why this is so. When might this be desirable? When would it not be desirable? ⓣ

18. Think about each element of good design. Make a chart with the headings "Element" and "Connection to Stability or Strength." For each element, describe how strength and stability might factor into the designer's thinking. ⓐ

6.0

19. Compare the thinking of a wise consumer with one who is not so wise. ⓒ

20. Why is it difficult to design and build a structure that will last forever? ⓣ

21. How are designing, building, buying, and disposing of structures related to the use of energy? ⓐ

22. In order to make responsible decisions, why should you consider the lifespan of structures? ⓣ

23. Describe the reasons to conduct market research. ⓚ

24. Describe a building in which you have observed the principles of universal design in use. ⓐ

(a) What was the form of the design?

(b) How did the form affect the function of the building?

25. What are the pros and cons of "planned obsolescence"? ⓒ

26. List three choices you have made in the past week that reflected a "greener option." ⓚ

27. How could you be encouraged to make even more "greener options"? ⓐ

Connect Your Understanding

28. Describe which parts of the following "combination structures" are solid, frames, and shells. ⓚ

(a) MP3 player

(b) umbrella

(c) car

(d) house

(e) canoe

(f) human body

29. Consider the items listed in question 28 (a) to (c). How is each structure designed for safety? ⓐ

30. Compare the different chairs you sit on at school (lab stool, chair, gym bench) in terms of centre of gravity and stability. *a*

31. List the different types of material that clothing and shoes can be made from. What are the trends in the relationship between the type of material and the type of clothing or shoe? *a*

32. Think of something you are using right now. It could be this textbook, your binder, or your pen. How could you extend the lifespan of this product? *t*

33. What products that you use have the shortest and longest lifespans? How might these lifespans be altered in length? *c*

34. Using your knowledge of the concepts in this unit, what do you think is the best type of structure to do the following tasks? Explain why for each one. *a*

(a) hold up a large mass

(b) span a gap

(c) act as a container

35. You have been asked to design a riding toy for a small child. How would you decide what materials and methods of construction to use? How might you modify the design to make it more suitable for an adult? Use diagrams to show your ideas. *a*

Practise Your Skills

36. If you had to redesign something in your home to increase its safety, what would it be? Why do you think it needs to be improved? How would you redesign it? *t*

37. Pick one of the building activities you did in this unit and re-do the activity with different materials, different shapes, or different structural components to increase the structure's efficiency. *t*

38. Consider how manufacturers listen to consumers. Write a letter to the manufacturer of a product that you think could be improved to lessen its impact on Earth. *c*

39. Your class is going to have a building competition to see who can build the strongest bridge out of craft sticks and glue. Prepare a handout sheet with instructions and criteria for success for this competition. *c*

40. The environmental club at your school has been given funding to build some seating in the yard for an outdoor classroom. You can use concrete or wood to build the seating. Create a chart that demonstrates the strengths and weaknesses of each choice. How would you make the final decision? *t*

Revisit the Big Ideas

41. Give possible functions for each of these descriptions of form. *k*

(a) a large piece of glass in the shape of cylinder with a bottom but no top

(b) a soft piece of foam covered in fabric

(c) a hard, heavy hunk of metal in the shape of a dog

(d) a reflective piece of material in a flat, rectangular shape

ACHIEVEMENT CHART CATEGORIES
k Knowledge and understanding   *t* Thinking and investigation   *c* Communication   *a* Application

42. Make up four more descriptions of form to share with a partner. *e*

43. The form of a structure depends on its function. Study the photographs and explain how you think the forms of these buildings relate to their functions. *c*

Question 43 Left: The addition to the Royal Ontario Museum was built to house artifacts. Right: The Ontario College of Art and Design is a school for future artists and designers.

44. You have installed a new bookshelf in your room. How might you monitor it to make sure that the structure is standing up to the forces it experiences? *e*

45. As you walk down the street, you notice a small crack in the sidewalk. How might the crack change if it were left over a long period of time? Would the season make any difference to your answer? *t*

46. In what types of structures (if any) would you consider: *t*

(a) form more important than function?

(b) function more important than form?

47. Building and maintaining structures such as roads and bridges is a continuous task. Discuss why this statement is true using the terms "forces," "structures," and "interactions." *c*

B53 *Thinking about Science, Technology, Society, and the Environment*   S T S E

Structures and You

When you design, modify, choose to buy, and dispose of structures, you are using science and technology. Your decisions about these issues can impact society and the environment.

What to Do

1. Pick a structure you use every day.

2. Think of a way to reduce your impact on society and the environment by changing how this structure was designed and modified, and how you choose it and dispose of it.

Consider This

3. Share your plan with a classmate.

4. Make a plan to meet in the near future and a little further in the future to check on each other's progress.

5. Meet to celebrate your success or modify your plans as necessary.

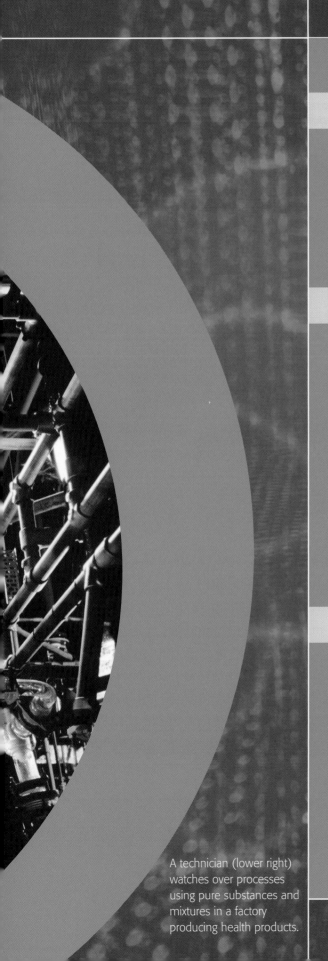

Unit Overview

Fundamental Concepts

In Grade 7 Science and Technology, six fundamental concepts occur throughout. This unit addresses the following two:

- Matter
- Systems and Interactions

Big Ideas

As you work through this unit, you will develop a deeper understanding of the following big ideas:

- Matter can be classified according to its physical characteristics.
- The particle theory of matter helps to explain the physical characteristics of matter.
- Pure substances and mixtures have an impact on society and the environment.
- Understanding the characteristics of matter allows us to make informed choices about how we use it.

Overall Expectations

By the end of this unit, you will be expected to:

1. evaluate the social and environmental impacts of the use and disposal of pure substances and mixtures
2. investigate the properties and applications of pure substances and mixtures
3. demonstrate an understanding of the properties of pure substances and mixtures, and describe these characteristics using the particle theory

A technician (lower right) watches over processes using pure substances and mixtures in a factory producing health products.

Exploring

Maple sap boils over an open fire to concentrate it.

Maple syrup production requires the separation of water from maple sap, which leaves behind a more concentrated mixture of sugar. According to historians, members of the Algonquin First Nation may have discovered the nutritional properties of maple sap. They made V-shaped cuts in sugar maple trees and collected the sap in birchbark containers. In time, many First Nations peoples, including the Algonquins, boiled the collected maple sap in clay pots over an open fire to concentrate the maple syrup, similar to what is shown in the above photo.

Sharing Technology

First Nations peoples showed French settlers how to tap maple trees in the spring to collect sap. These settlers used metal drills to bore into the trunks of maple trees so that they could insert homemade taps into the trees. They would then hang wooden buckets on the taps to collect the sap, as shown in the photo to the right.

Maple syrup production became an important part of the lives of 16th- and 17th-century settlers. To improve the efficiency of the boiling process, iron and copper kettles containing sap were suspended over fire pits. However, much of the heat from burning wood was able to escape. To reduce this heat loss, boiling of sap was moved indoors. Sugar shacks were built to block the wind and contain the heat from the fires. Also, the sugar shack's walls and roof helped to reduce contamination of the boiling sap by leaves and insects.

Early settlers collected sap in wooden buckets.

Impact of Technology

Over the next two centuries, innovations involved containing the heat in more efficient boilers. Sheet metal was fashioned into large, flat evaporators and fire boxes that contained the heat, increasing the surface area of the boiling sap. However, producing 1 L of maple syrup meant that 40 L of sap had to be carried to the evaporator, which made the process very labour intensive.

In the 20th century, the efficiency of maple sap collection for syrup production was greatly enhanced. Trees were tapped and connected to hoses, which allowed the sap to run downhill to collecting tanks or the evaporators in sugar shacks. Later, vacuum pumps were used to increase the amount of sap collected from each maple tree, as shown in the photo to the right.

Evaporator technology has also improved. Raw sap flows or is pumped into a large, relatively deep pan to begin the boiling process. As water is removed, the more concentrated mixture flows into a smaller, shallower pan. Here it is concentrated further. Finally, the more concentrated mixture flows into a third, very shallow pan, where boiling is managed to enable precise control of the sugar content of the syrup.

Maple sap is collected using pipelines connected to a vacuum pump.

...MORE TO EXPLORE

Concentrating a Mixture — A Simulation

Maple syrup is made by boiling a maple sap mixture to remove the water. In this activity, you will simulate that process with sand and marbles, where sand represents the water and marbles represent the sugar.

Purpose

To simulate the concentration of a mixture

Materials and Equipment

- 100-mL beaker (jar)
- sand
- marbles
- balance

Procedure

1. Measure and record the mass of an empty beaker.

2. Place marbles in the beaker. Measure the mass of the beaker and marbles. Subtract the mass of the beaker, and then record the mass of the marbles in a table as shown to the right.

3. Fill the beaker with sand. Measure the mass of the full beaker. Subtract the mass of the beaker and marbles, and then record the mass of the sand.

4. Remove some sand, then measure the mass of the beaker. Repeat this process two more times.

Table C.1 Comparing the concentration of different mixtures

Mass of Beaker (g)	Mass of Marbles (g)	Mass of Sand (g)	Mass of Marbles Divided by Mass of Sand

Questions

5. How does the concentration of marbles in the mixture change as sand is removed?

6. How does the ratio of mass of marbles to mass of sand change as sand is removed?

7. Explain how this simulation relates to concentration of maple syrup.

C2 *Thinking about Science, Technology, Society, and the Environment*

Environmental Impact of Maple Syrup Production

1. Make a list of both positive and negative effects of the production of maple syrup on society and the environment.

2. With a classmate or the whole class, discuss the significance of each effect mentioned above.

3. Based on your discussions of positive and negative effects, should we be producing maple syrup? Support your answer.

UNIT C

Contents

 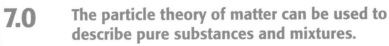
Unit Task

Many sources of water contain mixtures of naturally occurring substances and contaminants. In your unit task, you will investigate water samples taken from a number of surface water sources. You will use skills that you learn in this unit to purify the water samples. You will also be able to identify possible sources of contaminants from the sample.

Essential Question

What are some industrial and commercial sources of pure substances and mixtures that mix with surface water to make it impure?

Getting Ready to Read

Thinking Literacy

Probable Passage

You will be introduced to the following terms in this unit:

- pure substance
- mixture
- concentration
- solution
- particles

Which of these terms can you already define? Which of these terms are you unsure of? Based on what you already know, write one or two sentences that make a prediction about what you will learn in this unit.

Pure substances combine into a mixture to eventually become bread.

What You Will Learn

In this chapter, you will:

- distinguish between pure substances and mixtures
- state the points of the particle theory of matter
- use the particle theory to describe the difference between pure substances and mixtures

Skills You Will Use

In this chapter, you will:

- use appropriate science and technology vocabulary in oral and written communications
- follow established safety procedures for handling chemicals and apparatus

Why This Is Important

Everything that you see, touch, taste, and smell is made of particles. Your body is a complex mixture of particles that is maintained by eating nutritious foods, which are also made up of particles.

Before Reading

Thinking Literacy

Making Predictions

Making predictions before reading helps you to activate your prior knowledge and to anticipate what you will learn. Before reading this chapter, look at the headings and captions in the text. Record this information in a chart, along with your thoughts about what you will find out. Revisit your predictions during the chapter to confirm or revise your understanding of the topic.

Key Terms

- heat
- kinetic energy
- mechanical mixture
- mixture

- particle
- pure substance
- solution
- temperature

Figure 7.1 Crude oil is a mixture of pure substances that sticks to everything it contacts, creating a mess that is difficult to clean up.

When crude oil spills into a natural environment, such as from a damaged oil tanker at sea or a broken pipeline on land, the result is a sticky black mess. Everything in the immediate environment is changed by the contamination caused by the spill.

In July 2007, a crude oil pipeline was accidentally broken in Burnaby, British Columbia (Figure 7.1). More than 240 000 L of crude oil was released into the environment. The oily black mixture contaminated a residential area and eventually flowed into the Pacific Ocean.

Town residents reported that their lawns and gardens were coated with oil. Environmental experts determined that soil and ground water chemistry would be damaged, perhaps for a very long time. Also, birds, mammals, and marine wildlife would be severely injured, and some would die. Many people wondered how the oil could be separated from the water, soil, plants, and animals.

Understanding the properties of the substances that make up this oily mixture was essential to the clean-up effort. By studying the properties of substances, environmental experts can find new methods to treat environmental contamination (Figure 7.2).

You will also want to learn how to use substances. You may want to build a model with special glue, apply a styling product to your hair, or clean the mud off your bike. To do this, you will need to understand some key ideas about substances. In this chapter, you will study the points from the particle theory of matter and use them to classify substances.

Figure 7.2 Studying the properties of substances can help to save wildlife, such as this sea otter, from environmental contamination.

C3 *Quick Lab*

Animal, Plant, or Mineral

Although you may not give it much thought, you make classification decisions all of the time. Cars, music, and the food you eat are classified into categories to make it easier to understand, obtain, or use these items. In this activity, you will make some decisions about the categories of some items found in your classroom.

Purpose

To classify items found in your classroom as animal, plant, or mineral

Materials and Equipment
▪ paper ▪ pen or pencil
▪ magnet (optional)

Procedure

1. Make a copy of the following table with enough space for 10 items.

Table 7.1 Animal, plant, or mineral

Item	Animal	Plant	Mineral
pencil	no	yes	yes

2. Select 10 items found in your classroom. With a partner, decide if any part of each item is made up of something that is or comes from animals, plants, or minerals (e.g., metals, plastics).

3. Complete your table and then answer the following questions.

Questions

4. Is it always easy to determine what something is made from? Be sure to explain your answer thoroughly with at least one example.

5. Do some of the items belong to more than one category? Provide an example of an item that belongs to two or three categories.

6. Sometimes items do not fit conveniently into categories because the categories may not provide enough information or choice. Think of other categories that could be used to classify items in the classroom. Explain how you would use this category in a classification system.

Here is a summary of what you will learn in this section:

• Everything that we see is made up of matter.

• Matter can be classified as a pure substance or a mixture.

• Mixtures can be classified as solutions or mechanical mixtures.

Figure 7.3 Chocolate chip cookies and milk are made of matter.

Chocolate chip cookies, milk, the glass holding the milk, the plate under the cookies, and the air you breathe have something in common (Figure 7.3). They are all made of matter. **Matter** is anything that has mass and takes up space.

Matter can be classified by its physical state: solid, liquid, or gas. Textbooks, trees, cars, and running shoes are all made up of solid matter. Rainwater, orange juice, mouthwash, and gasoline are all made up of liquid matter. Air is made up of different types of gaseous matter, such as oxygen and nitrogen. You can also use an understanding of what makes up matter to classify substances by composition.

C4 Starting Point

Skills A C

Classify This

Look for similarities and differences in the physical appearance of 5 to 10 common substances (e.g., bread, juice, chocolate bar, butter, cereal). Come up with your own classification system, and provide reasons for how you classified each substance. Prepare a table like the one shown to record your reasons. Give your table a descriptive title.

Table 7.2 Classifying substances

Substance	Classification	Reasons for Your Classification
Milk	Liquid	Milk is a liquid.

Classifying Matter by Composition

Matter can be grouped in different ways. You may already know that matter can be classified as a solid, a liquid, or a gas. All matter can also be grouped into two basic categories: pure substances and mixtures.

Pure Substances

A **pure substance** is made up of only one type of matter. Sugar, distilled water, and copper wire are all types of pure substances. Figure 7.4 shows that all the parts of the packet of sugar are the same. Similarly, all the parts of the distilled water are the same, and all the parts of the copper wire are the same. A pure substance is the same throughout.

Pure substances appear uniform, or **homogeneous** [pronounced "hoh-moh-JEEN-ee-uhs"], throughout. This means that every part of that substance has the same composition as every other part. When you look at a container of salt or a glass of distilled water, every part of that substance looks the same.

Mixtures

A **mixture** is made up of two or more different types of matter. For example, pizza is a mixture of different types of edible ingredients placed on a flat dough (which is also a mixture of different substances, such as flour, eggs, and water), that is baked in an oven (Figure 7.5). Many soft drinks are mixtures that may contain the pure substances carbon dioxide and sugar mixed with water.

Each substance in a mixture keeps its particular properties, even though those properties may be difficult to identify. For example, when you look at a bowl of salad, you can see the different vegetables in the mixture, and you can taste the oil and vinegar in the salad dressing. However, when you pour a soft drink into a glass, you cannot see the sugar in the mixture, although you can probably taste the sweetness of the sugar.

Figure 7.4 All the parts in the packet of sugar are the same.

*Take It **Further***

Think of a common product found in a grocery store. Determine if its ingredients are pure substances or mixtures. Begin your search at PearsonScience.

Figure 7.5 This pizza is a mixture of different ingredients.

The particle theory of matter can be used to describe pure substances and mixtures.   195

A Hypothesis is a Prediction

The idea of making an "educated guess" based on prior knowledge is referred to by different names in different subject areas. In science, it is called hypothesizing.

In the Inquiry Activity on the following page, you are asked to consider which of the common substances in the following list are pure substances and which are mixtures: aluminum foil, baking soda, water, salt, sugar, vinegar, olive oil, baking flour.

Think about what you already know or have just learned about pure substances and mixtures, as well as what you know about each of the common substances. Based on this knowledge, predict whether each substance is pure or a mixture. Briefly explain why you think so. You have now developed a hypothesis for science.

Figure 7.6 The snack food is a mechanical mixture of different substances.

WORDS MATTER

The prefix "hetero" comes from the Greek word "heteros," which means "different."

Classifying Mixtures

Mixtures can also be grouped into two basic categories: mechanical mixtures and solutions.

When you look at **mechanical mixtures** closely, they do not have the same appearance throughout. You can see the differences with the naked eye. There are differing amounts of different types of matter throughout the mixture. Snack food is an example of a mechanical mixture, as it contains different substances (Figure 7.6). This type of mixture can also be called **heterogeneous** [pronounced "het-uhr-oh-JEEN-ee-us"]. This means that it is made up of many different substances, each with different appearances and characteristics.

Solutions have the same appearance throughout, but are made up of two or more substances. All solutions are homogeneous mixtures because they look the same throughout even though they are made up of different substances. For example, when you dissolve sugar in tea, the tea still looks the same throughout (Figure 7.7).

Figure 7.7 Sweetened tea is a solution of sugar and different chemicals extracted from tea leaves.

Classifying Substances by Composition

Figure 7.8 Looking closely at a substance can help you determine if it is a pure substance or a mixture.

Everything around you is made up of matter, including the food you eat, the air you breathe, and the liquids you drink. You will investigate the properties of common substances. Referring to these properties, you will classify each substance as either a pure substance or a mixture.

Question

Which of these common substances are pure substances, and which of them are mixtures?

Materials & Equipment
- common substances (e.g., aluminum foil, baking soda, water, salt, sugar, vinegar, olive oil, baking flour)
- hand lens (optional)
- microscope (optional)

CAUTION: Handle all substances as instructed by your teacher.

Procedure

1. Prepare a table like the one shown below to record your observations.

Table 7.3 Classifying substances by composition

Substance	Appearance	Pure Substance or Mixture
salt	white, granular	pure substance

2. Inspect each of the substances provided by your teacher. Note the appearance, using terms similar to the example. Relying on your observations and any other information available, classify each substance as a pure substance or a mixture of substances.

3. Return all substances and clean up your work area as instructed by your teacher. Wash your hands after the activity.

Analyzing and Interpreting

4. How did you determine if a substance was a mixture of more than one substance?

5. Was it possible to determine if a substance was pure just by its appearance? Please explain your answer.

Skill Builder

6. What findings did you use to draw the conclusions that you made?

Forming Conclusions

7. What must someone know about a substance in order to classify it as a pure substance?

Key Concept Review

1. Explain the difference in appearance between a pure substance and a mixture.

2. How do the components of a mixture differ from the components of a pure substance?

3. What are the differences between sand and potting soil? Are they both mixtures? How do you know?

4. What are the key differences between solutions and mechanical mixtures? Give two examples of each.

5. Categorize each item as either a pure substance or a mixture.

   (a) chocolate pudding

   (b) gold necklace

   (c) bleach

   (d) helium gas

   (e) unfiltered tap water

Connect Your Understanding

6. Many hockey sticks are made of composite materials instead of wood. How would you classify each type of hockey stick?

7. Explain why most foods and beverages are mixtures.

Practise Your Skills

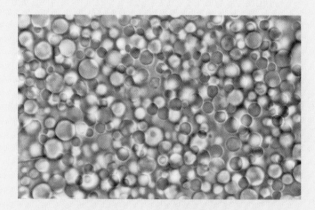

8. The above photo is a microscopic view of homogenized milk. Determine if homogenized milk is a mechanical mixture or a solution. Explain your answer.

For more questions, go to PearsonScience.

C7 Thinking about Science and Technology

Classifying Common Substances

At the beginning of this chapter, you created your own classification system to categorize common substances. This time, use the classification of matter flowchart to classify 5 to 10 common substances used in your home (Figure 7.9). Explain how each substance is commonly used.

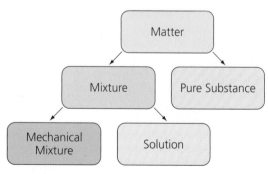

Figure 7.9 Standard classification diagram

Here is a summary of what you will learn in this section:

- The particle theory of matter describes the characteristics of matter.
- The spaces between particles are small in solids, larger in liquids, and largest in gases.
- Energy changes accompany changes of state.

Everything that you can see (e.g., cereal, milk), as well as everything that you cannot see (e.g., air, carbon dioxide), is made up of particles. **Particles** are very small portions of matter. These particles are so small that you cannot see them with your eyes alone. For example, a balloon is made up of particles (Figure 7.10). So is the air in the balloon. As the balloon fills with air, it expands. Air particles bump into each other and the balloon particles, which causes the balloon to inflate. If the balloon is filled with too many air particles, it will burst.

Figure 7.10 You cannot see the air particles in a balloon, but this student might feel their effects.

C8 *Starting Point* Skills **P** **C**

Sugar Cubes and Particles

Because particles are so small, you cannot see them. A sugar cube can give you a better understanding of particles. You can see the granules that make up the sugar cube.

Work with a partner. Obtain a sugar cube and a small piece of plastic wrap from your teacher. Use the plastic to wrap the sugar cube securely. Place the wrapped sugar cube on a desk, and then gently tap the sugar cube until it breaks apart. Observe what happens

Discuss the following questions with your partner, and be prepared to share your ideas with the class.

1. What are the similarities between the granules of sugar and particles?

2. When you hit the sugar cube, you must have done something to break it apart. What do you think you did to the sugar granules when you hit the sugar cube?

3. If all of the sugar granules were present after you hit the sugar cube, do you think they take up the same amount of space, less space, or more space than when the granules were arranged in the cube?

The Particle Theory of Matter

The six key points of the **particle theory of matter** are summarized here.

1. All matter is made up of particles.
2. All particles of one substance are identical.
3. The particles of matter are in constant motion.
4. Temperature affects the speed at which particles move.
5. Particles have forces of attraction between them.
6. There are spaces between particles.

Matter and Particles

All matter is made up of particles (Figure 7.11). Different substances are made up of different particles. The particle theory of matter can be used to explain the difference between pure substances and mixtures.

Particles of a pure substance are all identical. Figure 7.12 shows that substances A and B are both pure substances because each one is made up of only one type of particle. For example, distilled water is made up of water particles that are all the same. All the water particles look the same because they are the same. The particles that make up mixtures are different. Mixtures contain varying amounts of their component particles. For example, a soft drink consists of a number of different substances.

Particles in Motion

The particles of matter are in constant motion (Figure 7.13). They move and vibrate constantly. Particles move because they have kinetic energy. **Kinetic energy** is the energy of movement. In solids, the particles vibrate and wiggle in one place. In liquids, the particles slide around and over each other. The liquid takes the shape of the container. For each substance, its particles move more and have more kinetic energy when the substance is in a liquid state than when it is in a solid state. In gases, the particles move around as far as the space they are in allows, completely filling the space in the container. The particles of a substance move more and have more kinetic energy when the substance is in a gaseous state than when it is in a liquid state.

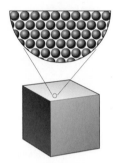

Figure 7.11 All matter is made up of particles.

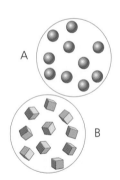

Figure 7.12 All particles of one substance are identical. A anb B are different substances.

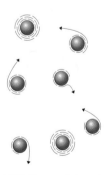

Figure 7.13 The particles of matter are in constant motion.

Particle Theory — Points to Ponder

Use a single term from the list that follows to complete each of the sentences at right.

- different
- mixture
- pure substance
- identical

1. The particles of a pure substance are _____ .

2. The particles of a mixture are _____ .

3. The composition of most foods can be classified as _____ .

4. Oxygen and carbon dioxide are each classified as _____ .

Temperature, Heat, and Motion

To understand the speed at which particles move, you need first to understand the concepts of temperature and heat. **Temperature** is the measure of the average kinetic energy of the particles in a substance. It measures how hot a substance is. **Heat** is the energy that transfers from a substance at a higher temperature to one at a lower temperature.

Temperature affects the speed at which particles move (Figure 7.14). As you just learned, particles in matter are in constant motion. When heat transfers from a hotter substance to a cooler one, the particles in the cooler substance start to move faster.

You can observe the effects of this motion by placing a spoon in a cup of hot chocolate and feeling the temperature increase in the spoon's handle (Figure 7.15). Even though parts of the spoon are not in the hot chocolate, the whole spoon gets warmer. Heat in the hot chocolate is transferred to the particles in the spoon. The particles in the spoon then move faster; you sense this as an increase in the spoon's temperature. If you then place the spoon in a glass of cold water, the temperature of the spoon will decrease. The particles in the spoon then move slower because heat is transferred from the spoon to the colder water.

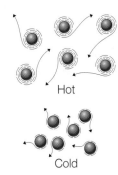

Hot

Cold

Figure 7.14 Temperature affects the speed at which particles move.

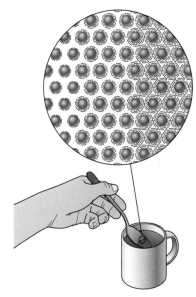

Figure 7.15 The particles of this spoon are moving faster because they are being heated by the hot chocolate.

Space and Attraction between Particles

There are spaces between particles. There are also forces of attraction between particles. Figure 7.16 illustrates how a substance has different amounts of space and attraction between particles when comparing that substance in its solid, liquid, and gaseous states.

Solid particles are much closer together and have greater attraction when compared to liquid particles. For example, the particles in a solid block of metal, such as lead, are closer together than the particles in a sample of lead that has been heated until it melts. Liquid particles are closer together and have greater attraction when compared to gas particles. For example, the particles in a glass of water are closer together and have greater attraction than the air particles in a balloon.

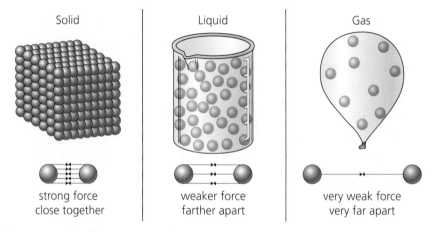

Figure 7.16 Particles have spaces and forces of attraction between them.

Temperature and Changes of State

Changes in temperature can also cause changes of state. All matter exists as a solid, a liquid, or a gas. Changing the temperature of matter in one state can cause it to change to a different state. Figure 7.17, on the next page, shows how heat is necessary to overcome the degrees of attraction between particles of matter and result in a change of state.

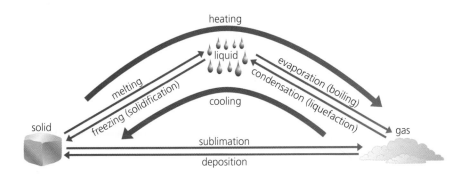

heating

liquid

melting

freezing (solidification)

evaporation (boiling)

condensation (liquefaction)

cooling

solid

sublimation

deposition

gas

Figure 7.17 Energy is necessary to overcome the degrees of attraction between particles to change state from solid to liquid, liquid to gas, or directly from solid to gas. Energy is released when the substance changes state from gas to liquid, liquid to solid, or directly from gas to solid.

The change of state from a solid to a liquid is called **melting**. Heat (e.g., flame from a match) must be added to make this happen. For example, think about a wax candle (Figure 7.18). Wax is a solid at room temperature. When the wick on the top of the wax candle burns, heat from the flame increases the temperature and melts the wax. The wax changes from solid to liquid.

The change of state from liquid to gas is called **evaporation**, or **boiling**. When you boil water for a hot drink, you see steam rising from the surface of the water. This is water as a gas (vapour) evaporating from the liquid water.

The change of state from gas to liquid is called **condensation**, or **liquefaction**. After you take a hot shower, you see water on the surface of the mirror in the bathroom. The mirror is cooler than the air so water vapour condenses from a gas to a liquid on the mirror.

The change of state from liquid to solid is called **freezing**, or **solidification**. Liquid candle wax will solidify after a candle is extinguished and allowed to cool. Heat is removed, causing a decrease in the temperature of the wax so it solidifies.

The change of state from solid to gas is called **sublimation**. The change of state from gas to solid is called **deposition**. In both cases, there is no change to a liquid state. A change of state from solid to gas would occur when heat is added. You can see this in the spring sometimes. On a warm sunny day, snow seems to disappear without melting. The solid water (snow) is changing directly to gas (vapour). A change of state from gas to solid would occur when heat is removed.

Figure 7.18 The wax in the candle changes state with changes in temperature.

Suggested Activity • · · · · · · · ·
C11 Inquiry Activity on page 205

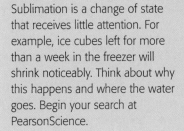

Take It Further

Sublimation is a change of state that receives little attention. For example, ice cubes left for more than a week in the freezer will shrink noticeably. Think about why this happens and where the water goes. Begin your search at PearsonScience.

Acting Out the Particle Model

It may be difficult to imagine how particles look when they are in solid, liquid, and gaseous form. Being able to see how they are arranged and move can give you a better understanding of particles. In this activity, you and your classmates will act like particles in the three states of matter.

Question

How can you and your classmates move and arrange yourselves to act like the particles that make up solids, liquids, and gases?

Materials & Equipment
- sheet of paper
- pen or pencil

Procedure

1. You will work in groups. Each group will work in a separate area. Treat each separate area as if it were a large container.

2. With your group, develop a way to represent a solid state of matter. Decide how to arrange yourselves and how to move to be particles of a solid.

3. Imagine that heat is being added to you. Your solid group changes positions and movements to represent liquid particles.

4. Now add more heat. Change your positions and movements again to represent gas particles.

5. Keep working together until your group is satisfied with the way you represent particles in the three states of matter. Then present one of these states to the rest of the class without saying what it is. Show yourselves change from that state to another state (e.g., from a solid to a liquid).

6. Draw two rectangles on a sheet of paper. The rectangles represent "containers." Use them to sketch the two states of matter your group represented. Draw arrows to show your movement. Include other information about the way and the speed that you (as particles) were moving.

Analyzing and Interpreting

7. As a class, judge each group's presentation based on the following criteria:

   - How easy was it to infer the state of matter being represented? What were the best clues? How accurately did the group represent the state of matter?

   - How well did the group's actions represent the level of kinetic energy of the particles? How accurate was this action?

   - How well did the group's actions show changes in volume?

Skill Builder

8. What criteria did you use to evaluate and decide upon a method of representing states of matter?

Forming Conclusions

9. Review the scores that you gave your classmates' presentations. Write three paragraphs that describe the best presentation for each state of matter: solid, liquid, and gas.

Melting and Freezing of Deodorizer Blocks

The deodorizer blocks found in washrooms, like all other matter, are composed of particles. You will closely observe the melting and freezing of samples of a deodorizer block. You will not be able to see the tiny particles, but you can imagine what they are doing inside the test tube.

Question

What happens to the particles of a sample of deodorizer block when it melts and freezes?

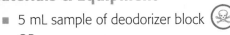
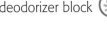

Materials & Equipment

- 5 mL sample of deodorizer block ☠
  OR
- 5 mL sample of salol (alternative to deodorizer block)
- test tube with stopper
- 50°C water bath

CAUTION: Do not eat or drink anything during this activity.

Procedure

Part 1 — Melting a Sample of Deodorizer Block

1. Obtain a sample of 5 mL of deodorizer block, a test tube, and a stopper. Be careful to hold the test tube securely with your fingers on the glass rim.

2. Observe the sample very carefully and make a note of its appearance in your notebook (e.g., white crystals resembling ice).

3. Place the sample in the test tube and place the stopper loosely in the tube. Mark your test tube as instructed by your teacher.

4. Place the test tube in the warm water bath. Write what happens to the crystals in your notebook.

Part 2 — Freezing a Sample of Deodorizer Block

5. Remove the test tube from the warm water bath by holding on to the rim at the top of the tube. **Do not hold onto the stopper.**

6. Hold the test tube upright in your hands. Note the appearance of the sample and any change of state.

Analyzing and Interpreting

7. What happened to the crystals when placed in the water bath?

8. What happened to the liquid when removed from the water bath?

9. Did the test tube feel cold when the liquid sample froze?

Skill Builder

10. What information will you use to draw conclusions in this experiment?

Forming Conclusions

11. What happened to the particles of the deodorizer block sample during the change of state from solid to liquid?

12. What happened to the forces between particles during the change of state from liquid to solid?

Key Concept Review

1. Explain why a solid substance occupies less space than the same substance in gaseous form.

2. Explain why the particles of a liquid are able to pour into a container and then take on the shape of that container.

3. Explain what happens to the particles of a substance that changes state from liquid to gas.

4. Explain why ice cubes placed in your refrigerator's freezer section become smaller over time.

Connect Your Understanding

5. Use the particle theory of matter to explain how the particles in an ice cube differ from the particles in a glass of water.

6. Use the particle theory of matter to explain what happens to the particles in a hot drink when it cools down.

7. Use the particle theory of matter to explain why heat is required to boil water.

Practise Your Skills

8. As shown in the photo below, particles of iodine form an amber solution in one liquid and a purple solution in another liquid. When combined with other substances, do iodine particles change or does the arrangement of iodine particles change? Use the particle theory of matter to explain your answer.

For more questions, go to PearsonScience.

C12 *Thinking about Science and Technology*

Using Models

We use models to help us explain things that we cannot see. For example, the particle theory of matter is a model that helps us to understand the structure of matter.

Work with a partner to identify and describe a model that you have seen or used to describe something. An example is the way textbooks show how planets orbit the Sun.

Carbon Dioxide: Dry Ice and Greenhouse Gas

Figure 7.19 Carbon dioxide is a pure substance that sublimes — it changes state from solid to gas, hence the name "dry ice."

Carbon dioxide is mentioned in the news all the time because its increasing concentration in the atmosphere is thought to be one of the main causes of climate change. Carbon dioxide is one of the by-products of the combustion, or burning, of different types of natural resource fuels, such as coal, oil, and natural gas. However, we should take a closer look at this pure substance because it has some interesting chemical properties.

Sources

As mentioned, carbon dioxide is one of the products of the burning of different types of organic substances, such as wood, paper, and sugar. Along with water, carbon dioxide is also a by-product of the respiration that occurs in all plants and animals. Every time you breathe, you exhale carbon dioxide. Additionally, plants take in carbon dioxide and release oxygen and water as part of the process of photosynthesis.

Common Uses

The most common industrial use of carbon dioxide is as a refrigerant. At temperatures below −78°C, carbon dioxide becomes solid, and solid carbon dioxide is commonly known as dry ice (Figure 7.19). At ordinary temperature and air pressure, carbon dioxide changes state directly from solid to gas in a process known as sublimation. Thus, dry ice can be carried in a suitable container to keep food or other substances at temperatures below the freezing point of water.

Another common use of carbon dioxide is as a fire extinguisher. Since carbon dioxide is denser than air, it replaces the less dense air surrounding a burning material, preventing oxygen from supporting combustion.

Greenhouse Gas

In recent years, it has become known that carbon dioxide, along with other so-called greenhouse gases, has the ability to retain or trap heat from Earth's surface. This is necessary for life on Earth. However, since the middle of the 19th century (around 1850), the amount of atmospheric carbon dioxide has risen steadily. There has also been an increase in average temperature. Some environmentalists predict that, by the year 2050, the amount of carbon dioxide will have doubled from before 1900. This will lead to an increase in the average temperature on Earth (perhaps by as much as 5°C), resulting in a major and dangerous change in climate.

Questions

1. How is carbon dioxide produced naturally?

2. What is sublimation?

3. Why is carbon dioxide known as dry ice?

Key Concept Review

1. Explain whether you would classify each of the following items as either a pure substance or a mixture. ⓒ

   (a) apple juice

   (b) fruit punch

   (c) distilled water

   (d) lemonade

2. A pure substance is made up of particles that are all the same, while a mixture is made of particles that are different. Use a diagram to show a mixture of distilled water, vinegar, and olive oil. ⓒ ⓚ

3. Explain what happens to a potato chip bag as it warms in the heat of the Sun. ⓐ

4. Describe what happens to the particles of a solid as it changes state to become a liquid. ⓚ

Connect Your Understanding

5. Use the particle theory of matter to explain why cooling a gas will eventually cause it to condense into a liquid. ⓐ

6. If all matter is made up of particles, what is between the particles? ⓣ

7. Use a diagram to explain why heat is released by the particles of a liquid substance when it becomes a solid. ⓒ

8. In cold weather, frost forms and coats everything with a white substance. What is this substance, and why does it appear only when the weather is cold? ⓣ

9. What would the particles in a block of chocolate look like compared to the same amount of chocolate in liquid form? Draw particle diagrams of the block of chocolate and liquid chocolate to support your answer. ⓒ

After Reading Thinking Literacy

Reflect and Evaluate

Revisit the predictions you made at the start of this chapter. What prediction did you make about the particle theory? Was your prediction confirmed or did you need to modify it as you read?

Use what you knew and what you learned to create a well-labelled diagram to represent the key points that describe the behaviour of matter. Which of the points of the particle theory of matter do you think is most important to remember? Explain why.

ACHIEVEMENT CHART CATEGORIES
ⓚ Knowledge and understanding ⓣ Thinking and investigation ⓒ Communication ⓐ Application

10. When you blow into a balloon, what makes it get bigger? Explain your answer with a particle diagram. ⊙

11. Give an example of a mechanical mixture or solution that is made of: ⊙

    (a) two or more solids

    (b) two or more liquids

    (c) a solid and a liquid

Practise Your Skills

12. Prepare a T-chart with the following title: Pure Substances and Mixtures as Foods. Label the columns Pure Substances and Mixtures. Make a list of five pure substances and five mixtures that you might eat or drink every day. Some examples to help get you started include salt, pepper, olive oil, and water. ⊙

13. When water freezes to become ice, energy must be removed. If this occurs in the freezer section of your refrigerator, where does the heat energy go? Explain your answer with a diagram that uses arrows to show the direction of heat flow. ⊙

Unit Task Link

In your unit task, you will investigate water samples taken from a number of sources. Commercial and industrial processes involve isolating particles and mixing particles from different substances to form useful mixtures. During these processes, particles may escape into water supplies as waste. Using the particle theory of matter, track the source of the waste particles that may contaminate water. Think about how the waste particles interact with the water particles.

C13   *Thinking about Science and Technology*

Common Uses of Pure Substances and Mixtures

Many of the products that you use in your garden, on your lawn, and around your home can be classified as either pure substances or mixtures.

Consider This

Consider the following examples of common substances found in the house and garden:

- ice melter
- fertilizer
- bug spray
- glass cleaner
- gasoline

With a classmate or as a whole class, discuss the following and be prepared to share your ideas.

1. Ice melter is usually a pure substance in solid form (e.g., salt). What happens to the space between its particles when it is working to melt ice?

2. What negative environmental effects could be caused by misuse of fertilizer, glass cleaner, or bug spray?

3. Gasoline is a mixture of several chemicals that come from crude oil. List some advantages of gasoline as a fuel source in comparison to other fuels (e.g., wood, coal, wax, natural gas).

8.0

Mixtures and solutions can be analyzed through concentration, solubility, and separation.

Chemists can use colour as an indicator to help determine the solubility and concentration of solutions.

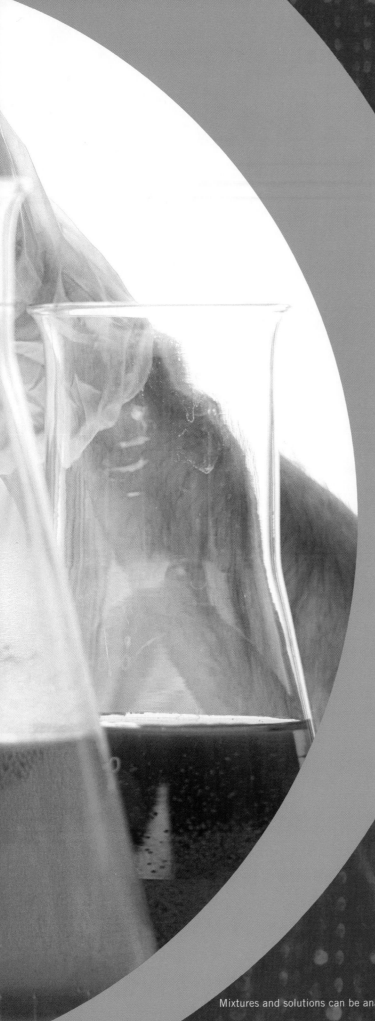

What You Will Learn

In this chapter, you will:

- identify the components of a solution
- describe the concentration of a solution in qualitative and quantitative terms
- describe the difference between saturated and unsaturated solutions
- describe the processes used to separate mixtures or solutions into their components

Skills You Will Use

In this chapter, you will:

- use scientific inquiry/experimentation skills to investigate factors that affect the solubility of a substance and the rate at which substances dissolve
- use scientific inquiry/experimentation skills to investigate the properties of mixtures and solutions

Why This Is Important

Preparing your favourite meal involves understanding the properties of the mixture. Concentration and solubility can affect the taste and quality of the meal.

Before Reading

Thinking Literacy

Monitoring Comprehension

A **KTW** chart is used to identify what you already **K**now about a topic, what you **T**hink you know, and what you **W**ant to know. Complete a KTW chart for the properties of mixtures and modify it as you read the chapter to monitor your comprehension.

Key Terms

- concentration
- distillation
- evaporation
- filtration
- saturated
- solubility
- solute
- solvent

Figure 8.1 Between May and July 2000, seven people died as a result of drinking contaminated drinking water.

When you take a drink of water, you assume that it will not make you sick. The people of Walkerton, Ontario thought their water was safe (Figure 8.1). But between May and July 2000, seven people in the town died because they drank contaminated water. More than 2000 people became ill. The government of Ontario made safe drinking water a priority because of the tragic events that took place in Walkerton.

To purify drinking water, various components of the mixture that make up untreated water must be separated and removed. The separation process is complex and involves many stages, including treatments that sort particles by size. The process eventually requires mixing the water with chemicals to kill bacteria and other harmful living components (Figure 8.2 on the next page).

Through research involving separation of mixtures, water purification experts have improved the processes involved in purifying drinking water. In addition, many other industrial processes (e.g., separating metals and minerals from mined rocks, separating oils and oil products from crude oil) rely on an understanding of mixtures and solutions. Many common household products and items that you use every day, such as dishwashing detergent, hair gel, and snack foods, have come about as a result of industrial uses of mixtures.

Wise use of consumer products is enhanced by understanding key ideas about mixtures and solutions. In this chapter, you will learn about different aspects of, and methods of separating, mechanical mixtures and solutions.

Figure 8.2 The components of the mixture that make up untreated water must be separated and removed.

C14 *Quick Lab*

Making a Solution

Many solutions involve mixing a substance in a liquid until the substance is completely dissolved. For example, you can mix powdered drink crystals with water to make a refreshing drink.

Purpose

To see what is involved in making a solution

Materials & Equipment

- 50-mL or 100-mL graduated cylinder
- water (room temperature)
- beaker
- 5-mL measuring spoon
- powdered drink crystals
- stir stick

Procedure

1. Use the graduated cylinder to measure 50 mL of water into the beaker.

2. Use the measuring spoon to measure 5 mL of the powdered drink crystals. Add the drink crystals to the water.

3. Stir the mixture until the substance has dissolved. Record your observations in a table similar to the one below.

Table 8.1 Making a solution

Amount Added	Observations
5 mL	

4. Keep adding the drink crystals, 5 mL at a time, until they will not dissolve in the water.

Questions

With a classmate or as a whole class, discuss the following questions.

5. How did you know that you could not dissolve more drink crystals in the water?

6. How did stirring the water affect the dissolving of the drink crystals in the water?

Here is a summary of what you will learn in this section:

- The concentration of a solution can be described in qualitative and quantitative terms.
- Solutes and solvents can be identified in various kinds of solutions.
- Water is sometimes referred to as the universal solvent.

Figure 8.3 Common ingredients used in baking can form solutions with water.

Cooks and chefs prepare and follow recipes for meals that call for specific amounts of ingredients (Figure 8.3). When those ingredients are properly mixed together, they produce great-tasting foods. For example, experienced cooks understand that just the right amount of salt dissolved in water will produce a desired taste. Too much salt may not completely dissolve in the amount of water necessary, or it may produce a flavour that is too salty. Hence, an understanding of concentration and solubility is necessary to prepare foods properly.

C15 *Starting Point*   Skills P C

Dissolving Common Kitchen Ingredients in Water

Salt, baking soda, and sugar are common ingredients used in baking. However, they dissolve in water at different rates.

Work with a partner; one person will perform the experiment, while the other will measure time and record the data in a notebook. Obtain a beaker or glass with 50 mL of water at room temperature. Measure 5 mL of one of the ingredients listed above. After the substance is added to the water, measure the amount of time required for it to dissolve in the water.

Record the colour and clarity of the solution. Repeat your procedure for the other ingredients, and then answer the following questions.

1. Which ingredient took the least amount of time to dissolve in water?

2. Which ingredient took the most time to dissolve in water?

3. Were all solutions identical in appearance? If not, what was the difference?

Thinking Literacy

Pause and Check

Readers can do many things when they realize their understanding of a concept is breaking down. On this page you are reading about the two components of solutions: the solute and the solvent. Can you distinguish between these two things? Focus on the solute and create a two column chart to record, "What it is" and "What it is not." Add information from the text to your chart. What do you notice about the column entitled, "What it is not"? What is it describing?

Solutions

As you learned in the previous chapter, a solution is a homogeneous mixture because it has the same appearance throughout. Solutions can occur as solids, liquids, or gases. Solid solutions are called **alloys**. The door knocker is made of a brass alloy, which is a mixture of copper and zinc (Figure 8.4). Liquid and gaseous solutions are simply called **solutions**.

Figure 8.4 The brass door knocker is a mixture of copper and zinc.

Solutions consist of solutes and solvents. A **solute** is the substance that dissolves. A **solvent** is the substance into which the solute dissolves. The solvent is usually the substance present in the greatest amount. For example, in the air you breathe, nitrogen is found in the greatest amount. It is the solvent into which solutes such as oxygen, argon, and carbon dioxide dissolve. In seawater, salt and other substances (solutes) dissolve in water (solvent). Examples of common solutions are described in Table 8.2.

Table 8.2 Examples of common solutions

Solute	Solvent	Solution
zinc (solid)	copper (solid)	brass
salt, minerals (solid)	water (liquid)	seawater
benzene (liquid)	rubber (solid)	rubber cement
ethylene glycol (liquid)	water (liquid)	antifreeze
carbon dioxide (gas)	water (liquid)	soda pop
oxygen, argon (gas)	nitrogen (gas)	air

Water — The Universal Solvent

Water is often referred to as the universal solvent because many different solids, liquids, and gases dissolve in it to form solutions. For example, seawater is a solution of water with many dissolved solids, such as salt and magnesium, and gases, such as oxygen and carbon dioxide.

Not all substances are soluble in water. For example, many oils and fats do not dissolve in water. However, fats and oils dissolve in soaps and detergents, which you can use to clean cookware and clothing.

Components of Solutions

1. Name three types of solutions — one solid, one liquid, and one gas.

2. Identify three common solutions used in the kitchen. List the solutes and solvents found in each solution.

3. Name a substance that dissolves in water. How can you prove that it is water soluble?

4. Make a list of three substances that cannot dissolve in water. For each substance, identify a solvent in which it will dissolve.

Suggested Activity • • • • • • • •
C18 Quick Lab on page 218

Take It Further

Most clothing is washed in water using laundry detergent. Most detergents work best in hot water. Some fabrics (e.g., wool) can be damaged by the heat from hot water (and hot air in dryers). Dry cleaners use different solvents to clean clothing. Find out more about these solvents. Begin your search at PearsonScience.

Solubility

Solubility is the relative ability of a solute to form a solution when added to a certain solvent. It is also defined as the maximum amount of solute you can add to a fixed amount of solvent at a given temperature. To form a solution, the solute particles must be attracted to the solvent particles, which allows the particles to spread evenly throughout the solution. For example, salt dissolves in water because the salt particles are attracted to the water particles (Figure 8.5, left). This forms a saltwater solution.

However, salt does not dissolve in olive oil because the salt particles are not attracted to the oil particles (Figure 8.5, right). When a substance does not dissolve in a solvent, that substance is **insoluble** in that solvent. A solution is not formed by the combination of the two substances when one of the substances is insoluble in the other other.

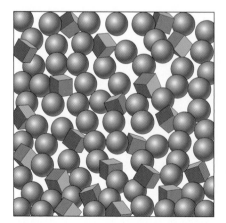
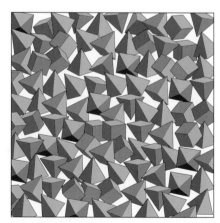

Figure 8.5 (Left) Salt (yellow) dissolves in water (blue) because the particles are attracted to one another. (Right) Salt particles (yellow) form clumps and do not dissolve in olive oil (green) because the particles are not attracted to one another.

Concentration — Qualitative

The amount of solute in a solvent can be expressed in qualitative terms. A **concentrated** solution is a solution that contains a large amount of dissolved solute and very little solvent. For example, frozen juice concentrate is a concentrated solution of orange juice solids (solute) and a small amount of water (solvent). Solutions are **dilute** when very little solute is dissolved in the solvent. By adding water (solvent) to the frozen juice concentrate (solute), you would be diluting the frozen orange juice. This would create a diluted solution of orange juice (Figure 8.6).

Concentration — Quantitative

The **concentration** of a solution is the amount of solute dissolved in a specific amount of the solution. For example, if 5 g of salt are dissolved in enough water to make 500 mL of solution, the concentration of the solution is 5 g/500 mL (or 1 g/100 mL). This can be read as "five grams per five hundred millilitres" or "one gram per one hundred millilitres." We could also call this a 1 percent solution. For example, a concentration of 1 g/100 mL means that 100 mL of the solution has 1 g of solute dissolved in it. This also means that the solute makes up 1 percent of the solution.

Figure 8.6 Frozen orange juice is diluted with water to form an orange juice solution.

Saturation

In all solutions, there is a maximum amount of solute that can be dissolved in a given amount of solvent at a given temperature. A solution is **saturated** when it has been formed from the maximum amount of solute for a given amount of solvent at a certain temperature. Every solution has a **saturation point** at a given temperature, which means that no more solute can be dissolved in a fixed volume of solvent at that temperature.

If more solute can be dissolved in a solvent at a given temperature, then the solution is **unsaturated**. You can dissolve more solute in an unsaturated solution. Under certain circumstances, a saturated solution can be cooled below a critical temperature to form a **supersaturated** solution, which contains more solute than would normally be dissolved in the solution.

Soluble or Insoluble

Although they are similar in appearance, salt and sugar do not necessarily share similar characteristics when it comes to solubility. In this activity, you will investigate if salt and sugar are soluble or insoluble in two different solvents — water and vegetable oil.

Purpose

To determine whether salt and sugar have similar characteristics of solubility in different solvents

---

Materials and Equipment

- 4 transparent plastic cups or beakers
- pen or marker
- 4 labels
- measuring spoons
- water
- vegetable oil
- salt
- sugar
- 4 stir sticks

Procedure

1. Make a table for your observations similar to the one shown below.

   Table 8.3 Solvents, solutes, and solubility

Container	Solvent	Solute	Observations
A			
B			
C			
D			

2. Label the 4 containers (i.e., plastic cups or beakers) A, B, C, and D.

3. Use a measuring spoon to pour 5 mL of water into containers A and B.

4. Dry the measuring spoon, and then pour the same amount (5 mL) of vegetable oil into containers C and D.

5. Predict whether each of the solutes will dissolve in one, both, or neither of the solvents. Record your predictions in your notebook.

6. Use a measuring spoon to add 2 mL of salt to containers A and C, and then add 2 mL of sugar to containers B and D.

7. Using separate stir sticks, stir each mixture and carefully observe the contents of each container to determine if the solutes have dissolved. Record your observations in the table.

8. Once you are done, clean up the materials as directed by your teacher and wash your hands thoroughly.

Questions

9. Which solutes were soluble in which solvents?

10. Were your predictions about the solubility of each combination of solute and solvent correct?

11. Which solvent appeared to be best able to dissolve when the solutes were tested?

12. Use the particle theory of matter to determine why the solutes dissolved as observed.

13. Use the particle theory of matter to explain why water is a very good solvent for many different solutes.

Key Concept Review

1. Explain how a metal alloy is a solution. Provide two examples of metal alloys.

2. Explain how to change a dilute solution to a concentrated solution.

3. Explain the meaning of the terms "saturated," "unsaturated," and "supersaturated" with reference to the amount of solute and solvent in solutions.

4. What is the concentration of a solution, expressed in g/100 mL, if 25 g of solute is dissolved in 40 mL of water? State the concentration in two different ways.

5. Why is water referred to as the universal solvent? Is this description of water accurate?

Connect Your Understanding

6. Use your understanding of the terms "soluble" and "insoluble" to explain why you must shake a bottle of salad dressing made with oil and vinegar before you use it.

7. Use your understanding of solutes and solvents to explain why a supersaturated solution tends to be unstable and likely to have the solute come rapidly out of solution when shaken or disturbed.

Practise Your Skills

8. In a classroom experiment, 5 g of sugar are added to 50 mL of water. If 1 mL of water has a mass of 1 g, calculate the concentration of the sugar solution and express your answer in units of g/100 mL.

For more questions, go to PearsonScience.

C19 Thinking about Science and the Environment

Solutes and Solvents

Chocolate and peanut butter are solutes that do not dissolve well in water. They are difficult to remove from kitchen cutlery and clothing. Solvents like oil and turpentine stain clothing.

In your notebook, make a list of two solutes and two solvents that might be difficult to clean up or dispose of safely. Identify at least two ways to minimize the impact of clean-up or disposal of these substances on the environment.

Here is a summary of what you will learn in this section:

- The particle theory of matter explains how solutes dissolve in solvents.
- Solubility is affected by temperature, type of solute or solvent, particle size, and stirring.

Salt has many different uses, and it also comes in different forms. Rock salt is used in water softeners to help remove unwanted particles of dissolved metal from water (Figure 8.7, top). Table salt is used to add flavour to foods (Figure 8.7, bottom). They both dissolve in water, since salt particles are attracted to water particles, but table salt dissolves more quickly than rock salt.

Solubility is an interesting property of solute particles and their interaction with solvent particles. For example, when you paint with water-based paints, it is easy to clean up and remove the paint from your brush with water. However, oil-based paints do not dissolve in water. Cleaning up is made more difficult because only certain solvents, such as turpentine, will dissolve oil-based paints.

Figure 8.7 Rock salt (top) takes longer to dissolve than table salt (bottom).

C20 *Starting Point*   Skills

One Lump or Two Teaspoons

If you have ever eaten at a restaurant or shopped in a grocery story, you may have seen that sugar comes in different forms. You can buy granular (loose) sugar by the bag or packet, and you can also buy sugar cubes. In this activity, you will determine which dissolves more quickly in water: one sugar cube or two teaspoons of granular sugar.

Work with a partner. Measure 50 mL of water into each of two colourless, transparent containers. At exactly the same time, add one sugar cube to one container while your partner adds two teaspoons of sugar to the other container. Do not shake either container or touch them in any way. Determine which sample finishes dissolving first: one sugar cube or two teaspoons of granular sugar.

Solubility and the Particle Theory

As stated in the previous chapter, all matter is made up of particles. According to the particle theory of matter, those particles are in constant motion. Particles are constantly rotating, vibrating, and moving about from one place to another. In a solution, this means that solute particles are always bumping against other solute particles as well as solvent particles.

Figure 8.8 shows that dissolving a salt crystal begins with water particles bumping into salt particles at the edge of the crystal. The water particles are attracted to the individual salt particles. With constant motion, they are able to free individual salt particles from the larger crystal. Individual salt particles are then carried away by bumping into water particles. This leaves room for other water particles to bump into and carry off other salt particles at the edge of the crystal. The process continues until all the salt particles are surrounded by water particles and are evenly distributed throughout the water.

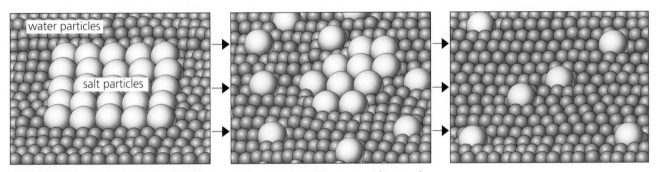

Figure 8.8 The constant motion of particles and the attraction of water particles to salt particles cause salt to dissolve in water.

Rate of Dissolving

How quickly a substance dissolves in a solvent is variable. A teaspoon of table sugar will dissolve rapidly in a hot drink (Figure 8.9). The same amount of sugar will take much more time to dissolve in a glass of ice water. Similarly, table salt dissolves rapidly in water at room temperature. Large pieces of salt, like those used in home water softeners, dissolve much more slowly, which makes this type of salt ideal for use over long periods. The rate of dissolving is affected by stirring, temperature, and particle size.

Figure 8.9 A teaspoon of sugar dissolves quickly in a hot drink.

Suggested Activity •·········
C24 Inquiry Activity on page 225

Figure 8.10 Stirring makes the flavour crystals dissolve more quickly.

Stirring

Stirring a solution increases the rate at which a solute dissolves in a solvent. For example, you may have tried to make a soft drink by dissolving flavour crystals in a pitcher of water (Figure 8.10). The flavour crystals are the solute and water is the solvent. If the package of flavour crystals is poured into the water, dissolving begins, but clumps of powder may remain. To speed up the process, you probably used a spoon to stir the water with the flavour crystals. This results in a more uniform arrangement of flavour crystals and water particles and makes dissolving occur more quickly. You can actually see the flavour crystals being stirred until they dissolve in the water. The end result is a solution, as all parts of the soft drink mixture look the same.

Figure 8.11 is a particle diagram of water particles surrounding salt particles. It illustrates how particles dissolve more quickly in water that is stirred compared to salt particles in water that is not stirred. As shown in the left part of the diagram, the water particles at the edge of a salt crystal tend to remain near the edge of the crystal. This limits the number of water particles that can interact with individual salt particles and it limits the amount of dissolving that can occur. As shown in the right part of the diagram, stirring the water pushes some of the salt particles surrounded by water particles away from the edge of the crystal and increases the number of water particles that are able to interact with salt particles. Thus, more salt particles are exposed to and come in contact with more water particles. This speeds up the dissolving process.

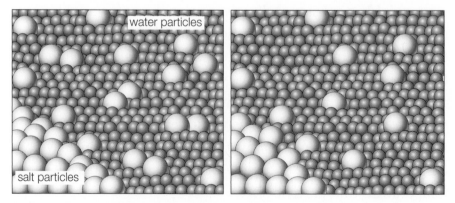

Figure 8.11 (Left) Water particles surround salt particles at the edge of a salt crystal and tend to remain near the edge. (Right) When the water is stirred, more water particles are free to bump into salt particles and surround them.

Using a Particle Diagram to Explain Rate of Dissolving

John Dalton (1766–1844) was a chemist, meteorologist, and physicist. He is best known for developing ideas about particles. His early records contain particle diagrams, which he used to represent the chemicals he was studying.

In your notebook, make a particle diagram to show why stirring tends to increase the rate of dissolving (Figure 8.12).

Figure 8.12 Use a particle diagram to explain the rate of dissolving.

Temperature

As you learned in the previous chapter, temperature affects the speed at which particles move. Particles move more rapidly at higher temperatures, as heat is transferred by the movement of the particles. Since the rate of dissolving depends on solute particles bumping into solvent particles, when the particles move more rapidly, more solvent and solute particles will bump into one another. In addition, the solvent particles at the edge of a piece of solute will more rapidly carry away the solute particles that they meet. This will quickly spread the solute particles throughout the solvent. With increasing temperature, most solutes dissolve more rapidly in most solvents. This explains, for example, why a teaspoon of sugar dissolves more quickly in a cup of hot tea than in a glass of iced tea.

Particle Size

Particle size also affects the rate of dissolving. Large particles take longer to dissolve than smaller particles of the same substance. For example, sugar cubes dissolve more slowly than granular sugar, and rock salt dissolves more slowly than table salt. You learned that solvent particles must bump into solute particles for dissolving to occur. Particles of a solvent will contact solute particles at the surface of a clump or crystal of solute particles. Therefore, large pieces of a solute must be broken apart to enable solvent particles to come in contact with solute particles.

Take It *Further*

To survive, fish need oxygen, which they obtain from oxygen dissolved in the water. Temperature affects the amount of gas that dissolves in liquids. At higher temperatures, the content of oxygen dissolved in water decreases. With climate change and global warming, water temperatures in rivers and lakes are expected to increase. Determine how the increased temperature will affect fish in Ontario and around the world. Begin your search at PearsonScience.

SKILLS YOU WILL USE
- Designing an experimental procedure
- Recording and organizing data

Growing Crystals

Crystals can be grown from solutions made from common solutes with water as the solvent. This is a slow process involving the growth, particle by particle, of a solute on a seed crystal suspended in a supersaturated solution. The resulting crystals are often quite beautiful in colour and demonstrate some of the characteristic shapes of the solute particles from which they are made.

Question

How can you grow crystals from a solution?

Design and Conduct Your Investigation

1. Form a research team with a partner.

2. Decide what type of solute you will select from the following list:
   - sugar
   - salt
   - alum
   - copper sulfate
   - Rochelle salt

3. Determine where you will conduct the investigation.

4. Decide on what apparatus will be needed for you to complete that activity.

5. Determine how much solute and solvent will be necessary to form a supersaturated solution.

6. Make a plan that clearly identifies how you will conduct your investigation, including how much time you intend to spend on the investigation to monitor progress each day.

7. Discuss your plan with your teacher. Once the plan has been approved, conduct the investigation.

8. When your work is finished, be prepared to bring your crystal to class for comparison with others.

C23 *Quick Lab*

Sugar Is Sweet, Candy Is Dandy

Purpose

To investigate the effect of particle size on the rate of dissolving

Materials & Equipment

- 2 mL granular sugar
- 2 mL icing sugar
- 50 mL beaker or small jar
- tablespoon
- teaspoon
- water
- stopwatch

CAUTION: Do not taste anything during this activity.

Procedure

1. Use a teaspoon to obtain 5 mL of granular sugar.

2. Place the granular sugar in a small jar or beaker.

3. Add one tablespoon of water and determine the time required for granular sugar to dissolve.

4. Repeat steps 1 to 3 with icing sugar.

Questions

5. Which type of sugar dissolved in the shortest time?

6. Were your findings the same as the rest of your class?

7. Use a particle diagram to explain how particle size affects the rate of dissolving.

Factors Affecting Rate of Dissolving

Question

How do temperature, stirring, and size of particles affect the rate of dissolving?

Materials & Equipment

- rock salt 🜂
- 8 small beakers or glasses
- masking tape
- small but sturdy plastic bag
- cold tap water
- warm tap water
- stir sticks

Procedure

1. Read through the procedure. Write your predictions in your notebook about the effect that temperature, stirring, and size of particles will have on the rate of dissolving of the rock salt samples.

2. In your notebook, prepare a table similar to the one shown below.

Table 8.4 Factors affecting rate of dissolving

| Treatment | Time to Dissolve (s) | | | |
| | Cold Water | | Hot Water | |
	Stirred	Not Stirred	Stirred	Not Stirred
clumped				
crushed				

3. Obtain 8 small beakers and use masking tape to label 4 of them Cold Water and the other 4 Hot Water.

4. Obtain 8 clumps of rock salt. Place one clump each in 2 beakers labelled Cold Water and one each in 2 beakers labelled Hot Water.

5. Place a clump of rock salt in a plastic bag and step on it to crush the clump. Divide the contents of the bag into 2 empty beakers labelled Cold Water. Crush the last clump of rock salt as above and place in 2 empty beakers labelled Hot Water.

6. Fill 2 beakers labelled Cold Water with 50 mL of cold tap water. Fill 2 beakers labelled Hot Water with 50 mL of hot tap water.

7. Without stirring, record the time each sample of rock salt takes to dissolve.

8. Repeat steps 5 and 6 with the other beakers, but this time, stir the water with the stir sticks.

Analyzing and Interpreting

9. Was your prediction for the effect of temperature correct? Explain how you used the particle theory of matter to help with your prediction.

10. Was your prediction for the effect of particle size correct? Explain how you used the particle theory of matter to help with your prediction.

11. Was your prediction for the effect of stirring correct? Explain how you used the particle theory of matter to help with your prediction.

Skill Builder

12. What did you use to measure time for the experiment? Do you feel confident that you were accurate in your measurement of time?

Forming Conclusions

13. If you want to dissolve a solute explain what you must know about the solvent and what you must do to the solute to minimize the time required for dissolving.

Key Concept Review

1. Identify two factors about particles that enable them to form solutions.

2. List three factors that influence the rate at which dissolving occurs.

3. Use the particle theory of matter to explain why table salt dissolves more rapidly than rock salt.

4. Use the particle theory of matter to explain why hot chocolate powder dissolves more rapidly in hot water than in cold water.

Connect Your Understanding

5. Use the particle theory of matter to explain why laundry detergents tend to work better in hot water than in cold water.

6. Use the particle theory of matter to explain why icing sugar dissolves more rapidly than granular sugar.

Practise Your Skills

7. Use the particle theory of matter and the information in the graphs below to explain the solubility of solids and gases in liquids.

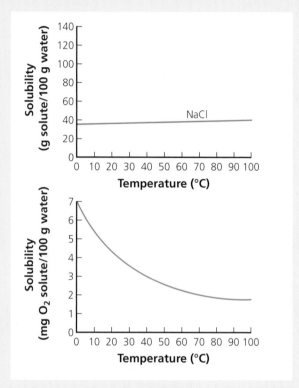

For more questions, go to PearsonScience.

C25 *Thinking about Science and the Environment*

Winter Safety and Salt on Roads

During periods of cold weather, salt is spread on roads to melt ice and snow and make driving safer. Later, the salt is still present to dissolve in rainwater and flows into wetlands, rivers, streams, and lakes.

1. With a partner, brainstorm some possible environmental problems and record them in your notebook.

2. With a partner, brainstorm possible ways of solving these problems and record them in your notebook.

Here is a summary of what you will learn in this section:

- Solutions can be separated by filtration, paper chromatography, evaporation, or distillation.
- Mechanical mixtures can be separated by sorting, sifting, or magnetism.

The manufacturing of cheese involves a process of separating the solid and liquid parts from milk, which is a mechanical mixture. Certain chemicals can be added to milk to cause solid globs called curds to appear and drop away from the liquid part called whey. This process is known as curdling. After this process takes place, the cheese solids can be treated in different ways, usually involving removal of additional water to make many different varieties of cheese (Figure 8.13).

Figure 8.13 Cheese is made by separating milk into different substances.

C26 *Starting Point*   Skills **A C**

Coffee Filter Chromatography

Obtain a 10-cm strip of coffee filter from your teacher. Draw a line in pencil with a ruler 2 cm from one end. Place a dot of ink from a black marker on the middle of the line. Fill a small container with water to a depth of 1 cm. Place the filter strip in the water with the dot about 1 cm above the water, and tape the strip to a pencil (Figure 8.14).

1. Which colour was carried the farthest? Which colour travelled the least distance?

2. Why did the different colours of ink separate and travel different distances? Use the particle theory of matter to explain your answers.

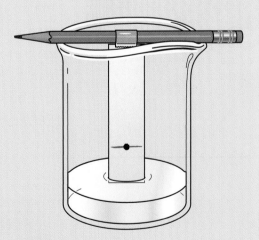

Figure 8.14 Determine which colours of ink move the farthest.

Separating Solutions

The components of a solution have very similar properties and characteristics, which makes them difficult to separate. The most common strategy involves making either the solute or the solvent change state (e.g., changing the solute from solid to liquid) so that it can be removed from the solution.

Filtration

Filtration is the mechanical process of separating solids from liquids (or gases). A filter can be used to separate the solid bits from a mixture of dirt and water (Figure 8.15). When the solution is poured into the filter, the solid parts become trapped in the filter, while the water passes through the filter. Salt or other minerals dissolved in the water will pass through the filter and remain in the water.

Automatic coffee makers use a filter to make coffee. The water passes through the coffee grounds, which creates the coffee solution, leaving the coffee grounds in the filter.

Paper Chromatography

In **paper chromatography**, a highly concentrated solution is placed on a single spot and is absorbed by the paper (Figure 8.16). The paper is dipped in a solvent, such as water, so that the spot is above the solvent. The solvent moves through the paper because the solvent particles are attracted to the paper particles and to one another. Different substances within the mixture dissolve and are carried by the solvent through the paper. The distance that a substance moves depends on its solubility in the solvent and its attraction to the paper. Different compounds travel different distances from the starting point and become separated.

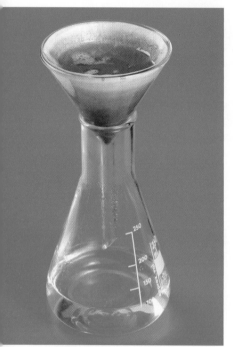

Figure 8.15 Water passes through the filter, but larger particles of dirt are trapped by the filter.

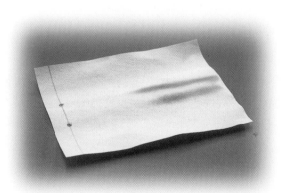

Figure 8.16 In paper chromatography, colours separate based on solubility and attraction to paper.

Evaporation

During the process of **evaporation**, water particles in a container leave the liquid (as vapour) and mix with surrounding air particles. Figure 8.17 shows that the escaping water particles have more energy and are moving faster than the remaining particles. They have enough energy to escape from the surface of the liquid. If the liquid is a solution, then the concentration of solute will increase because the number of solute particles remains constant while the number of water particles decreases. Over time, if all of the water particles leave the solution, then only the solute particles will be left behind, as they have been separated from the water. Thus, evaporation allows the solute to remain but not the solvent.

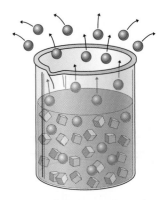

Figure 8.17 Evaporating solvent particles leave solution, while solute particles remain in greater concentration.

You already learned that maple syrup is made by boiling maple sap. This process causes the water in the maple sap to evaporate, which leaves behind a concentrated solution of maple syrup.

Distillation

Distillation enables you to retain both the solute and the solvent from a solution. During the distillation process, the solution is boiled. This vaporizes the solvent (turning it into a gas) and separates it from the solute (Figure 8.18). Then the gas condenses on a relatively cool surface and is collected. This separation technique is useful for substances with large differences in boiling points.

Some types of bottled water are created by distillation. This process is common when creating drinking water from salt water. Distillation removes the salt from the water, which makes it drinkable.

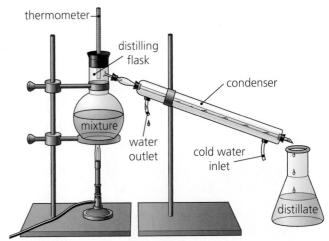

Figure 8.18 Distillation separates substances using boiling and condensation. In this apparatus, cold water is used to cool the vapour in the condenser.

Thinking Literacy

Checking the Meaning of Key Words

Slowing the pace of reading, rereading, or pausing to think are effective strategies to monitor comprehension. Checking the meaning of key words is another.

While reading this section, write down a list of terms that you do not understand. You can make vocabulary cards to help you understand their meaning (Figure 8.19). To get you started, here are a few terms from the first part of the section:

- chromatography
- filtration
- distillation
- evaporation

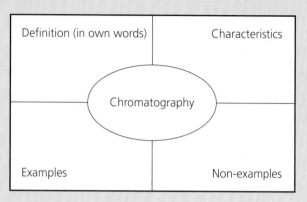

Figure 8.19 Vocabulary cards are useful for helping you to understand terms.

Separating Mechanical Mixtures

Generally speaking, separating mechanical mixtures is easier than separating solutions because the components of the mechanical mixture are usually quite different from each other. In some cases, the components of mechanical mixtures are easy to see and are easily identifiable.

Sorting

Sorting is a technique that involves separating substances on the basis of appearance, which may involve colour, size, texture, or composition. Figure 8.20 shows a blue box with a number of recyclable items. Some curbside recycling programs require the driver of the recycling truck to place the contents of the blue box into appropriate bins. Metal objects are separated from glass items, and plastic containers are separated from paper products. These separate groups of objects are then recycled. For example, aluminum cans are melted down and recycled as new aluminum cans. Some paper products are recycled for use in printing newspapers.

Figure 8.20 You can sort recyclable materials into different bins for easier recycling.

Sifting

Sifting is a means of separating solids by component size. It involves shaking or agitating a solid material while it passes through a screen or mesh. For example, bakers sift flour to remove larger clumps, which helps to make the pastries light and fluffy (Figure 8.21). Components of the solid materials that are small enough to pass through openings in the sifting device are separated from larger components that cannot fit through the same openings.

Although it seems like they are similar techniques, sifting is different from filtration. Filters tend to have much smaller holes than screens used for sifting. As a result, a solid that would pass through a screen would not pass through a filter. Also, filtration is used to separate solids from liquids or gases, whereas sifting separates solids from other solids.

Figure 8.21 Pastry chefs sift flour to keep cakes and pastries light and fluffy.

Magnetism

Some metals are **magnetic** because their component particles are attracted to the particles within magnets. Iron, steel, nickel, and some compounds are highly attracted to magnets, whereas most other substances are not. Therefore, a magnet can be used to separate magnetic materials, such as automobile parts made with iron, from those materials that are not magnetic, such as plastic dashboards, foam insulation, and the rubber tires of cars (Figure 8.22).

Figure 8.22 A magnet will pick up some types of metal but not others.

Take It *Further*

Recycling programs are in place throughout Canada and around the world. These programs successfully divert waste items from disposal in solid waste landfills. Many products that you use everyday have been made from recycled materials. Find out more about the sources of recycled materials. Begin your search at PearsonScience.

Designing a Method to Separate a Mixture

Recognize a Need

Many industrial and manufacturing applications involve the need to separate components of a mixture of different substances. This may involve removing precious stones, minerals, or metals from rocky raw material, making cheese by separating clumped material called curd from raw milk, or some other application. In this activity, you will work with a team to design a method to separate the components of a mixture determined by your teacher.

Problem

How can you separate this mixture into each of its component parts?

Materials & Equipment
- as determined by the teacher

Criteria for Success

- A method of separation for each component part is approved by the teacher.

- The mixture is sorted into each component part.

Brainstorm Ideas

1. Classify each of the substances known to be in the mixture using the following criteria:

   - pure substances or mixtures

   - water soluble or water insoluble

   - magnetic or non-magnetic

   - large particle size or small particle size

2. Determine which separation methods will be allowed by your teacher.

Make a Drawing

3. Show on your flowchart when and how each substance is separated from the mixture.

4. Ask your teacher to approve your process.

5. Revise your process as necessary, and repeat steps 3 and 4 until your flowchart is approved by your teacher.

Test and Evaluate

6. Using the flowchart you prepared as your guide, conduct the separation as you have planned.

7. Be prepared to demonstrate your separation technique by modelling the procedure for your class. As much as is possible, use real examples and include the thinking process you used to design your technique.

8. When finished, clean up your work station and wash your hands thoroughly.

Communicate

9. Prepare a brief presentation (2 min) of your separation technique and deliver this to your class. Be sure that all team members contribute to the presentation.

10. Use simple examples to get your point across. Try to include extensions that would enable other students, groups, or industries to use your technique for other mixtures.

Separating a Mixture of Nails, Salt, Sand, Oil, and Water

Question

What methods are necessary to separate and retain all components of a mechanical mixture?

Figure 8.23

Materials and Equipment

- small jar with lid
- 5–10 small nails
- 5 mL table salt
- 5 mL fine sand
- 50 mL tap water
- 50 mL vegetable oil
- 2 small beakers
- bar magnet
- paper towel
- metal tray

Procedure

1. Work with a partner. Combine the nails, table salt, sand, water, and oil in the small jar.

2. Firmly secure the lid to the jar and shake the contents vigorously to dissolve and thoroughly mix the components of the mixture.

3. As a team, discuss and determine how to separate **and retain** all of the components of the mixture.

4. Discuss your procedure with your teacher, and get approval before you proceed with the method.

Analyzing and Interpreting

5. What component did you separate from the mixture first?

6. How did your choice in question 5 affect what you separated next?

7. How did you ensure that the maximum amount of each component of the mixture was retained?

8. Check with other students in your class. Did all students follow the same sequence to separate components from the mixture?

9. Use your understanding of the particle theory of matter to explain why your procedure worked to separate and retain the components of your mixture.

10. Wash your hands thoroughly after completing this investigation.

Skill Builder

11. How did you and your partner decide on the method you eventually used to complete this activity?

Forming Conclusions

12. What property of solutions was most useful to enable separation of the mixture?

13. What property of solids was most useful to enable separation of the mixture?

Key Concept Review

1. Use the terms "dilute" and "concentrated" to explain the difference between maple sap and maple syrup.

2. Explain the difference between evaporation and distillation. Provide an example of each method of separating solutions.

3. Explain why separating a solid mixture is often easier than separating components of a solution.

4. Most types of commercial flour are sifted before they are packaged and sold in the store. What effect do you think this has on the quality of the flour?

5. Explain how paper chromatography could be used to separate a mixture of different-coloured inks.

Connect Your Understanding

6. Explain what steps you could take to purify water for drinking if you were not sure about the water quality.

7. Explain why landscapers might sift soil that they use to construct gardens.

Practise Your Skills

8. You are given a mixture of chalk dust, larger pieces of blackboard chalk, paper clips, and salt. Draw a well-labelled flowchart to explain how you would separate each substance in the mixture.

For more questions, go to PearsonScience.

C30 *Thinking about Science and the Environment*   S T S E

Carbon Removal and the Environment

In Ontario, four generating stations burn coal to produce electricity. The resulting mixture of waste gases includes a great deal of carbon dioxide. In the future, it may be possible to separate carbon dioxide from the waste gases and store it underground, perhaps in abandoned mines.

Work with a partner. Think about some of the benefits that might come from carbon dioxide removal. Additionally, think about some of the negative consequences that could result. Write your ideas in your notebook, and be prepared to discuss your thoughts in small groups or with the rest of the class.

Careers in Consumer Products Safety

Figure 8.24 Careers in consumer products safety may involve testing different products to ensure that they are safe to use by consumers.

Every year, hundreds of people are injured or killed by the improper and unsafe use of consumer products. The Canadian government has established a branch of Health Canada called Consumer Products Safety to help protect Canadians from poorly manufactured products (Figure 8.24).

Safety Services

On its website, Health Canada lists a number of ways in which the Consumer Products Safety Branch works to serve Canadians. These include:

- supporting the development of safety standards and guidelines

- enforcing legislation by conducting investigations, inspections, seizures, recalls, and prosecutions

- testing and conducting research on consumer products

Educational Requirements

Each one of the identified roles requires well-trained people to ensure that the job is done thoroughly and correctly. Generally speaking, to begin a career in consumer products safety will require that you complete a secondary school graduation diploma and that you take math and science courses each year.

Additional requirements include the completion of a two- to three-year college, hospital, or university degree program in biology, chemistry, physics, or the health sciences. It may also require additional qualifications, including clinical training. Supervisors and instructors in this area require considerable experience in their respective fields.

Questions

1. Identify the branch of government responsible for maintaining the safety of consumer products in Canada. Explain why this work is necessary.

2. List three roles performed by this branch of government. Identify how knowledge of pure substances and mixtures would help in performing this role.

3. A career in consumer products safety will involve considerable interaction with people. Consider the types of people skills and qualities you will need to display in this career.

Key Concept Review

1. What is the difference between a solute and a solvent in a solution? Give an example of each. *(k)*

2. Describe the components of an air solution using the terms "solute" and "solvent." *(c)*

3. (a) Why is water called the universal solvent? *(k)*

   (b) List two examples of substances that dissolve in water. *(t)*

   (c) List two examples of substances that do not dissolve in water. Why is it good that they do not dissolve in water? *(t)*

4. Create a Venn diagram to identify and explain two factors that affect the rate at which a solute dissolves in a solvent. *(t)*

5. Compare and contrast the properties of dilute and concentrated solutions. *(c)*

Connect Your Understanding

6. A solution is made when 50 g of sugar is dissolved in 500 mL of water. What is the concentration of the solution in units of: *(a)*

   (a) g/mL?

   (b) g/1000 mL?

7. Use the particle theory of matter to explain the effect of particle size on rate of dissolving. Draw a particle diagram to illustrate your explanation. *(c)*

8. Salt dissolves more rapidly in hot water when compared to cold water. Why is this so? Use the particle theory of matter to explain your answer. *(c)*

9. Many fish species prefer cold water and some cannot survive in water above 20°C. Use your understanding of solubility of solids and gases to explain why these fish cannot survive in warm water. *(k)*

After Reading Thinking Literacy

Reflect and Evaluate

You will work in pairs or small groups to respond to the statements that follow these instructions. Use the marker colour assigned to your group to write a response to the first statement you are given. At your teacher's signal, move to the next statement. Read what has already been written, changing or adding as necessary to monitor the class' comprehension of each concept. What strategies did you use to monitor the comprehension of others during this activity?

ACHIEVEMENT CHART CATEGORIES
(k) Knowledge and understanding   *(t)* Thinking and investigation   *(c)* Communication   *(a)* Application

10. While you are adding salt to a garden salad, the top of the shaker comes off, and a large amount of salt falls into a salad bowl to which you have already added lettuce, pepper, and vinegar. Explain how you could separate the salt from this salad mixture using your understanding of solutions and mixtures. ⓒ

11. Antifreeze is a liquid used in car engines to prevent freezing of the coolant system. If 1 L of antifreeze is added to 1 L of water, the combined volume is less than 2 L. Why is this so? Use the particle theory of matter to explain what happens to the particles of antifreeze (solute) and water (solvent). ⓣ ⓐ

12. Identify two different methods that you have used to separate a solution or mechanical mixture. Describe the purpose and end results. ⓒ

Unit Task Link

In your unit task, you will investigate water samples taken from a number of sources. What properties of mixtures will enable you to understand how some pure substances and mixtures may enter and contaminate water supplies? Be sure to include key ideas like solubility and the effect of temperature on mixtures when you continue work on your unit task.

C31 Thinking about Science and the Environment

Separating Mechanical Mixtures

Mechanical mixtures consist of more than one substance, and each substance within the mechanical mixture looks different. As you complete this task, think about what you know about each component that enables you to separate it from the mixture.

What to Do

1. Reach into your pencil case, pocket, drawer, or desk, and then place the items you find in a pile on your desk.

2. Select similar items (e.g., things you write with, metals, plastics) from the pile and arrange them in separate groups.

Consider This

With a classmate or as a whole class, discuss the following questions.

3. What techniques did you use to separate and group these items?

4. Were your groupings the same as those of the rest of your class?

5. Energy is often required to enable separation of mixtures. Who or what supplied the energy in this case?

The commercial process of making maple syrup has an impact on society and the environment.

What You Will Learn

In this chapter, you will:

- identify industrial applications of the processes used to separate mixtures or solutions

- assess the impact on society and the environment of different industrial methods of separating mixtures and solutions

- assess positive and negative environmental impacts related to the disposal of pure substances and mixtures

Skills You Will Use

In this chapter, you will:

- investigate processes used for separating different mixtures

- use a variety of forms to communicate with different audiences and for a variety of purposes

Why This Is Important

Industrial methods used to separate and dispose of mixtures and solutions can have dramatic effects on where and how we live and may have lasting environmental effects.

Before Writing

Thinking Literacy

Procedural/Sequential Pattern

Some types of writing give step-by-step instructions (procedural pattern), or present a series of events in order (sequential pattern). Scan this chapter for examples of writing that follow a procedural/sequential pattern. When might you use this pattern in your writing?

Key Terms

- aeration
- herbicide
- insecticide
- landfill
- overburden
- radioactive
- salt pan
- surface mining

Figure 9.1 The use of pesticides can produce spotless fruits and vegetables, but at a price.

If you walk past your grocery store's fresh produce section, you may see fruits and vegetables that look healthy and delicious, and practically shine with freshness (Figure 9.1). However, some of these products may have been treated with herbicides to kill competing plants during the planting and growing process. Farmers may also have used insecticides to kill insects and pests that may spoil or damage the appearance of the crops. Even if the use of these chemical mixtures does not affect the immediate quality of the foods you eat, other side effects, such as contamination of rivers, lakes, and ground water, could result from the use and disposal of these chemicals.

Examples of the dangers to the environment of improper disposal of pure substances and mixtures are, unfortunately, too common (Figure 9.2 on the next page). One way to lessen the chance of this happening is to learn more about methods used by industries to dispose of pure substances and mixtures safely.

In this chapter, you will learn about some industrial methods used to separate mixtures. You will learn about the impact of those methods on society and the environment. You will also consider the effects of use and disposal of pure substances and mixtures on the environment. As you read through this chapter, think about your personal use of consumer products and consider how you influence the environment.

Figure 9.2 Industrial seepage from oil processing plants has created algae blooms, which deplete oxygen in the water and suffocate local fish populations. The green areas in this photo are algae.

C32 *Quick Lab*

Sifting for Precious Metals

Commercial mining often involves separating material known as ore (which contains precious metals, such as gold or silver) from rock. You can simulate this process in your classroom.

Purpose

To separate pennies, nickels, and quarters from a mixture of coins, sand, and stones

> ### Materials & Equipment
> - several pieces of paper
> - sand
> - small stones
> - scissors
> - plate
> - various coins

Procedure

1. Obtain scissors, paper, coins, and quantities of sand and stones from your teacher.

2. Use scissors to cut holes in the paper. The holes should be small enough that the coins will not fit through the holes but large enough that the sand and stones will fit through the holes.

3. You may wish to measure the size of each coin to ensure that the size of holes cut in the paper is slightly less than the size of a coin. This may mean that you use more than one piece of paper and that you perform the sifting more than once.

4. Carefully sift the mixture above a plate, allowing the sand and stones to pass through the holes in the paper but not the coins.

Questions

5. How big were the holes you cut in the paper to allow passage of the sand and stone mixture but not the coins?

6. Were you able to complete the sifting process in one try, or were multiple siftings needed to separate each type of coin?

7. Provide some examples to explain how mining companies might improve upon the efficiency of sifting to separate a mixture.

9.1 Industrial Methods to Separate Components of Mixtures

Here is a summary of what you will learn in this section:

- There are different methods of separating components from mixtures.
- There are many industrial applications of the different methods of separating solutions and mechanical mixtures.

Figure 9.3 Many common products are produced from metals separated from rocks mined from the ground.

There are many different types of substances and consumer products manufactured every day that involve industrial methods of separating pure substances and mixtures into different components. Bicycles, computers, and even cellphones are produced from materials that are created by separating metals from rocks mined from the ground (Figure 9.3). Crude petroleum is refined to produce fuels, plastics, and edible oil-based products, such as synthetic whipping cream. Many foods and drinks that you consume every day, from maple syrup to diet cola, are made using processes that involve separating mixtures.

C33 *Starting Point*   Skills **A** **C**

Distillation of Antifreeze

Antifreeze helps to protect an automobile's engine from damage. It is used to prevent water in the radiator from freezing or boiling. Table 9.1 shows the boiling points of three components of antifreeze.

1. Work with a partner and use the information in the table to predict what would happen if the antifreeze solution were gradually heated to 200°C.

2. What would be the components of the antifreeze solution at 50°C, 75°C, 100°C, and 150°C?

3. Why might one substance have a higher boiling point than another substance?
   Hint: Use the particle theory of matter to help explain your answers.

Table 9.1 The boiling points of some common components of antifreeze

Substance	Boiling Point (°C)
water	100
methanol	65
ethylene glycol	197

Separation Using Distillation

Fractional distillation is used to separate different substances or fractions that make up crude petroleum oil based on differences in their boiling points (Figure 9.4). Crude petroleum oil in liquid form is pumped through pipes into a furnace where it is heated and changed into gaseous form. The resulting mixture of very hot gases is passed into a fractionation or distillation tower. As the gases rise in the tower away from the heat, the gas mixture cools. Substances with higher boiling points, like paraffin wax, condense and are captured near the bottom of the tower where the temperature is greater. Substances with lower boiling points, like gasoline, remain as gases as they move up the tower until they condense and are captured at higher levels.

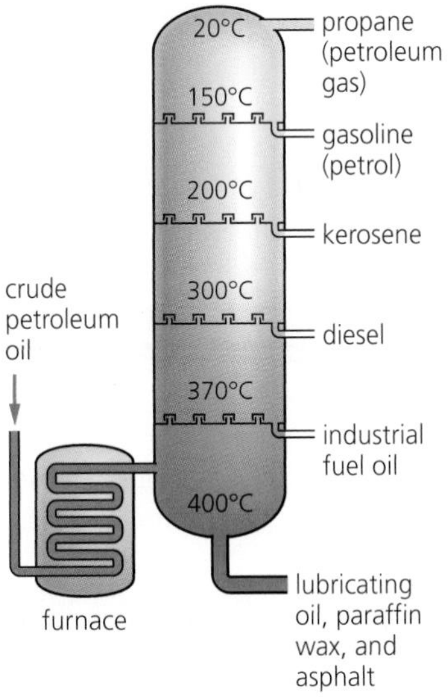

Figure 9.4 Crude petroleum oil is separated into different parts.

Separation Using Evaporation

Every spring, millions of litres of maple sap are collected in eastern Canada to make maple syrup. The sap is boiled to evaporate most of the water (Figure 9.5). What remains is a sweet mixture of sugar, water, and substances from the tree that give maple syrup its distinctive flavour.

For thousands of years, people living near oceans have used the heat from sunlight to evaporate seawater and obtain salt. Seawater flows into a large, low-lying area called a **salt pan**, which is surrounded by dikes. When the water has evaporated, the remaining solid is about 96 percent salt (sea salt).

Figure 9.5 It takes about 40 L of maple sap to make 1 L of maple syrup.

C34 Learning Checkpoint

Fractional Distillation

1. If crude petroleum is a mixture of different substances, is it a solution or a mechanical mixture? Explain your reasoning completely.

2. Explain how gasoline, kerosene, and crude petroleum are related.

3. Explain why substances with a lower boiling point are removed near the top of a petroleum fractional distillation tower.

Separation Using Filtering

Water purification uses very fine filters to separate dirt and some bacteria from water. Water filters can be used to improve the taste and purity of tap water (Figure 9.6). Commercial water filters are often used to remove impurities from the water during the production of different food products.

Air filters are often used in building ventilation systems and industrial clean rooms to ensure that the air is free of dust and other substances. Fans force air through microfilters, which have tiny pores that trap dust particles, pollen, and tiny particulate matter.

Figure 9.6 This water filter removes particles of dirt and some bacteria.

Separation Using Magnetism

Recyclers of solid waste often use magnets to separate metals (e.g., iron, steel) from other waste products. Figure 9.7 shows that iron and steel are attracted to the magnet and can be removed from non-magnetic substances, such as wood and plastics. Steel and iron recovered by this process can be melted down and remanufactured into other useful products. Bits of iron and steel (e.g., paper clips, staples) can be removed with magnets from waste paper and corrugated board, which can then be reprocessed into recycled paper products.

Figure 9.7 This industrial magnet removes steel and iron from other metals at a metal-recycling plant.

Separation Using Sifting

Rocks containing metals (ore) are sifted before metal is extracted from ore by melting. This sifting process separates the denser metal-containing rocks from lighter rock material (which has very little metal content) to make it easier to remove the metals from the rocks.

Sifting flour is also an important process in baking. Most flour bought from grocery stores is pre-sifted. Sifting flour breaks up lumps to ensure that the flour can be measured properly. In addition, when flour is sifted, air is added so that when flour is mixed with liquid ingredients (e.g., eggs, water), the dry flour can be fully and evenly moistened, which results in light, fluffy baked goods.

Take It *Further*

Panning for gold is a separation process developed by early prospectors. They needed to separate gold from sand and gravel in streams. To do this, they would shake a pan containing water and a small amount of sand and gravel so the gold would sink to the bottom. Learn more about panning for gold and other mining techniques. Begin your search at PearsonScience.

Using Magnetism to Separate Recycled Metals

Aluminum soft drink cans have a very high value for recycling. Unfortunately, the value of this resource is often reduced because of contamination from metallic cans that contain iron and steel. Recycling centres use large magnets that attract iron and steel to remove the contaminant metals and increase the value of the recycled aluminum. In this activity, you will learn to use a magnet to separate different magnetic and non-magnetic materials.

Purpose

To separate the steel and iron cans in your recycling box from aluminum cans

Materials & Equipment

- clean metal containers for recycling
- permanent magnet (larger is better)

Procedure

1. Make a table in your notebook like the one shown below.

Table 9.2 Magnetic properties of cans for recycling

Type of Container	Attracted to Magnet (Yes or No)
soft drink	

2. Select a number of metal containers (i.e., 4 to 6 different types of cans) from your recycling box.

3. Hold the magnet close to each container.

4. Make a note in the table about whether or not the container is attracted to the magnet.

Questions

5. What types of containers were attracted to the magnet?

6. Why are these types of metals attracted to the magnet?

7. Describe a process that would enable the large-scale separation of metallic cans from aluminum cans.

8. Why do you think it is necessary to separate certain types of metals from other metals before heating them?
   Hint: Think about what happens to a metal's magnetic properties when it is heated.

Key Concept Review

1. Identify two industrial uses of distillation and what components of mixtures are separated in each use.

2. List three commercial products that could have been separated using sifting.

3. List at least three uses of filters to separate components of mixtures.

4. Explain how a magnet could be used to separate different types of metals at a recycling centre.

Connect Your Understanding

5. Use the particle theory of matter to explain why evaporation of seawater can be used to obtain salt.

6. Use the particle theory of matter to explain why air filters used in automobiles and furnaces must be changed regularly.

7. Explain why gasoline and propane are removed near the top of a distillation tower, whereas diesel fuel and industrial fuel oil are removed nearer the bottom of a distillation tower.

Practise Your Skills

8. If you were designing a recycling centre that collected cardboard as well as different types of metal and glass, explain how and in which order you would separate these items from any other household waste.

For more questions, go to PearsonScience.

For more questions, go to PearsonScience.

C36 *Thinking about Science, Technology, Society, and the Environment* **STSE**

Separating Industrial Mixtures

Industries like mining focus on separating metals from rock mixtures. The resulting metals are used in everything from automobiles to airplanes. Most industries use technology to increase efficiency of metal extraction and to minimize costs and environmental impacts.

With a partner, consider some costs and benefits of mining by answering the following questions.

1. How does mining directly benefit you and your school?

2. What are some costs to the economy and environment that result from mining?

Impact of Industrial Methods of Separating Mixtures and Solutions

Here is a summary of what you will learn in this section:
- Mining and other methods of separating mixtures often have a negative impact on the environment.
- Some methods of separating mixtures, such as filtering, can be positive for the environment.

Many commonly used commercial products, including gasoline and plastics, are produced in refineries. A **refinery** is an industrial plant that purifies crude substances, such as petroleum or sugar. As you learned in the previous section, mixtures such as crude petroleum are separated into different substances at refineries (Figure 9.8). These refineries are often built at a considerable distance from cities and towns. The production process often produces offensive odours and may also create by-products that can contaminate air and ground water. Many industrial separation processes have requirements and consequences that influence where they are located.

Figure 9.8 Oil refineries separate crude petroleum into different substances.

C37 *Starting Point* Skills A C

Industrial Methods of Separating Pure Substances and Mixtures

Mining, metal extraction, oil refinement, and many other industrial processes separate useful pure substances and mixtures from other mixtures and solutions. Each method or process contributes some benefit to society or the economy. Work with a partner to determine what you already know about these processes and what you would like to learn by answering the questions that follow.

1. Identify two or more industrial processes that operate in your community.

2. What consumer products are produced by each process?

3. What waste products are produced by each process?

4. Where are the industrial plants located with respect to water bodies and houses?

Mining

Surface mining involves removing a large amount of soil and rock on the surface in order to access the valuable material underneath. This surface material is called the **overburden**. Surface mining can result in vast destruction of the environment if steps are not taken to replace the overburden and rehabilitate the disturbed area.

Open pit mining involves the removal of all materials in a large pit. This mining process is used when the material being mined is uniformly scattered in overburden that is also relatively consistent in texture. It can be used to obtain metals located near the surface (Figure 9.9). **Strip mining** involves removal of long strips of overburden in areas where the material being mined is concentrated in veins. It can also be used when the overburden is found on the sides of hills and in valleys, much like the oil that is trapped in the soil of the tar sands in Alberta.

Figure 9.9 This is an open pit mine from which iron ore was extracted.

Coal Mining

Coal is often found in large, flat deposits at or near Earth's surface. Mining can occur at or below the surface. In the Appalachian Mountains of the eastern United States, coal is found in layers beneath the tops of mountains. A method of mining called mountaintop removal has been adopted by coal mining companies and has had a large influence on this environment (Figure 9.10).

The **mountaintop removal** process starts with clearcutting and removal of the mountaintop forest, as none of the vegetation can survive this coal extraction process. Next, all soil on top of the mountain is removed and set aside for possible reclamation. Explosives are used to blast away the land and rock above the coal. This overburden is then pushed into a nearby valley to fill the hollow. Large trucks or draglines are used to transport coal to washing and processing plants.

During this process, millions of litres of waste water are stored in nearby pools created by the construction of earthen dams. After the coal is removed, the stored topsoil may be deposited on the exposed surface, and steps can be taken to replant trees to ensure revegetation.

Figure 9.10 This type of coal mining is called mountaintop removal.

Elements of Procedural/Sequential Writing

Writers sometimes use the procedural/sequential pattern when describing information in paragraphs. Reread the information on the mountaintop removal process in the last two paragraphs on the previous page. What signal words did the author use that tell you this is an example of procedural/sequential writing? Can you think of other signal words a writer using this pattern might use?

How could you visually display the steps in the mountaintop removal process? Develop a graphic organizer to do this. Think about how you will organize the boxes and the kind of lines you will use to connect the boxes. Share your ideas with a partner.

Extracting Metals from Ore

Most metals found in Earth's crust are combined with other substances and must be separated by chemical means. For example, gold is extracted from ore by combining it with cyanide, which makes the gold able to dissolve in water. Cyanide is a very toxic chemical. However, cyanide loses its toxicity when exposed to sunlight.

As a result, many gold extraction plants have **tailing ponds** (Figure 9.11). These are large pools where the cyanide compounds (mixed in with crushed rock) break down in sunlight. However, during periods of heavy snow, rain, or floods, the ponds may overflow. Harmful chemicals can escape these ponds and enter ground water, which may lead to environmental damage.

Figure 9.11 Refining gold involves cyanide, which can poison aquatic habitats.

Refining Oil

When oil is refined, very large amounts of gases are released into the atmosphere, along with a noticeable smell. As a result, refineries are usually located far from populated areas. Waste gases produced by the refining process, such as methane or natural gas, are released and sometimes set aflame in a process known as **gas flaring** (Figure 9.12). Waste methane is a significant greenhouse gas. It has 25 times the ability to trap heat in the atmosphere that carbon dioxide has. Some refineries have attempted to recapture and recycle this gas for use as fuel.

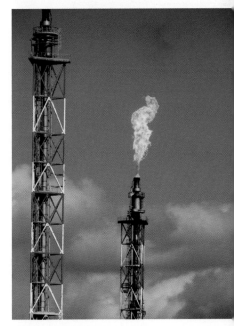

Figure 9.12 Waste gases are burned off during "flaring."

The everyday use of mixtures and solutions has an impact on society and the environment. **249**

Figure 9.13 Large amounts of fuel are consumed to evaporate water to produce maple syrup.

Figure 9.14 Water filters are used to purify drinking water.

Figure 9.15 Filters in your furnace can remove dust and pollen from the air.

*Take It **Further***

An automobile air filter allows the engine to "breathe." Find out how the air filter works. Begin your search at PearsonScience.

Evaporation and the Environment

Nearly every industrial separation process that relies on evaporation (such as the production of certain fuels, distilled spirits, and many types of plastics) uses heat from fuel combustion to speed up the process. For example, to produce 1 L of maple syrup, 40 L of water must be separated by evaporation (Figure 9.13). This may involve burning of fuel wood from maple trees or some other fuel. This process produces a considerable amount of carbon dioxide, which can have a negative impact on the environment.

Filters and the Environment

Some methods of separating mixtures can have a positive impact on the environment. Filtering is an example of a separation method with positive consequences. Air and water filters are the two most common types of filters.

Filtering Liquids

Waste water treatment involves the use of filters that separate impurities from water. This process helps to make it possible for municipalities to provide large amounts of pure treated water for domestic use. Where treated water is not available or when you want the additional assurance of purity, water filters can be used to obtain pure water for home use (Figure 9.14). In this case, an industrial process of separating mixtures (water filtration) has a positive impact on society and the environment.

Filtering Air

Many people suffer from asthma or allergies that are made worse by breathing air contaminated with dust, pollen, and other matter produced by combustion of fuels. Smog can make it impossible for some people to leave their house. Filters can greatly improve the quality of air both inside and outside the home, making it healthier for people to breathe. For example, air filters are used in furnaces and air purification devices to help clean the air inside the home (Figure 9.15). This is another industrial process (air filtration) that has a positive impact on society and the environment.

Benefits of an Air Filter on Indoor Air Quality

Air filters are beneficial to the environment, as they can improve the air quality in the surrounding area. They are used to separate impurities, such as dust, pollen, and by-products of combustion, from the air you breathe. Like most filtering processes, larger particles are blocked by the filter while smaller particles are allowed to pass through tiny openings in the filter.

Purpose

To demonstrate the benefits of an air filter on indoor air quality

Materials & Equipment

- 2 plastic drinking straws
- facial tissue
- cellulose tape
- eraser
- cheesecloth (optional)

Procedure

1. Cut a small piece of facial tissue into a circle. The circle should be just large enough to cover the end of a straw.

2. Place the tissue circle between the ends of two straws. Tape the two straws together, end to end, with the tissue circle between the straws.

3. Breathe in through the straws to test if air passes through the tissue filter and the straw-and-tissue apparatus. Adjust the tissue filter and straws to allow the passage of air.

4. Use the eraser to make rubber crumbs by rubbing the eraser on your desk or a sheet of paper.

5. Attempt to suck up the rubber crumbs by drawing air through the straw-and-tissue apparatus. Be careful not to inhale the rubber crumbs.

6. After several attempts, remove the tissue filter from its location between the two straws. Examine the tissue for evidence of trapped particles.

7. (Optional) Repeat steps 1 to 6 using cheesecloth instead of tissue.

Questions

With a classmate or as a whole class, discuss the following questions.

8. Why was air able to pass through the straw-and-tissue apparatus?

9. Why were other particles not able to pass through the tissue?

10. What modifications could you make to the straw-and-tissue apparatus to make this more effective for use with smaller particles?

11. What did this experiment tell you about the effectiveness of air filters in improving indoor air quality?

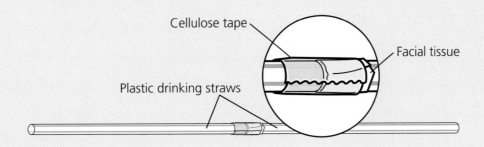

Cellulose tape

Facial tissue

Plastic drinking straws

Removing Carbon Dioxide from Air

Question

How can carbon dioxide be removed from air?

Materials & Equipment

- 50 mL limewater solution
- 100-mL beaker or jar
- plastic drinking straw
- dark piece of paper

CAUTION: Do not eat or drink anything during this activity.

Procedure

1. Obtain 50 mL of limewater solution from your teacher and place it in a 100-mL beaker.

2. Observe the colour and clarity of the limewater solution and make note of it in your notebook.

3. Place the limewater solution on top of a dark piece of paper.

4. Blow air through a straw to make bubbles in the limewater solution. Observe and make note of any changes that you observe.

5. Wash your hands thoroughly after completing this investigation.

Analyzing and Interpreting

6. What changes did you observe when you exhaled air through the straw into the limewater solution?

7. What substances are present in the air that you exhale?

8. What substances were present in the limewater solution?

9. How do you know that something in the air that you exhaled through the straw was responsible for changing the appearance of the limewater solution?

10. If you had been able to measure, what should have happened to the mass of the limewater solution when it reacted with the air that you exhaled?

Skill Builder

11. How could you organize the observations that you made during this activity to present your findings clearly?

Forming Conclusions

12. What happened to the carbon dioxide that you exhaled through the straw into the limewater solution?

13. What normally happens to the carbon dioxide that you exhale?

Key Concept Review

1. (a) Distinguish between the terms "open pit mining" and "strip mining."

   (b) Why are open pit mining and strip mining both considered to be surface mining?

2. Oil refining separates crude petroleum into different pure substances and mixtures by the method of fractional distillation.

   (a) List two ways in which oil refining benefits society and the environment.

   (b) List two ways in which oil refining negatively affects society and the environment.

   (c) List two strategies followed by oil refineries that minimize their harmful influence on society and the environment.

Connect Your Understanding

3. Filtering technologies involve the use of something that blocks some particles, but leaves most particles able to pass through the filter. List three ways in which filters affect you or one of your family members.

Practise Your Skills

4. Air purifiers, like the one shown below, dramatically reduce the concentration of indoor pollutants. Draw a simple diagram of an air purifier to show how it might work. Be sure to include the following labels: unfiltered air, filtered air, filter, and fan.

For more questions, go to PearsonScience.

C41 *Thinking about Science, Technology, Society, and the Environment*

S T
S E

Air Purifiers

Many people heat their home with forced-air furnaces that come equipped with air filters to trap dust, pollen, and other air-borne pollutants. However, many homes are heated by other means. For example, other heating solutions include use of wood stoves, electric space heaters, or hot water radiators, none of which come with air filters. Should people using this heating technology be required to use air purifiers? With a partner, decide whether or not you would support some type of law or by-law requiring air purification technology in every home. Be prepared to report your thinking to the class.

Here is a summary of what you will learn in this section:

- Careless use and disposal of pesticides has a harmful effect on the environment.
- The release of raw sewage has a negative effect on waterways.
- Disposal of industrial substances and mixtures, as well as by-products of industrial processes, has a negative impact on the environment.

The headlines screamed, "Raw sewage streams into Toronto creeks." Of course, everyone was concerned and wondered how this could happen. Raw sewage can make people sick and it can also damage the environment. Upon further investigation, it was revealed that cities across Canada treat their sewage differently. Partially treated sewage is regularly discharged into the waterways around many large urban centres in Canada.

C42 *Starting Point*

Skills

Dilution versus Pollution

Many pure substances and mixtures have very little impact when they occur at very low levels. For example, chlorine can be diluted to allow people to swim safely in a pool. However, other substances retain the ability to harm even in very small concentrations.

Starting with blue food colouring that is 87 percent blue dye by volume, do the following:

- Add 1 mL of blue food colouring to 99 mL of tap water (Figure 9.16).
- Collect 1 mL of the resulting solution and add it to another 99 mL of tap water.
- Repeat the process until you can no longer see the blue colour.

Consider This

1. After how many dilutions can you no longer see the blue colour?

2. Some substances are toxic at levels of less than one part per million. If the blue dye were toxic, do you think dilution with water would be an effective treatment method?

Figure 9.16 The blue food colouring represents a toxic substance.

Sewage and Waste Water Treatment

Sewage is the liquid waste water from toilets, baths, showers, and sinks. The water may also contain run-off from roofs, urban green spaces, and roadways, and liquid waste from industries. It is treated at a waste water treatment plant, and the treated water is eventually returned to the environment. Figure 9.17 illustrates that waste water treatment usually involves a three-stage process that includes mechanical, biological, and chemical treatments.

Figure 9.17 Waste water usually goes through three levels of treatment: mechanical, biological, and chemical.

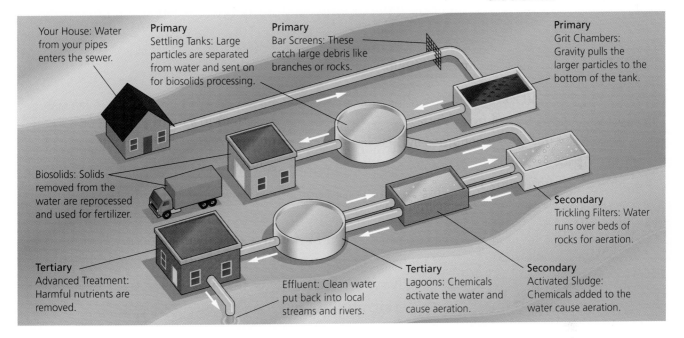

Your House: Water from your pipes enters the sewer.

Primary Settling Tanks: Large particles are separated from water and sent on for biosolids processing.

Primary Bar Screens: These catch large debris like branches or rocks.

Primary Grit Chambers: Gravity pulls the larger particles to the bottom of the tank.

Biosolids: Solids removed from the water are reprocessed and used for fertilizer.

Secondary Trickling Filters: Water runs over beds of rocks for aeration.

Tertiary Advanced Treatment: Harmful nutrients are removed.

Effluent: Clean water put back into local streams and rivers.

Tertiary Lagoons: Chemicals activate the water and cause aeration.

Secondary Activated Sludge: Chemicals added to the water cause aeration.

Primary, Secondary, and Tertiary Treatment

Water flowing into the treatment plant is full of solids that must be removed before further processing. **Primary treatment** involves separation of a mechanical mixture, including removal of suspended solids, rocks, sand, and grit. It allows heavy matter in the mixture to settle to the bottom of a sedimentation tank before moving on to secondary treatment.

Secondary treatment is a biological process involving **aeration**, which mixes waste water with large volumes of air. Living organisms, such as bacteria and protozoa, help to break apart larger particles, which then drop to the bottom of retention tanks and are removed.

Tertiary treatment involves application of chemicals, such as chlorine, to disinfect and kill remaining germs, and to remove phosphates. Other treatments include exposure to

Suggested Activity •••••••••
C44 Decision-Making Analysis on page 260

high-intensity ultraviolet (UV) light and treatment with ozone gas, which also kill germs.

Environmental Impact

In Canada, completely treated waste water is usually safe to return to the environment. However, during periods of heavy use or very rainy weather, water treatment plants become overwhelmed and waste water is not retained long enough to ensure purity. This commonly leads to the release of contaminated water. Recent upgrades to waste water treatment plants in Ontario have greatly increased the capacity to store and treat waste water effectively.

Pesticides

As you learned at the beginning of this chapter, farmers use pesticides, such as insecticides and herbicides, to protect their crops. An **insecticide** is a chemical mixture that is used to destroy insects that are harmful to cultivated plants or animals. A **herbicide** is a chemical mixture that is used to destroy unwanted vegetation, such as weeds. Home-owners often use insecticides to maintain their lawns and gardens. Farmers use herbicides to control weeds to enable the maximum growth of crops (Figure 9.18). However, the widespread use of pesticides has had a significant impact on the environment.

Figure 9.18 Insecticides and herbicides are used to control harmful pests and weeds.

Residues

According to environmental studies, almost every lake, river, and stream in the more populous areas of North America contains varying levels of **residues**, which are chemicals that come from pesticides. Contamination levels are very low in some areas, but in waterways that flow into the Great Lakes, the level of pesticide contamination is significant. The Ontario Ministry of the Environment recommends that, "Women of childbearing age and children under 15 should restrict their consumption of most sport fish caught in Ontario waters and some freshwater fish should not be consumed at all."

Obviously, we should try to prevent pesticides from entering our water supply. However, these chemicals are not always introduced directly into the water supply. Figure 9.19 shows a number of ways that pesticides and residues can enter waterways. For example, some chemicals are introduced to the water supply through **percolation**, or **leaching**, where they seep into the ground and later enter the water supply. The nature of these chemicals means that pesticides can remain able to kill or cause damage to the environment for years.

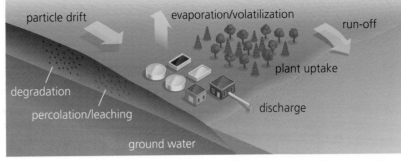

Figure 9.19 Pesticides and their residues can enter waterways in different ways.

Environmental Impact

The effects of pesticide use have been noted in farmers, in the environment, and in residues found in foods. Farmers have reported headaches, dizziness, nausea, and vomiting as a result of using pesticides, even though their use is deemed to be safe. Long-term health problems include respiratory and digestive problems, memory disorders, and skin and eye problems.

Environmental contamination from pesticides has led to reduced diversity of living things in soil and waterways. This means that plants and animals that were native to an area are now either completely gone or greatly reduced in numbers, which directly affects the environment. Also, many fruits (e.g., apples, pears, oranges) and vegetables (e.g., lettuce, spinach) are regularly found to contain pesticide residues or have residues present on their surfaces.

C43 *During Writing*

Thinking Literacy

Using Procedural/Sequential Pattern

List, in sequential order, all the pure substances and mixtures you have used since you woke up this morning. Much of what we use in a day produces some form of waste product, such as paper waste or water waste. Re-examine your list and think about ways you could reduce the amount of waste you produce. Use your ideas to write a procedural paragraph outlining an action plan that could reduce the waste products created at your school. Remember to include signal words appropriate to this type of writing.

Figure 9.20 Burlington Bay is one of the main locations for steel production in Canada.

Figure 9.21 Industrial processes sometimes result in chemicals being released into the air.

Figure 9.22 Household solid waste is buried under soil and stored in landfills.

Disposal of Pure Substances and Mixtures

Burlington Bay, located in the extreme west of Lake Ontario, is an example of the influence of industry on the landscape (Figure 9.20). The water, air, and environment have been polluted by steel manufacturers for years. An unknown amount of industrial waste material has been released into the environment by the steel industry since it began in Hamilton nearly 100 years ago. The amount of waste is surely very large, but we are still just learning about its effect on the environment and human health.

Sudbury is another example of an area damaged by the disposal of industrial waste mixtures. Much of the land has been damaged by acid rain, which is caused by sulphur released into the air, (Figure 9.21). In addition, a by-product of nickel and copper smelting is **slag** (a mixture of waste rock), which was discarded over a large area of land in the greater Sudbury area. This damaged the natural environment.

Landfills

Household solid waste, including garbage and waste from lawns and gardens, is usually disposed of in large landfills (Figure 9.22). A **landfill** is an area where garbage is disposed of and buried under layers of soil. Many items pose no hazard with this type of storage. However, many hazardous liquids are not suitable for landfill and must be treated in another manner. For example, some oil-based paints contain lead, which is a very toxic pure substance. Latex paint does not contain lead and is safe for disposal in a regular landfill.

Hazardous chemicals must be stored in special sites for the disposal of hazardous wastes. Examples include mercury, a pure substance found in fluorescent light bulbs, and cadmium, a pure substance found in rechargeable batteries. These disposal sites have undergone treatment to contain the solid and liquid substances placed within and prevent the movement of ground water, which could carry away harmful liquids.

Nuclear Energy and Uranium

Uranium is the fuel source most commonly used in generating electricity from nuclear power (Figure 9.23). The uranium is not burned like fossil fuels, so there is no release of air pollution or carbon dioxide. Instead, energy is released in a controlled nuclear reaction. However, the use of uranium as a fuel source for nuclear power has some significant social and environmental implications.

Uranium is not uncommon in Earth's crust. In fact, it can be found in small amounts in most rocks, dirt, and in the oceans. However, to be used as a fuel source in most reactors, the uranium must be enriched in a process that creates toxic and radioactive waste. A **radioactive** substance gives off radiation, which is a form of energy that is dangerous and possibly fatal to all living things exposed to it.

Figure 9.23 Nuclear power plants generate electricity using uranium as fuel.

Storage and Disposal

Typically, the uranium used as a fuel source can last for a period of about six years. The spent fuel must be stored temporarily in a large pool of water, where it cools and loses some of its radioactivity. After about five years in a spent fuel pool, the uranium is cool and stable enough for transportation to a reprocessing site. About 95 percent of the uranium can be reprocessed and used again as fuel. Unfortunately, the remaining 5 percent remains dangerously radioactive and must be prepared carefully for long-term storage.

Waste uranium material from nuclear power generation remains dangerously radioactive for a very long time. Some estimates suggest that spent nuclear fuel will pose a hazard for at least 10 000 years. Given that an average nuclear power plant produces up to 30 tonnes of waste fuel per year, the safe disposal of nuclear fuel is a very large problem. Some radiation and environmental experts recommend storage of spent nuclear fuel in deep underground deposits that can be monitored for leakage. The actual uranium fuel would first be sealed in dry storage casks made of steel and further encased in concrete containers, which would be moved to a final storage location, possibly kilometres underground.

*Take It **Further***

Canadian technology is behind a type of nuclear reactor used in Ontario. CANDU stands for **CAN**ada **D**euterium **U**ranium. This type of nuclear reactor has a very impressive safety record and uses cheaper natural uranium as fuel. Learn more about CANDU reactors. Begin your search at PearsonScience.

Community Treatment of Waste Water

Issue

How is waste water treated in your community?

Background Information

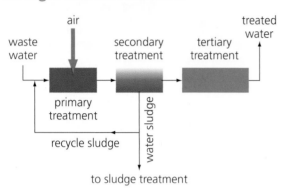

Municipalities across Ontario have established locations to treat waste water. Find out where your local waste water treatment plant is located and how it operates. In this activity, you will have a chance to learn more about waste water and its treatment in your community.

Before Field Trip

1. Find out the current population of your community.

2. Bring with you the materials requested by your teacher.

After Field Trip

3. Determine the volume of water treated daily at your local waste water treatment facility.

4. Calculate the per capita volume of water treated (the total amount of waste water treated divided by the population of the municipality).

5. Drawing on what you learned at the waste water treatment plant, list two or three problems that complicate the process of waste water treatment.

Analyze and Evaluate

6. What are some ways that people could reduce the amount of water that they discharge from their homes?

7. Explain how severe storm activity can affect the capacity of a waste water treatment facility.

8. List three ways to reduce the amount of water consumed and the amount of waste water produced at your school.

9. Use information collected during your field trip to answer the following questions. Be prepared to present your information to the class in a form determined by your teacher.

   (a) Explain how waste water is treated in your community.

   (b) Identify the major source or sources of raw water, the volume of water treated, and the average time required for water to pass through the water treatment facility.

   (c) Identify the major physical components and chemicals used in primary, secondary, and tertiary treatments of waste water.

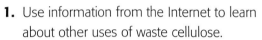
Dealing with Dangerous Disposal Practices

must be able to dispose of this mixture safely. Otherwise, it could be hazardous for the soil and the environment. Some environmental experts claim that the slurry is good for soils if it is applied under certain conditions in a limited amount.

Analyze and Evaluate

1. Use information from the Internet to learn about other uses of waste cellulose.

2. Identify alternatives to spreading cellulose on agricultural fields.

3. Try to determine the exact contents of the waste cellulose mixture.

4. Determine the potential benefits of spreading cellulose or other waste paper on agricultural fields.

5. Use the information you have developed to make a plan for the safe use and disposal of waste cellulose.

6. Prepare a list of precautions that must be exercised to ensure the safe and proper working of your plan.

7. Could you make an informed decision about safe disposal practices based on the information you collected? If so, how did you know your information was true and complete? If not, what steps could you take to ensure that the information you obtain is complete and reliable?

8. Share the results of your inquiry with the class as directed by your teacher.

Issue

How can you determine whether or not a mixture of cellulose is hazardous waste or a soil conditioner that can benefit agriculture?

Background Information

A by-product of paper production is a **slurry**, or mixture of cellulose, chemicals, heavy metals, and other unknown solutions. Paper manufacturers

Key Concept Review

1. What is a pesticide, and why would a farmer want to use pesticides ?

2. Identify and explain three ways in which pesticides find their way into waterways.

3. Explain the difference between primary and secondary treatment of waste water.

4. Identify two chemicals added to treated waste water to kill germs and disinfect.

5. Explain why emissions from an industrial smokestack are mixtures and not solutions.

Connect Your Understanding

6. Use the particle theory of matter to explain how sedimentation tanks help to remove solid wastes in the treatment of waste water.

7. Identify at least two ways in which heavy rain can affect the efficiency of waste water treatment facilities.

8. Use the particle theory of matter to explain the connection between air pollution and the disposal of industrial wastes.

Practise Your Skills

9. A mining company wishes to build a smokestack at a factory. What advice would you give the company about where to build and what pollution-control technology to install to ensure that environmental damage is minimized?

For more questions, go to PearsonScience.

C46 **Thinking about Science, Technology, Society, and the Environment**   S T S E

The Cost of Generating Electricity

The government of Ontario is planning to shut down all coal-fired electricity generating stations within approximately five years. Until the stations are shut down, they will release a great deal of pollution. However, the government does not want to install pollution-control equipment, perhaps because they believe this would not be a wise use of taxpayers' money. What do you think? Discuss your opinions with a partner and be prepared to share them with your class.

Making Connections

Jay Ingram

Jay Ingram is an experienced science journalist and is the host of Daily Planet on Discovery Channel Canada.

The Brazil Nut Effect

The next time you open a can of mixed nuts, take a careful look before you start munching. Which ones are sitting on top? The big ones! But the big ones are heavier, and gravity should have pulled them to the bottom. You are looking at a strange phenomenon called The Brazil Nut Effect.

Amidst all the peanuts, cashews, and walnuts, the Brazil nuts are the biggest and the most impressive demonstration of this gravity-defying effect. How do they get to the top? Believe it or not, physicists have been trying to figure this out since the 1930s.

First of all, the container has likely been shaken a lot from the time it was sealed in the factory until you opened it. That is the key to the effect. As a result, smaller nuts (or pieces of nuts) are jostled, slip down, and fill in the tiny spaces under the big ones, and with time, the big ones end up on top. But that's not the whole answer.

That shaking also triggers a flow inside the container, with nuts moving in a slow stream up the middle, across the top, and down the sides. Small nuts just keep going around and around like that, but big ones get stuck at the sides of the can. They were able to push smaller nuts out of the way on their way up, but they can't squeeze them aside on the way down – the downward stream is just too thin. So they stay on top.

And even that isn't the whole story. Scientists at the University of Chicago have discovered the weirdest thing: the density of the nut is crucial. If you have three large nuts, all the same size but different weights, the lightest and heaviest move up the fastest; the one in the middle is slowest. Even stranger is their discovery that the air in the can must be responsible for that: if the can is put in a vacuum, these nuts of different densities all move at the same speed. They aren't yet able to explain all this.

Try a Brazil Nut Experiment yourself: open a can, take out all the nuts, mix them up, put them back in, and shake the can. I bet you'll see the big ones on top. But imagine: scientists aren't really sure exactly why that happens.

Key Concept Review

1. In the manufacture of maple syrup, what substance is separated from the mixture? What is left behind in the mixture? *t*

2. List five consumer products that result from the fractional distillation of crude petroleum. *k*

3. (a) Which of the following products has the lowest boiling point: kerosene, propane, or gasoline? *k*

   (b) How does boiling point affect the location at which a substance is removed during the process of fractional distillation? *k*

4. List the methods of separation used in water purification. *k*

5. Filters are used to separate components of mixtures. Identify examples of filters, the substances separated, and the mixtures from which they are separated in the following items. *k*

   (a) car

   (b) furnace

   (c) kitchen tap

Connect Your Understanding

6. In many rural households, the quality of water for drinking, cooking, and other general uses is not consistent, especially in times of heavy rain. Surface run-off causes bits of soil and bacteria to enter wells. What advice would you give these home-owners with regard to treatment methods for drinking water? *c*

7. Evaporation is used commonly in tropical regions to collect salt from seawater. Why is this process not used extensively in North America? *a*

After Reading *Thinking Literacy*

Reflect and Evaluate

Reflect on the processes involved in writing a procedural paragraph. When would a writer choose to use this organizational pattern? What special features do writers include when they write in this way? Are there other words you have encountered in your own reading and life that mean the same thing as "procedure"? How does the ability to recognize procedural writing help you as a reader? Write a summary of 35 words or less describing procedural writing.

ACHIEVEMENT CHART CATEGORIES
k Knowledge and understanding   *t* Thinking and investigation   *c* Communication   *a* Application

8. Climate change has been occurring for a number of years. It is believed by most environmental experts to be caused by an increase in the amount of atmospheric carbon dioxide as a result of the human-influenced burning of fossil fuels. What would you need to know about carbon dioxide to be able to do each of the following? ⓐ

(a) identify a method to separate carbon dioxide from air

(b) burn only certain fossil fuels to meet industrial and household needs and reduce the amount of carbon dioxide produced from the burning of these fuels

(c) put carbon dioxide into the ground or oceans

> ## Unit Task Link
>
> In your unit task, you will investigate water samples taken from a number of sources. You have just examined some consequences of industrial methods of separating mixtures and disposing of mixtures and pure substances. As you continue to work on your unit task, consider how local industrial and commercial processes might affect water quality near you.

C47 | **Thinking about Science, Technology, Society, and the Environment**

Bottled Water

Many school boards in Ontario have discouraged the use, and some have banned the sale, of bottled water in schools and school board buildings.

There are many reasons for this decision. First, the amount of oil needed to produce the plastic mixture necessary to manufacture the bottles is considered an unnecessary and wasteful use of resources. Second, a great deal of waste is generated when empty plastic bottles are later disposed of. Some sources suggest that up to 90 percent of plastic water bottles eventually end up in landfills. Third, there is concern about who owns the water that is eventually put in bottles, and the price that bottling companies pay for the water, and whether or not that price is fair. Others say that the quality of water in bottled water, which may be treated by filtering alone, is no better, and possibly worse, than regular tap water.

Work with a partner to make a list of the benefits that can be obtained from the use of bottled water. Include in the list examples from your own experience that support your opinion. Make another list of the costs associated with the use of bottled water. These costs should include examples from your own experience and also opinions that you may hold.

Use these lists to help as you discuss the following questions. Be prepared to discuss your findings with your class.

1. Do you think your school or school board should ban the sale of bottled water?

2. If so, what alternatives are possible to provide clean, fresh drinking water for students and school staff?

3. If not, what steps can you take to address the previously mentioned concerns?

7.0 The particle theory of matter can be used to explain pure substances and mixtures.

KEY CONCEPTS

- A mixture can be classified as either a solution or a mechanical mixture.
- There are six points of the particle theory of matter (e.g., all matter is made of particles, there are large spaces between particles).

CHAPTER SUMMARY

- Everything that we see is made up of matter.
- Matter can be classifed as a pure substance or a mixture.
- The elements found in pure substances are all the same, while the elements found in mixtures are different.
- The particle theory of matter describes the characteristics of matter.

8.0 Mixtures and solutions can be analyzed through concentration, solubility, and separation.

KEY CONCEPTS

- Solutions consist of solutes and solvents.
- Solutions can be dilute or concentrated, and saturated, unsaturated, or supersaturated.
- The concentration of a solution is the amount of solute dissolved in a specific amount of solvent.

CHAPTER SUMMARY

- The concentration of a solution can be described in qualitative and quantitative terms.
- Solutes and solvents can be identified in various kinds of solutions.
- Solubility is affected by temperature, type of solute or solvent, particle size, and stirring.
- Solutions and mechanical mixtures are separated in different ways.
- Water is sometimes known as the universal solvent.

9.0 The everyday use of mixtures and solutions has an impact on society and the environment.

KEY CONCEPTS

- Commercial products consisting of solutions and mechanical mixtures can be separated in different ways.
- The improper use and disposal of pure substances and mixtures can have a harmful effect on society and the environment.

CHAPTER SUMMARY

- There are many industrial applications of the methods used to separate components from mechanical mixtures and solutions.
- Many industrial methods of separating mixtures have a negative impact on the environment.
- Some methods of separating mixtures, such as filtering, can be positive for the environment.
- Disposal of industrial substances and mixtures, as well as by-products of industrial processes, has a negative impact on society and the environment.

"Clearly" You Can Drink This Water

Getting Started

It was not that long ago that people could safely drink water directly from springs, streams, and creeks. Today, we would not think about doing this! Pollution, in many forms, has entered nearly all surface water bodies.

In this unit, you have developed many skills of investigation that are used to maintain supplies of clean water. These skills include differentiating between pure substances and mixtures as well as techniques to separate them. Most consumer goods are made from pure substances and mixtures. When the goods are no longer needed, there is a risk that the components will find their way back into our environment if they are not recovered properly.

These streams may look safe to drink from, but one is definitely not.

Your Goal

You will investigate water samples taken from a number of surface water sources. In each case, you will use your skills of observation and investigation to purify the water as thoroughly as possible. As well, you will match the recovered components of the sample to a "creek profile" that will allow you to determine the source of each of the samples.

What You Need

- equipment that was used throughout this unit for separating mixtures
- water samples from each of the creeks
- profile cards for each of the creeks

Steps to Sucess

1. As a class, review techniques for separating pure substances and mixtures.

2. As a group, review the properties of solutions and mechanical mixtures.

3. Create an observations table that will allow you to record your results.

4. With each of the water samples, separate all of the impurities that form the mixture with the water. Set them aside for identification.

5. Using what you have learned about the particle theory of matter, make a hypothesis as to the identity of the impurities.

6. When your analysis is complete, match it to a "profile card" that identifies the creek from which the sample was taken.

How Did It Go?

7. How pure were you able to make the samples? What was the final test that you used before deciding that you were finished?

8. Was there any equipment or materials that you know would have improved your investigation?

9. Were you able to determine which creeks your samples came from?

10. Create a brief report of the requirements for water treatment before water reaches your tap.

UNIT C Review

Key Terms Review

1. Create a mind map that illustrates your understanding of the following terms.

- aeration
- concentrated
- distillation
- evaporation
- filtration
- heat
- herbicide
- insecticide
- kinetic energy
- landfill
- mechanical mixture
- mixture
- overburden
- particle
- pure substance
- radioactive
- salt pan
- saturated
- solubility
- solute
- solution
- solvent
- surface mining
- temperature

Key Concept Review

7.0

2. Explain the difference between a mechanical mixture and a solution. *(a)*

3. List all six points of the particle theory of matter. *(k)*

4. If all matter is made up of particles, what is between them? *(k)*

5. How does heat affect the speed of particles and distance between particles? *(k)*

6. How does an increase in temperature account for the fact that substances change state? *(a)*

7. Use the particle theory of matter to explain the difference between a pure substance and a mixture. *(k)*

8. Explain how heat is involved in the sublimation of carbon dioxide (dry ice) when it changes from a solid to a gas. *(t)*

9. Describe the changes in the state of matter when you light a wax candle on a birthday cake. *(a)*

10. People are composed of at least 70 percent water. Explain why people can be described as mechanical mixtures. *(c)*

8.0

11. Use the terms "solute" and "solvent" to explain the difference between a dilute and a concentrated solution. *(c)*

12. Use the particle theory of matter to explain the difference between a saturated and an unsaturated solution. *(a)*

13. Explain why solute particles must be attracted to solvent particles to enable formation of a solution. *(c)*

14. Does water dissolve all solutes? Explain your answer using examples. *(c)*

15. Steel is an alloy made up of iron and carbon. Explain why iron is considered the solvent and carbon is the solute. *(a)*

16. Use the particle theory of matter to explain why stirring speeds up dissolving. *(t)*

17. Use the particle theory of matter to explain why latex paint dissolves in water. *(t)*

ACHIEVEMENT CHART CATEGORIES
(k) Knowledge and understanding *(t)* Thinking and investigation *(c)* Communication *(a)* Application

18. Describe a method to separate aluminum cans from steel cans. *ⓐ*

19. Explain the difference between distillation and evaporation. *ⓚ*

20. Explain how air filters work to remove dust particles. *ⓚ*

21. Ore is sifted before it is heated and melted to extract metal. Explain how sifting makes this process more efficient. *ⓐ*

22. Why are oil refineries located at a large distance from populated areas? *ⓚ*

23. Strip mining and open pit mining are both types of surface mining. Identify at least one negative environmental consequence of this type of mining. *ⓣ*

24. Explain why strip mining is suitable for obtaining oil from tar sands in Alberta. *ⓚ*

25. Explain why mountaintop removal is potentially so destructive to the local environment. *ⓣ*

26. Use the particle theory of matter to explain why gold might become soluble in water when combined with cyanide. *ⓐ*

27. Evaluate the use of cyanide as a means to extract gold from ore. Provide reasons to support your opinion. *ⓣ ⓐ*

28. Tailing ponds are built to prevent environmental contamination but may lead to release of contaminants into streams and rivers. Explain how mining companies could minimize this risk. *ⓣ ⓐ*

Connect Your Understanding

29. Explain why liquid laundry detergent is particularly useful for washing in cold water. *ⓐ*

30. Some paint can be dissolved in water, while other paints must be dissolved using mineral spirits. How could you determine which solvent to use? Explain at least two ways. *ⓣ*

31. Water treatment facilities require the use of sedimentation tanks. Use the particle theory of matter to explain how these tanks help to separate materials in the waste water mixture. *ⓐ*

32. Explain how filters placed on faucets in your home could actually result in water that is more pure than bottled water. *ⓣ*

33. Pesticides tend to kill all types of insects, including those that actually feed on pest species. Describe two methods that you could use around your lawn and garden to reduce the need for pesticides. *ⓐ ⓣ*

34. Explain why recommendations about consumption of fish are generally more severe for women of childbearing age and for children under the age of 15. *ⓣ*

35. Most people do not apply pesticides and herbicides directly to or spill these chemicals in waterways. Yet, these mixtures are found in many lakes and streams. Explain how this happens. *ⓐ*

36. Many lakes and rivers experience sharp increases in contamination from bacteria after summer thunderstorms. Explain why this happens. ⓐ

37. Balloons filled with air tend to remain inflated for a much longer time than balloons filled with helium do. Use the particle theory of matter to explain the difference. **Hint:** The particles of helium are not the same size as most particles that make up air. ⓣ ⓐ

38. Salad dressings made with oil and vinegar tend to separate and must be shaken before use. Use the particle theory of matter to explain why oil does not dissolve in water. ⓣ ⓐ

39. Tennis racket technology has changed in the past five years. Rackets made from composite materials have made weaker players more competitive. Use the particle theory of matter to explain your classification of the composition of the materials that make up new rackets. ⓐ

40. Use the particle theory of matter to explain why a pizza is classified as a mixture but salt is a pure substance. ⓣ

41. Use the particle theory of matter to explain why steam, ice, and water are all considered to be the same thing. ⓣ ⓐ

42. On a hot summer day, a glass of cold water warms rapidly. However, if an ice cube is added, the same amount of water will not warm up until the ice cube is melted. Explain why this is so using the particle theory of matter. ⓣ ⓐ

43. Use the particle theory of matter to explain why 5 g of water occupies the space of 5 mL in the liquid state but completely fills a room when it evaporates. ⓣ ⓐ

44. Describe one situation where you observed the contributions of science and technology to the understanding of pure substances and mixtures. ⓣ ⓒ

Practise Your Skills

45. The concentration of acetic acid in a vinegar mixture is approximately 5 percent. Use the terms "solute," "solvent," "dilute," and "concentrated" to describe the meaning of this value. ⓚ

46. Air is approximately 21 percent oxygen and 78 percent nitrogen. Describe this solution using the terms "solute" and "solvent." ⓚ ⓒ

47. DDT is a pesticide that can cause harm when 1 mL is present in 1 000 000 L of water. If water has a mass of 1 g/mL, what is the concentration of such a solution of DDT? ⓣ

48. People living in the high Arctic also use wash lines to dry clothes, even when the temperature is well below the freezing point of water. Use your understanding of changes of state and the particle theory of matter to explain how this can happen. ⓣ ⓐ

ACHIEVEMENT CHART CATEGORIES
ⓚ Knowledge and understanding   ⓣ Thinking and investigation   ⓒ Communication   ⓐ Application

270   UNIT C

Revisit the Big Ideas

49. Select five items that can be found in your refrigerator at home. Classify the items as either pure substances or mixtures. **k**

50. Write a short paragraph that shows clearly how these three words are related to one another: solute, solvent, and solution. **c**

51. Explain the meaning of these terms in your own words: distillation, filtration, and evaporation. **k**

52. Use the particle theory of matter to explain the differences between pure substances and mixtures. Provide examples of each. **c**

53. Explain how temperature is involved in the process of changing between different states of matter. Use the particle theory of matter in your explanation. **k**

54. Write a five-sentence paragraph focusing on the mining industry that supports or refutes this statement: "Mining is all about collecting and separating pure substances from mixtures." **t c**

55. A supersaturated solution contains more dissolved solute than could be dissolved by the solvent under normal circumstances. Use the particle theory of matter to explain how this occurs. **t**

56. Some municipalities have banned the use of pesticides on lawns and gardens. Write a five-sentence paragraph to either support or refute this universal ban. Be sure to support your opinion with examples. **t c**

57. Ketchup appears to be uniformly red in colour and consistent in texture, but it is classified as a mechanical mixture rather than a solution. Use the particle theory of matter to explain why this is so. **t a**

C48 *Thinking about Science, Technology, Society, and the Environment*

Changing Your Consumption Habits

We use pure substances and mixtures every day. Think about what you have eaten today, the content of the air that you have breathed, and the substances produced by your use (e.g., carbon dioxide, waste products). Now, multiply this by about six billion, and you will have an estimate of the impact of humans on the environment.

If you could change anything you wanted, what would you do to change your consumption and production of pure substances and mixtures at school, in your home, in your community, or in Canada? Brainstorm some ideas with a partner, and then share them with your class.

Heat in the
Environment

Fundamental Concepts

In Grade 7 Science and Technology, six fundamental concepts occur throughout. This unit addresses the following three:

- Energy

- Sustainability and Stewardship

- Systems and Interactions

Big Ideas

As you work through this unit, you will develop a deeper understanding of the following big ideas:

- Heat is a form of energy that can be transformed and transferred. These processes can be explained using the particle theory of matter.

- There are many sources of heat.

- Heat has both positive and negative effects on the environment.

Overall Expectations

By the end of this unit, you will be expected to:

1. assess the costs and benefits of technologies that reduce heat loss or heat-related impacts on the environment

2. investigate ways in which heat changes substances, and describe how heat is transferred

3. demonstrate an understanding of heat as a form of energy that is associated with the movement of particles and is essential to many processes within Earth's systems

A flare in the Sun's outer layer, the corona

Exploring

Increasing temperatures affect polar bears in Canada's Arctic.

The polar bears in the picture above are living with rapid changes in their habitat. The ice in Canada's Arctic is melting faster than expected because of increasing temperatures. This warmer climate is making it harder for polar bears to hunt and live where they usually do.

The news is full of stories like these about environmental problems such as pollution and climate change. What can we do about them? Environmentalists have a saying that can help us find a way to make a difference: Think Globally, Act Locally. It means thinking about the big, worldwide problems but finding ways locally to help solve them. Acting locally means making changes in your activities, your home, and your school.

In this unit, you will learn about heat and about global environmental concerns related to heat and climate change. For example, you will learn why we have to reduce our use of certain types of fuel for heating and electricity.

Energy-Saving Buildings

One way to do this is through constructing buildings that use less energy for heating and cooling. The Earth Rangers Centre in Woodbridge, Ontario, is an example of how different types of building materials and technologies can save energy. This building is not special just because of its energy use. It is both an environmental education centre for students like you and a hospital for wild animals. The building was designed to use very little energy and still be comfortable for both humans and animals.

The extra-thick concrete walls trap and hold heat during the warmth of the day. Then, as the air temperature drops at night, the walls release heat. The Sun's energy heats water for washing. Skylights let in both light and warmth from the Sun.

Hailey the striped skunk and Scarlett the red-tailed hawk are Animal Ambassadors at the Earth Rangers Centre. The Earth Rangers building is a comfortable environment for animals and humans.

A Green Roof

The Earth Rangers building is unusual because of who uses it. But ordinary buildings, like school buildings, can also conserve energy. Fleming College in Lindsay, Ontario, has a new environmental technology wing that includes a green roof. The roof is green because it actually has plants growing on it! A green roof helps to keep a building warmer in winter and cooler in summer. To heat the new wing, the college uses heat from below Earth's surface — 122 m below. Wells bring water naturally heated from deep within Earth. Pumps circulate the water through pipes to heat the school building.

Living plants form the green roof at Fleming College.

Saving Energy at Home

New technologies are important for today and into the future, but we can reduce our need to burn fuel for heat even without them. Turn down the thermostat in the house at night or when no one is home. In the summertime, keep the temperature higher so that the air conditioning system does not have to work so hard. Doing what you can to save energy locally — in your own home — helps everyone globally.

Light coming through skylights makes a bright student area at Fleming College.

...MORE TO EXPLORE

Heat in Your Home

Heat produced in people's homes contributes to the warming of the environment.

Purpose

To collect information about heat produced and used in your home

Materials & Equipment

- pen and/or pencil
- ruler
- paper

Procedure

1. Imagine that you are sitting at home in your kitchen. Think about the household items in your kitchen that produce or use heat.
2. Design and label a chart to record the name of the room and these items. Be specific.
3. In your head, take a tour of your home. For each room, identify the household items that produce or use heat.
4. Add your items, room by room, to your chart. You could also draw a floor plan that includes each room and the items you have identified.

Questions

5. Which room contains the most household items that produce or use heat?
6. Categorize the items in your chart. For example, one category could be "items used for cooking or reheating foods." Below your chart, record the names of your categories. Select a symbol (icon) or letter for each category. Then complete your chart by placing a symbol or letter beside each item.

The Environment in the News

What are you doing to think globally and act locally? In this unit, you will read about and discuss issues related to heat in the environment.

What to Do

1. Locate several newspaper, magazine, or Internet articles that refer to thinking globally and acting locally, sustainability, or stewardship, or use the article(s) supplied by your teacher.
2. Select one of the articles. In your own words, summarize the details of the article.

Consider This

3. Share your article and summary with your classmates. Ask them to provide comments about the article. Below your summary, describe their comments.

UNIT D

Contents

10.0   Heat causes changes in solids, liquids, and gases.

11.0   Heat plays an important role in nature.

12.0   Heat technologies offer benefits and require choices.

Unit Task

Insulation materials help prevent heat loss from homes and reduce the amount of energy needed to keep the house warm. In this Unit Task, you will use a variety of materials as insulation blankets to test how well the materials prevent heat loss from a plastic bottle containing hot water. You will then list the samples in order, from best heat insulator to worst heat insulator.

Essential Question

What materials help keep a house warm in winter?

Getting Ready to Read   *Thinking Literacy*

Activating Prior Knowledge

Read the contents list. Without looking through the unit, record several facts that you know about each of these topics. In a separate paragraph, indicate which topics are new to you.

Colourful balloons expanding against an early morning sky

What You Will Learn

In this chapter, you will:

- use the particle theory to compare how heat affects solids, liquids, and gases
- identify ways in which heat is produced
- explain how heat is transmitted through conduction, convection, and radiation

Skills You Will Use

In this chapter, you will:

- follow appropriate safety procedures
- investigate the effects of heating and cooling
- investigate heat transfer by conduction, convection, and radiation

Why This Is Important

Heating and cooling cause many of the changes you encounter every day. By understanding these changes, you can predict how they will affect your life and the environment.

Before Reading

Thinking Literacy

Determining Importance

Readers often have to decide what is interesting information and what is important information. This textbook includes features to help you do this. Scan the top of this page and the summary boxes starting each section in this chapter. Look for patterns that help you determine what is important. Create a mind map for the main concepts in this chapter; the particle theory, heat production, and heat transfer.

Key Terms

- thermal energy
- heat
- particle theory of matter
- conduction
- convection
- radiation

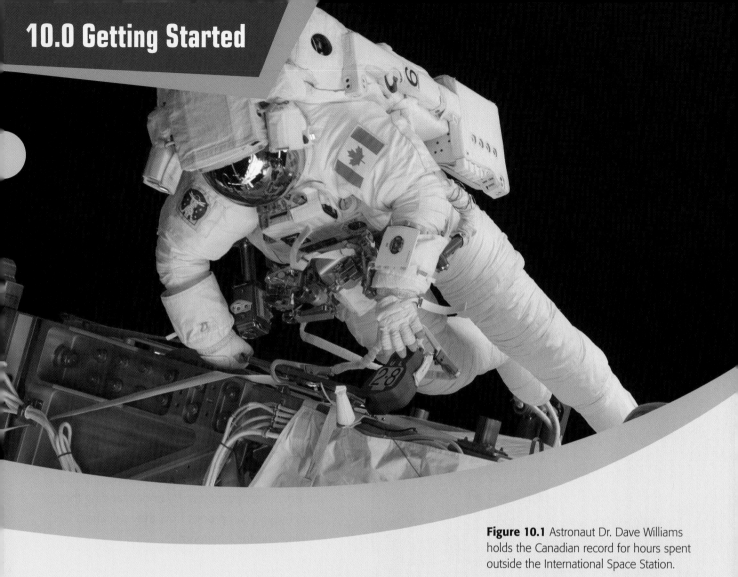

Figure 10.1 Astronaut Dr. Dave Williams holds the Canadian record for hours spent outside the International Space Station.

Figure 10.2 Cold temperatures are useful for some outdoor activities.

Your environment includes the atmosphere — a thick layer of air that protects you from the strong energy of the Sun and other objects in space. To work in space, outside the space shuttle, Canadian astronaut Dr. Dave Williams needed to take his environment with him (Figure 10.1).

An astronaut's spacesuit provides protection from the extreme heat and cold of space. The side of the suit facing the Sun may be heated to a temperature as high as 120°C. The other side, exposed to the darkness of deep space, may get as cold as –160°C.

These extreme temperatures never occur on Earth, where the temperature ranges from about –89°C to about 57°C. The coldest temperature ever recorded in Canada was –63°C in Snag, in Yukon Territory, on February 3, 1947. The hottest day on record in Canada was in Saskatchewan on July 5, 1937; the temperature reached a scorching 45°C.

Canadians often talk about how hot or how cold it is outside, and heat plays many roles in our daily activities (Figures 10.2 and 10.3). At school, at home, in a car, or out shopping, you need to know how to control heat so that you can feel comfortable.

Producing, using, and controlling heat helps people survive around the world. People also use heat in manufacturing and other industries. However, some of the methods used to produce heat can harm plants, animals, and other living things in the environment.

Canadians are working to reduce the harmful effects of heat in the environment. To play your part, you need to understand what heat is and its impact on our planet. In this chapter, you will learn about heat, thermal energy, and temperature.

Figure 10.3 A warm, sunny day is a great time to be outside.

D3 | *Quick Lab*

What Is Hot? What Is Not?

Purpose

To compare sensations of hot and cold under different conditions

Figure 10.4

(a)

Materials & Equipment

- 3 buckets or other containers
- stopwatch or clock
- water: cold, warm, and room temperature

Procedure

1. At the same time, stick one hand into a container of cold water and the other into a container of warm water (Figure 10.4(a)).

2. Keep your hands submerged for 1 min.

3. During the minute, predict what your hands might feel like when you place them into a third container of water at room temperature. Have a classmate record your prediction.

4. After 1 min, place both hands into a third container of water at room temperature (Figure 10.4(b)).

(b)

Question

5. Was your prediction in step 3 correct? Try to explain what happened and record your explanation.

Here is a summary of what you will learn in this section:

- There are many forms of energy.
- Energy can be changed from one form to another. This is called an energy transformation.
- Thermal energy is the total energy of the moving particles in a solid, a liquid, or a gas.

You get off your bicycle and park it next to your home. Entering your home, you immediately head for the refrigerator. You take a snack from the refrigerator. You see a note under a fridge magnet that reminds you to take tonight's dinner out of the freezer so that it can thaw. You open the freezer compartment of the fridge and remove the package. All the while, you are listening to great music on your MP3 player.

In this brief time, you have participated in several changes in energy. In fact, energy is changing from one form to another in each of the examples described above and around you as you read this paragraph! What are the different forms of energy? What is an energy transformation? To learn the answers to these and other questions, read on.

D4 | *Starting Point*

Skills **P** **C**

Talking about Forms of Energy

An apple and a slice of pizza are delicious foods full of energy. The energy in food is in the form of chemical energy. In other grades, you learned about many different forms of energy.

Look at Figure 10.5. Name as many different forms of energy as you think are represented there. Share your list with a classmate. Check your answers after reading the next section.

Figure 10.5 There are several forms of energy represented in this scene.

Forms of Energy

Energy is the ability to make objects move. For example, the energy stored in fuels like gasoline can be used to make a car move. The energy in gasoline is a form of energy called chemical energy. There are 10 **forms of energy**, as shown in Figure 10.6.

Take It *Further*

Choose one of the types of energy shown below. Research ways in which people use this type of energy in everyday life. Begin your search at PearsonScience.

Figure 10.6 (a) Thermal energy is the total energy of the moving particles in a solid, a liquid, or a gas.

Figure 10.6 (b) Chemical energy is the energy stored in matter such as food, fuels, and clothing.

Figure 10.6 (c) Magnetic energy (magnetism) is the energy that causes some types of metal, such as iron, to attract or push away from certain other metals.

Figure 10.6 (d) Light energy is the form of energy that our eyes can detect.

Figure 10.6 (e) Gravitational energy is the stored energy an object has when it is above Earth's surface.

Figure 10.6 (f) Nuclear energy is the stored energy at the centre of particles of matter. Nuclear power plants produce electricity from nuclear energy.

Figure 10.6 (g) Electrical energy (electricity) is the energy of particles moving through a wire or through an electrical device.

Figure 10.6 (h) Elastic energy is the energy stored in objects that are stretched, compressed, bent, or twisted.

Figure 10.6 (i) Sound energy is the form of energy that we can hear.

Figure 10.6 (j) Mechanical energy is the energy of objects in motion.

Ten Terrific Forms of Energy

1. Name all 10 forms of energy.

2. Which forms of energy are used and produced when you:
   (a) listen to your MP3 player?
   (b) surf the Internet?
   (c) prepare dinner using a kitchen stove that burns natural gas?

3. Identify the form(s) of energy that are described in the following situations. You may need to list more than one form of energy for some of these.
   (a) playing a violin
   (b) throwing a baseball
   (c) stretching an elastic band

Figure 10.7 Every appliance in this kitchen can transform electrical energy into other forms of energy.

Energy Transformations

An **energy transformation** is a change from one form of energy to another. When you eat a banana, your body breaks down the chemicals in the food. This process releases the stored chemical energy. Your body can transform the chemical energy into thermal energy that keeps you warm and comfortable.

Energy is being transformed around you continuously. The ceiling lights transform electrical energy (electricity) into light. Moving automobiles transform the chemical energy of gasoline into mechanical energy. All of the appliances in Figure 10.7 transform one form of energy into another.

Suggested Activity •·········
D6 Inquiry Activity on page 285

Figure 10.8 The devices inside a computer transform electrical energy into mechanical energy, light energy, magnetic energy, sound energy, and thermal energy.

Hidden Energy

Consider the energy transformations inside a laptop or desktop computer (Figure 10.8). The spinning hard drive transforms electricity into mechanical energy. Some of the mechanical energy produces thermal energy. This is one of the reasons why the outer case of your computer feels warm. The hard drive also transforms electricity into magnetic energy to store your important data. You can hear the whirring of the computer's fan converting electrical energy into mechanical energy and sound. The DVD or CD drive uses the light energy of a small laser to read or burn information. All of these are examples of energy transformations that are hidden.

Amazing Transformations

Question

What energy transformations can you observe in this activity?

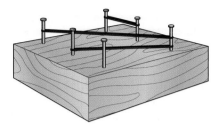

Figure 10.9 Set-up for Inquiry Activity D6 Station 1

Materials & Equipment

- wooden block with 6 nails
- 3 elastic bands
- 1 commercial heat packet
- 1 battery
- 2 wires
- 1 switch
- 1 light bulb

Procedure

1. Visit each station and carry out the steps described below.

Station 1 Bouncing Sounds

2. This station has three elastic bands and a piece of wood with six nails (Figure 10.9). Stretch each of the elastic bands across two of the nails. Draw your own arrangement of the elastic bands.

3. Gently pluck each of the elastic bands. Describe what you hear as you pluck each elastic band. Identify the energy transformations you observe.

4. Place the rubber bands and wooden block with nails back where you found them when you arrived at this station.

Station 2 Warming Up

5. This station has one heat packet. Your teacher will have activated the packet. Describe what you feel on your hand when you hold the packet.

6. Identify the energy transformation you observe while holding the heat packet. Place the heat packet back where you found it when you arrived at this station.

Station 3 A Bright Idea

7. This station has a battery, a switch, two wires, and a light bulb. Turn on the switch. Draw and label the equipment set-up. Describe what happens when the switch is turned to the "on" position.

8. Identify the energy transformations you observe while the light is on. Move the switch to the "off" position and make sure the light bulb is off before you leave this station.

Analyzing and Interpreting

9. List the different energy transformations you observed.

10. Which energy transformations produced heat?

Skill Builder

11. Think of an energy transformation that you have not discussed in class but could observe at a station like the three in the activity. Write a procedure your classmates could follow to observe the energy transformation.

Forming Conclusions

12. Using a table or other graphic organizer, summarize what you observed at each station. Your summary should include the name of the station, a description of what you observed, and a description of the energy transformations that occurred.

Key Concept Review

1. Which forms of energy are used when:

(a) you ride in an automobile?

(b) you bounce a basketball?

(c) you boil water to make hot chocolate?

Connect Your Understanding

2. A student suggests that he could easily live without electrical energy. Write a paragraph to describe what his life would be like in that situation.

Practise Your Skills

3. Examine the typical street scene on the right. Draw and fill in the table. In column A, name five activities shown in which there is an energy transformation. In column B, name the *starting* form of energy that is being transformed. In column C, name the form of energy that is being *produced* in that activity.

 For more questions, go to PearsonScience.

A: Activity in Street Scene	B: Starting Energy	C: Energy Produced
1		
2		
3		
4		
5		

D7 *Thinking about Science and Technology*

Exciting Energy

Imagine your daily activities from waking up until going to bed at night. Brainstorm the activities that involve an energy transformation. In your notebook, record as many of these activities as you can in three minutes. Group the activities in your list into categories of your choice. Give a name to each category. For each activity, identify the form of energy at the start and end of the transformation. Consider adding a drawing or image to represent each category. Share your list with your classmates.

What technologies do you use related to these activities? What are their sources of energy?

Here is a summary of what you will learn in this section:

- Temperature is a measurement of the average energy of the moving particles of a solid, a liquid, or a gas.
- Heat is the thermal energy transferred from an area of higher temperature to an area of lower temperature.
- We use a thermometer to measure the temperature of solids, liquids, and gases.
- Heat transfer can raise the temperature of a solid, a liquid, or a gas.

We need to produce a huge amount of heat to keep buildings warm and comfortable, cook food, and make all the consumer products that we use. We obtain this heat from the Sun and many different kinds of fuels, such as wood, coal, oil, and natural gas. As you read about heat in this section, think about how important heat is in your life.

D8 *Starting Point*   Skills A C

Heating Things Up and Cooling Things Down

Examine the photographs in Figure 10.10. Decide which ones show a solid, a liquid, or a gas heating up. Record your answers under the title "Heating Things Up." Write a sentence for each photograph to explain how you know this.

Next, decide which photographs show a solid, a liquid, or a gas cooling down. Record your answers under the title "Cooling Things Down." Describe how you know this.

When you have finished, you should have described all four photographs.

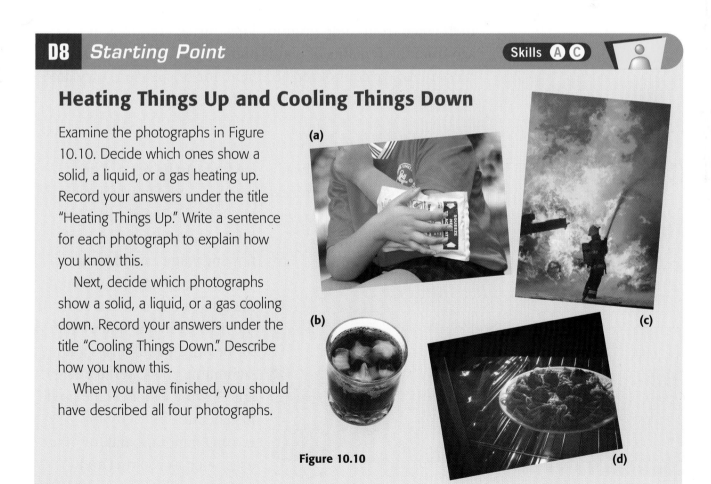

(a)

(b)

(c)

(d)

Figure 10.10

Heat causes changes in solids, liquids, and gases. **287**

Figure 10.11 Extreme physical activity produces large amounts of body heat.

Heat Production

You are waiting for a bus on a cold day, so you try to keep warm by moving around. The more you move, the warmer you become. As you learned in section 10.1, your body produces heat. It transforms the chemical energy in the food you eat into mechanical energy of motion and heat (Figure 10.11). But your body heat and clothing are not enough to keep you warm all the time. We need a variety of heat sources to keep our homes and other buildings warm. Sources of heat are also needed for cooking, manufacturing, and other uses.

Fossil Fuels

Our main source of heat is the burning of **fossil fuels** — oil, natural gas, or coal. You may have an oil furnace or natural gas furnace in your home. If your home is heated with electricity, the electricity may have come from a process that involves burning coal, oil, or natural gas. These fossil fuels come from underground. They formed millions of years ago from the remains of plants and animals. Once we use these fuels, we cannot replace them; for this reason, they are called **non-renewable** energy sources.

Renewable Heat Sources

Figure 10.12 Energy in the wind can be converted into electricity by wind turbines like these.

A **renewable** source of heat is one that can be re-used or replaced. That is what "renew" means — we can use it again and again or replace it. The Sun's energy, the wind, and flowing water are all forms of renewable energy. Heat from the Sun can be used for some of the heating in our homes and for heating greenhouses and swimming pools. Wind energy and flowing water can be used to generate electricity for heating buildings and for other uses, such as cooking and manufacturing (Figure 10.12).

"Waste" Heat

Not all the heat around us is produced on purpose. For example, you turn on a lamp so that you have enough light to read by at night. But if you put your hand close to the bulb, you can feel the heat coming from it (Figure 10.13). A light bulb transforms electrical energy into light and heat. The heat from the bulb is considered "waste" heat because we do not need it.

Heat is produced in all energy transformations, whether it is wanted or not. Whenever energy is converted from one form to another, some heat is produced. In Chapter 12, you will learn how the different ways we produce heat affect our global environment.

Figure 10.13 A light bulb produces more heat than useful light energy.

D9 *During Reading*

Thinking Literacy

Important vs. Interesting Information

Reading large amounts of information can be overwhelming, but there are strategies to help you. As you read the next few pages, you will find information about temperature, thermal energy, and heat. Make a Heat InfoBox as shown in Figure 10.14. In each section of the InfoBox, draw a T-chart with the headings "Important Information" and "Interesting Information." As you read, add information to the appropriate T-chart in the appropriate column. When you are finished reading, compare your T-chart with a partner's. Did you record the same information in the "Important" columns? How is this an effective way to determine what is important information?

> **Temperature, Thermal Energy, and Heat**
>
> **A:** Temperature
>
> | Important Information | Interesting Information |
> |---|---|
> | | |
>
> **B:** Thermal energy
>
> | Important Information | Interesting Information |
> |---|---|
> | | |
>
> **C:** Heat
>
> | Important Information | Interesting Information |
> |---|---|
> | | |

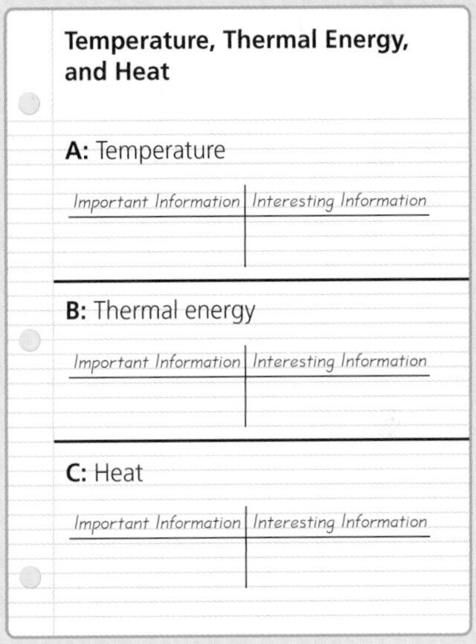

Figure 10.14 Heat InfoBox

Temperature

In your own local environment, it is important for you to know how hot or cold it is. You can tell how hot it is outside by going out. But if you want to know how hot it is before you go out, you can listen to the radio for the temperature. You decide whether to wear a coat or not based on the temperature outside. Temperature is a measure of how hot or cold matter is. But what is temperature actually measuring?

Figure 10.15 This tea is hot because of the rapid movement of particles.

To understand temperature, think about the particles that make up all matter. Everything is made up of particles, and these particles are constantly moving. Moving particles have energy because of their motion. All of the particles in the cup of hot tea in Figure 10.15 are moving quickly, so the tea is hot. But the tea particles do not all move at the same speed. Some move faster than others.

Temperature is a measurement of the average energy of all the particles in a solid, liquid, or gas. So, for example, the particles in the cup of hot tea in Figure 10.15 are moving faster than those in a cup of iced tea. The temperature of the hot tea is higher than the temperature of iced tea. When the particles of the tea in the cup slow down, the tea becomes cooler, so its temperature drops.

Measuring Temperature

You can measure the temperature of the tea by using a thermometer (Figure 10.16). A **thermometer** is an instrument used to measure the temperature of solids, liquids, and gases. Scientists have invented a wide range of thermometers for measuring temperatures from hundreds of degrees below zero Celsius to thousands of degrees above zero Celsius.

WORDS MATTER

Therm or thermo: The prefixes *therm* and *thermo* come from the Greek *thermos*, meaning warm or hot.

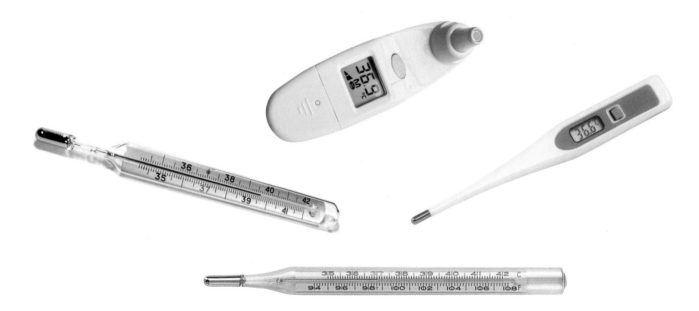

Figure 10.16 Mercury thermometers and digital thermometers are common types of household devices for measuring body temperature.

Thermal Energy and Heat

There are three important terms that you need to know to understand heat. One is temperature, which you just read about. Another one is thermal energy. And the third one is the word "heat" as a scientific term.

In section 10.1, you learned that thermal energy is one of 10 forms of energy. **Thermal energy** is the total energy of all the moving particles in a solid, liquid, or gas. The more moving particles there are in a sample of matter, the greater the thermal energy.

Suppose you have a pot of hot tea, and you pour some into a cup. You immediately measure the temperature of the tea in the pot and the tea in the cup. The temperatures are the same. That means the *average* energies of the tea particles in the pot and in the cup are the same. But the tea in the pot has much more thermal energy than the tea in the cup because there are more tea particles in the pot than in the smaller cup of tea (Figure 10.17). Therefore, the *total* energy of all the particles in the pot is greater than the total energy of all the particles in the cup.

Take It *Further*

Think of all the uses we have for thermometers in our homes, schools, and workplaces, or during leisure activities. Find out about different types of thermometers. Begin your search at PearsonScience.

Transferring Thermal Energy

When we boil water to make the pot of tea, we say that we are *heating* the water. We actually mean that we are transferring energy to *all* the particles of the water, thus increasing the total energy of all the water particles. As a result, the average energy of motion of each particle increases. This means that the temperature increases.

Suppose you pour a cup of steaming hot tea from a teapot (Figure 10.17). You touch the cup with a finger. Somehow, the cup has become hotter, maybe hot enough to burn your finger. Thermal energy in the tea has transferred to the cup and then to your finger. This transfer of thermal energy is called **heat**. Heat is the thermal energy transferred from a solid, a liquid, or a gas at a higher temperature to a solid, a liquid, or a gas at a lower temperature. Heat also refers to the thermal energy that transfers within a solid, a liquid, or a gas.

Figure 10.17 A pot full of tea has more thermal energy than a cup of tea at the same temperature.

Heating Up

In this activity, you will investigate the rate of heating of two different liquids.

Question

Does tap water or salt water boil faster?

> **CAUTION:** Be careful around hot objects and hot water.

Materials & Equipment

- salt solution (10 g salt per 250 mL of solution)
- 2 beakers
- 250 mL tap water
- stirring rod
- 2 thermometers
- hot plate
- tongs or oven mitts
- graph paper

Procedure

1. Create a data table in your notebook similar to the table below.

Table 10.1 Heating of two liquids

Tap Water		Salt Water	
Time (s)	Temperature (°C)	Time (s)	Temperature (°C)
0		0	

2. Pour 250 mL of tap water into a beaker. Measure the temperature of the water and record this "Temperature" value in your table beside the 0 (zero) value in the "Time" column.

3. Add 250 mL of salt solution to the second beaker. Measure the temperature of the solution and record this "Temperature" value in your table beside the 0 (zero) value in the "Time" column.

4. Place both containers on a hot plate. Turn the hot plate on. Predict which liquid will boil first.

5. Measure the temperature of the liquid in each beaker every 30 s. Record in your data table when each liquid begins to boil. Continue to take two more temperature readings of each liquid after boiling.

6. Turn off the hot plate and allow the two liquids to cool. Your teacher will tell you when it is safe to pour the water down the sink. Use tongs or oven mitts to carry your beaker.

Analyzing and Interpreting

7. Use the data you collected to draw a line graph that shows the rate of heating for both liquids. The vertical axis is for temperature and the horizontal axis is for time. The line on your graph for each liquid is called the heating curve for that liquid.

8. Is there a difference between the two heating curves? Describe the differences.

9. How does your graph show that one liquid reached boiling point before the other? Was your prediction accurate?

Skill Builder

10. Suppose you were to repeat this experiment with a salt solution that contained 20 g of salt in 250 mL of solution. Predict and sketch the heating curve of the new liquid.

Forming Conclusions

11. Write a summary paragraph that answers the question for this experiment. Make sure you support your answer with the data you collected and the graph you created.

Key Concept Review

1. What is the difference between thermal energy and heat?

2. What is temperature?

3. How do we measure temperature?

4. State which of the following are sources of energy: wood, bicycle, oil, gasoline, paper, and light bulb. Give a reason for including or excluding each choice.

5. How are renewable and non-renewable energy sources different? List two examples of each of these types of energy sources.

Connect Your Understanding

6. In the past, many Canadians used wood stoves or fireplaces to heat their homes. Today, most Canadian homes burn oil or natural gas or use electric heating. Suggest more than one reason why this change has occurred.

7. People who live in northern Ontario experience cold temperatures for long periods of time in winter. How do you think their homes are built differently from homes in southern Ontario?

8. Many electrical devices in your home are designed to maintain a constant temperature. Name at least three of these devices. Suggest why it is important to keep temperature constant.

Practise Your Skills

9. The photograph below shows a person on a camping trip. Explain what he is trying to do.

For more questions, go to PearsonScience.

D11 *Thinking about Science and Technology*

Heat Technologies in Your Life

In this section, you have learned about temperature, thermal energy, and heat. You have also read about ways that people have used their understanding of these three concepts to meet their needs. For example, understanding how to produce heat has allowed people to live comfortably in houses during cold winters. Think about and describe a situation where an understanding of temperature, thermal energy, or heat has helped create a technology that improves the lives of you and your classmates. Include any situations that you can think of where this technology might affect the environment or your community negatively.

Here is a summary of what you will learn in this section:

- The particle theory describes how particles of solids, liquids, and gases move.
- The particle theory explains how matter can change from one state to another.
- Heat causes particles to move faster.
- The particle theory explains the expansion and contraction of solids, liquids, and gases.

Figure 10.18 Ice cream tastes good, even when it melts.

When you eat ice cream on a hot summer day, it does not take long for the ice cream to start melting (Figure 10.18). Why does the cold ice cream start to melt? Where is the heat coming from to cause the change of state from a solid to a liquid?

These changes in the ice cream can be explained using the particle theory of matter. In this section, you will investigate changes in matter and the reason for these changes.

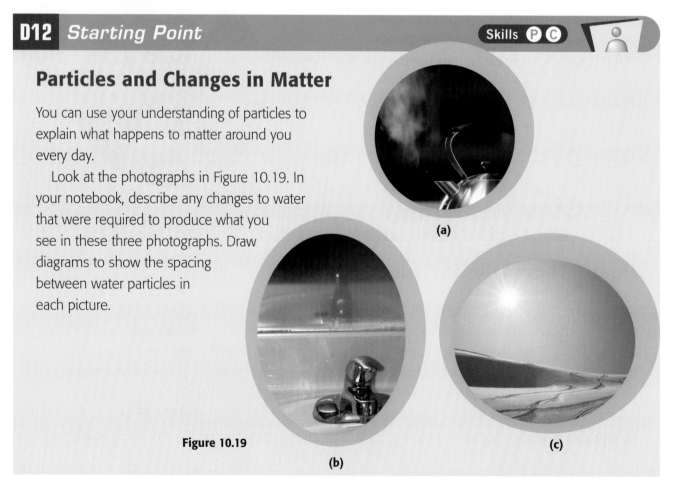

D12 | *Starting Point*   Skills **P** **C**

Particles and Changes in Matter

You can use your understanding of particles to explain what happens to matter around you every day.

Look at the photographs in Figure 10.19. In your notebook, describe any changes to water that were required to produce what you see in these three photographs. Draw diagrams to show the spacing between water particles in each picture.

(a)

Figure 10.19

(b)

(c)

Matter Can Change

You may have learned that solid, liquid, and gas are the names of the three **states of matter**. Ice melting is an example of a **change of state**. Solid water (ice) changes to liquid water. A change of state is a change from one of the three states of matter to another.

There are six changes of state, as shown in Figure 10.20. A change from a solid to a liquid is **melting**. A change from a liquid to a gas is **evaporation**. (This is also known as vaporization.) A change from a gas to a liquid is **condensation** and from a liquid to a solid is **freezing**. A solid can also change directly into a gas. This process is called **sublimation**. And a gas can change directly to a solid. This is called **deposition**.

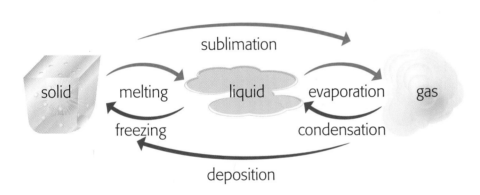

Figure 10.20 Changes in states of matter. The red arrows indicate increasing temperature. The blue arrows indicate decreasing temperature.

The Particle Theory and Changes of State

We can use the particle theory to explain each of the changes of state. The chart in Figure 10.21, on the next page, shows what happens to the particles of a solid when heat is added. The particles of the solid move more quickly and spread apart as the solid slowly melts. As more heat is added, the particles of the liquid have more energy and move more rapidly until they break free from the liquid, forming a gas.

Suggested Activity • • • • • • • •
D13 Inquiry Activity on page 298

Particle Theory

1 Solid
- Particles of a solid are packed closely together.
- Strong attractions, or bonds, hold the particles together.
- Solids have a fixed shape.
- The particles vibrate, or shake back and forth, in a fixed position.

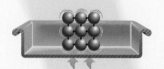

2 Heating a Solid
- Transferring heat to a solid makes the particles vibrate more energetically.
- Some of the particles move farther away from one another.
- The solid expands—its volume increases.

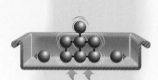

3 Melting a Solid
- As more heat is transferred to a solid, the particles vibrate even more.
- The particles bump against one another.
- Some of the particles break loose.
- The solid structure begins to break down—the solid melts.

4 Liquid
- The particles have more energy to move about.
- The bonds that hold the particles together are weak.
- Liquids take on the shape of their containers.

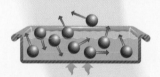

5 Heating a Liquid
- Transferring heat to a liquid makes the particles move more vigorously.
- The particles move farther apart.
- The liquid expands—its volume increases.

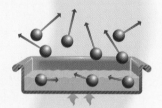

6 Boiling a Liquid
- As more and more heat is transferred to a liquid, the particles bump and bounce around even more.
- Some of the particles are "kicked" out of the liquid.
- The liquid boils—it changes to a gas.

7 Gas
- Particles of gas move about very quickly in all directions.
- Bumping and bouncing keep them far apart.
- Gas particles will fill up the space of any container.
- On heating, gas particles spread out even more—the gas expands.

Figure 10.21 Stages in the conversion of a solid into a gas

Heat Affects the Volume of Solids, Liquids, and Gases

It is going to be a home-made pizza for dinner, complete with sliced olives. You pick up a jar of olives, but, trying as hard as you can, you cannot turn the metal lid to open the jar (Figure 10.22). A friend suggests that heating the lid with hot water would help. You carefully hold the jar so that hot water runs over the lid. After you dry it off, you can turn the lid easily.

You can use the particle theory to explain what happened to the lid. Thermal energy transferred from the hot water to the particles of the lid of the jar. This caused the particles of the metal in the lid to vibrate faster and move farther apart. As a result, the size of the lid increased slightly — just enough that the lid became looser on the jar. When a solid increases in size, we say that it **expands** (grows larger). The glass in the jar also expands when heated but not as much as the metal lid does.

Expansion and Contraction in Liquids and Gases

We can see an example of expansion and contraction of a liquid in a thermometer. Liquid is placed in a narrow glass tube. As the liquid becomes warmer, it expands and rises in the glass tube. As it cools, contraction takes place and the liquid drops down.

Similar principles are at work when there is a change in the thermal energy of a gas. Imagine that you are invited to a party in January. At the end of the party, you take home some helium balloons tied to ribbons. It is very cold, so you walk quickly. The farther you go, the more the balloons "wilt." They no longer pull at the ribbons, but now bob near your shoulders. By the time you reach home, the balloons are smaller and wrinkled (Figure 10.23). However, after they have been in your bedroom for an hour, they look the same as when you left the party. Both contraction and expansion have been at work!

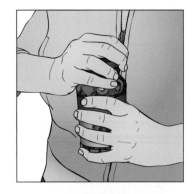

Figure 10.22 The particle theory explains why heating the lid of a jar makes it easier to twist off.

Take It Further

When a bridge is built, gaps are present in the road surface. Find out why these gaps are included in the design. Begin your search at PearsonScience.

Figure 10.23 The gas in the balloons is affected by the warm air indoors and the cold air outside.

Melting Away

You have often seen ice cubes melting. In this chilling activity, you will predict and then measure how long it takes for an entire ice cube to melt.

Question

How long would it take for an entire ice cube to melt in your hand?

> **CAUTION:** Stop holding the ice cube if your hand becomes too cold.

Materials & Equipment

- 1 ice cube per student
- triple-beam balance
- waxed paper
- digital watch or clock
- margarine tub or small beaker
- cloth or paper towels
- graph paper and ruler

Procedure

1. Draw Table 10.2 in your notebook.
2. Predict how long (in minutes) it would take for an ice cube to melt in your hand. Record your prediction.
3. Use the triple-beam balance to measure the mass of your ice cube (Figure 10.24). Record the mass in your table.
4. Place the ice cube on waxed paper. Pick up the ice cube and waxed paper together, so that the ice cube is surrounded by the paper.
5. Hold the ice cube in your fist for 2 min. Allow any water to drip into the tub or beaker.
6. After 2 min, quickly wipe any liquid from the surfaces of the ice cube. Measure the mass of the ice cube. Record the mass.

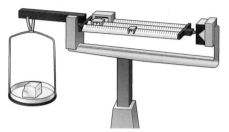

Figure 10.24 Set-up for Inquiry Activity D13

7. Repeat steps 4–6 for another 2 min. Use your other hand this time.
8. Repeat steps 4–6 for two more trials (total of 8 min).
9. Pour the melted water into the sink. Dry your work area.

Table 10.2 Melting of an ice cube

Time (min)	Mass of Ice Cube (g)
0	

Analyzing and Interpreting

10. Calculate the total loss of mass in grams of your ice cube over 8 min. Show how you calculated the change in mass.

11. Calculate the rate at which your ice cube was melting. In your notebook, write the following formula and then calculate the rate of melting.

$$\text{rate of melting (g/min)} = \frac{\text{overall change in mass of my ice cube (g)}}{8 \text{ min}}$$

12. Calculate how long it will take the entire ice cube to melt in your hand. In your notebook, write the following formula; then calculate the expected melting time for the entire ice cube.

$$\text{expected melting time for the entire ice cube} = \frac{\text{starting mass of unmelted ice cubes (g)}}{\text{rate of melting (g/min)}}$$

Skill Builder

13. Use a ruler and pencil to draw the *x*-axis and *y*-axis of a graph. The *x*-axis will represent time while the *y*-axis will represent the mass of your ice cube. Label the *x*-axis and *y*-axis (Figure 10.25).

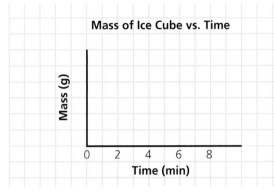

Figure 10.25

14. Use a pencil to plot the data from Table 10.2.

Forming Conclusions

15. How close was your prediction of the melting time to the value calculated in step 12?

16. Extend the line on your melting graph down to the *x*-axis (completely melted). What value for time do you obtain? Compare this value with the value you calculated in step 12.

17. Suggest one or more reasons to explain why your calculated time for the entire cube to melt is different from the value from the graph.

18. Use the particle theory to explain why an ice cube melts. Include words like "energy," "motion," and "space" in your answer.

D14 Quick Lab – Teacher Demonstration

Fast Change

Purpose

To observe the effect of cooling a gas

Materials and Equipment

- aluminum can
- water
- 5-mL measuring spoon
- hot plate
- large, clear bowl
- ice cubes
- tongs

Procedure

1. Pour 5 mL of water into an aluminum can and place the can onto a hot plate. Turn the hot plate on.

2. Add water to a large, clear bowl. Add ice cubes. The ice cubes will cool the water.

3. When the water in the can is boiling, use the tongs to carefully remove the aluminum can from the hot plate.

4. In a quick turning motion, flip the can over and immerse the can in the ice water to a depth of approximately 2 cm.

Questions

5. Describe what happened to the aluminum can after it was immersed in the ice water.

6. How does the particle theory explain your observations of the aluminum can after it was immersed in the ice water?

7. Would the same effect occur if the aluminum can was immersed in hot water? Explain your answer.

Key Concept Review

1. Name the six changes of state.

2. For each of the six changes of state, list the starting state of matter and the ending state of matter. Devise your own chart for your answers.

3. What happens to the particles of solids, liquids, and gases when they are heated?

4. What happens to the volume of solids, liquids, and gases when they are heated. Devise your own chart for your answer.

5. (a) Predict what might happen to the size of a blown-up ball if you place it into a refrigerator or freezer.

   (b) If possible, test your hypothesis for part (a). Include labelled diagrams in your report of the test.

Connect Your Understanding

6. Sealed bottles of juice or other drinks are not filled to the top. Use the particle theory to suggest a reason for this.

7. When Ontario hydro workers set up electrical cables during the summer, they allow the cables to sag. Suggest a reason for this. In your answer, refer to the particle theory. (**Hint:** Consider what will happen in the winter.)

Practise Your Skills

8. Compare the motion of the particles in a solid, a liquid, and a gas. Illustrate your descriptions and label your drawings.

9. How would the particle theory be useful to explain the situation shown below?

The coffee mug cracked after boiling water was poured into it.

For more questions, go to PearsonScience.

D15 *Thinking about Science and Technology*

Keeping the Warm Air In

Consider the entrances to your school. Inside, the door is warm from the heat of the air in the school. Outside, in winter the door is cold from the outside air. The door expands and contracts as these temperatures change. This is true for the doors of any building. If possible, take a look at an entrance door to your school. Draw and label a diagram to explain how we prevent warm air from leaking out through the space between a door frame and a door.

Here is a summary of what you will learn in this section:

- Heat is transmitted through the environment by conduction, convection, and radiation.
- Conduction is the transfer of heat through a solid or between a solid and another solid, a liquid, or a gas that it is touching.
- Convection is the transfer of heat through a fluid (a liquid or a gas).
- Radiation (radiant energy) is the transfer of heat in the form of waves.

On a hot summer day, you open your lunch bag to find a warm drink and a melted and mushy cheese sandwich. It would be much more appetizing to have both the drink and the sandwich at the right temperature. Understanding how heat transfers between materials is the first step to creating the properly cooled drink and sandwich for your lunch.

This warm lunch is only one of many examples where heat can be undesirable. Often, the transfer of energy is very useful. When is heat transfer helpful? What can we do to reduce heat transfer when it is not helpful? Figure 10.26 shows examples of heat transfer.

(d)

(a)

(b)

(c)

Figure 10.26 Heat is transferring in different ways in these situations.

D16 | *Starting Point* — Skills Ⓐ Ⓒ

Thinking Things Through

You have learned about heat as being the thermal energy transferred from an area of higher temperature to an area of lower temperature. Now, consider common situations where heat is useful. In your notebook, write a title and five or more situations where heat is useful at home, school, work, or leisure. Then, under a separate title, list five or more situations where heat is *not* useful or may even be harmful. Illustrate some of the situations you listed.

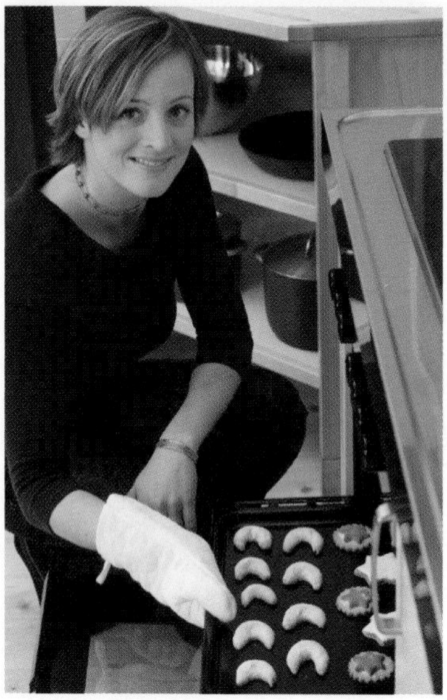

Three Types of Heat Transfer

There are three types of heat transfer. The word *"transfer"* means to carry across. When heat transfer occurs, the energy is carried through or across from one solid, liquid, or gas to another. In the following section, you will learn about all three types of heat transfer—conduction, convection, and radiation.

Conduction

If you have ever tried to remove a hot cookie sheet filled with cookies from an oven, you will know how quickly heat can transfer from one solid, the cookie sheet, to another solid, the oven mitt covering your hand (Figure 10.27). This is an example of rapid heat transfer by the heating of a solid, the oven mitt.

Conduction is the transfer of heat through a solid or between a solid and another solid, a liquid, or a gas that is in contact with it. The oven mitts are an example where solids are touching. Conduction also occurs where energy is transferred between a liquid and a solid or a gas and a solid (Figures 10.28 and 10.29). Notice that conduction occurs in one direction only — from a region that is warmer to a region that is cooler.

Figure 10.30 shows a pot of soup heating up on the element of a stove. The particles in the stove element are moving rapidly. They are vibrating rapidly, bumping into their neighbours — the particles on the bottom of the pot. Some of the energy of the particles in the red-hot element transfers to the metal pot. This makes the particles of the pot vibrate faster. Some of this energy transfers to the particles of the soup at the bottom of the pot, making the soup hotter. Conduction has played a role twice in this example. The result? A bowl of delicious hot soup, courtesy of conduction.

Figure 10.27 Oven mitts prevent the rapid transfer of heat to this person's hands.

Figure 10.28 Heat conducts from the hot water to the thermometer.

Figure 10.29 Heat is transferring by conduction from the hot air to the baby.

Figure 10.30 A pot of soup heating up on the element of a stove

Convection

In the example of the tasty hot soup, there is also another type of heat transfer occurring. Heat first transfers from the hot element to the bottom of the pot by conduction. In turn, heat transfers from the hot bottom of the pot to the soup at the bottom of the pot. This is also conduction. Then the soup particles at the bottom of the pot begin to move around rapidly. They bump into each other and spread apart. This is just like a curling rock bumping into several curling rocks on a sheet of ice (Figure 10.31). In other words, the hot soup at the bottom of the pot expands (pushes out and up).

Figure 10.31 Curling rocks are models for how rapidly moving particles transfer energy by bumping into each other. The collision transfers energy from the yellow curling rock in the centre to the red curling rocks on the left and right.

Movement of Particles

The hot soup begins to rise to the surface of the soup, pushing the cooler particles at the surface to the sides of the pot. There, the cooler particles sink to the bottom to take the place of the rising hot particles. When the cooler particles reach the bottom, they bump into the hot bottom of the pot and the circular pattern continues (Figure 10.32).

When the circulating hot liquid reaches the top of the pot, energy from the particles of the liquid transfers to the air particles. These particles of liquid, therefore, become somewhat cooler. They are pushed to the side of the pot as more hot liquid rises to the surface. As they drop down to the bottom, they again transfer energy to the sides of the pot, which are in contact with cooler air outside. This continuous motion sets up a pattern that continues as the soup is heated.

Figure 10.32 (a) The soup was cool to begin with. Heat from the hot element reaches the soup particles at the bottom of the soup by conduction.

Figure 10.32 (b) The soup particles near the bottom of the pot vibrate quickly, bumping into the particles of the cooler soup above them. The hot soup pushes upward, forcing the cooler soup to the side of the pot.

Figure 10.32 (c) The particles of the cooler soup sink closer to the bottom of the pot and begin to circulate.

Figure 10.32 (d) As the particles reach the bottom of the pot, they are heated and begin to rise up the middle, creating a convection current.

Suggested Activity ● ·········
D18 Quick Lab on page 306

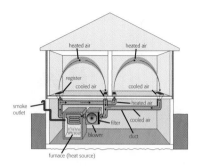

Figure 10.33 Forced-air heating creates convection currents.

This transfer of thermal energy by moving particles occurs in **fluids** — liquids and gases. It is called **convection**. The circular pattern of moving particles within fluids is called a **convection current**. Convection currents transfer heat from the hotter region to the cooler region, just as in conduction.

Convection Currents Affect Your Life

Convection currents occur in many places in nature and in structures such as buildings. These currents can make a big difference to your living conditions. Think about being in a cold room that has a heater in one corner or a hot-air vent in the floor (Figure 10.33).

When you turn the heater on or when the furnace pushes hot air through the vent, the first part of the room that warms up is near the heater or vent. As the particles of air move more rapidly, they push out and up. The hot air rises and meets the ceiling of the room, where it transfers some energy to the ceiling. The air then cools and drops down along the walls. A convection current forms in the room until the entire room becomes warm, just like the pot of soup did.

D17 *Learning Checkpoint*

Identifying Heat Transfers

Here is a chance to practise your skills in non-fiction writing as you share what you have learned about heat transfer. Think about interesting and fun ways to inform your classmates.

1. Describe how heat transfer occurs when you place your hand in a sink full of hot water.

2. Why does convection not occur in solids?

3. How does heat flow in these situations?
  (a) an egg on a hot frying pan
  (b) a candle in air

---

*Take It **Further***

Fire walkers walk across red-hot coals with bare feet but do not burn themselves. Find out how they do it. Begin your search at PearsonScience.

Heat Transfer by Radiation

Conduction and convection are two ways in which heat transfers between solids, liquids, and gases. Radiation is the third way. Both conduction and convection involve the movement of particles. Radiation does not. **Radiation** (radiant energy) is the transfer of energy by invisible waves given off by the energy source.

Thermal energy is one of the many forms of energy radiated by the Sun and other stars. Thermal energy from the Sun reaches Earth by radiation. Heat is the radiant energy that you feel on your skin. On the opening pages of this unit (pages 272 and 273), the photograph of the Sun reveals details that our eyes cannot see. Heat is transferred by invisible waves called **infrared waves**. All hot solids (including you), liquids, and gases radiate invisible heat waves (Figure 10.34). Images taken with a camera capable of recording infrared waves give information that we could not get from visible-light pictures.

Scientists use infrared waves to detect many things in nature that otherwise could not be observed. For example, satellites that orbit Earth can detect infrared waves that reflect off Earth and into space. These infrared images help people to discover how pollution spreads, where insects are damaging forests, and what the weather might be like in your region for the next several days (Figure 10.35).

Figure 10.34 This image gives a different view of a familiar animal. It was taken using a camera capable of recording infrared waves. The orange areas are the warmest and the white-blue areas are the coldest.

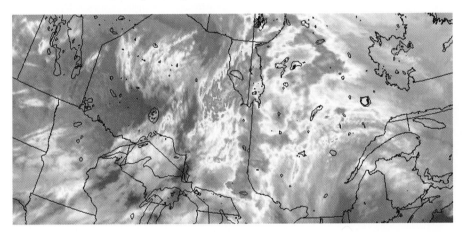

Figure 10.35 This infrared image of Ontario can be used to forecast the weather. High clouds are very cold. They are composed of ice crystals. The colours show the range of temperatures with orange-red being the coldest.

How Radiant Energy Warms Up Objects

When invisible waves of radiant energy come into contact with a solid, the particles in the solid vibrate faster. The solid becomes hotter. The solid can in turn, reradiate some of this energy back into the area where it is standing (Figure 10.36).

Suppose you open the doors of your family car on a sunny day in winter. The air in the car may feel quite warm. Touch the plastic dashboard beneath the windshield. It might feel hot, yet the windshield and other windows in the car may feel almost as cold as the air around the vehicle. This example shows that coloured solids can absorb and reradiate infrared waves, but transparent solids, liquids, and gases allow infrared waves to pass easily through them.

Figure 10.36 Even on a cold day, radiation from the Sun can warm the floor and objects inside a room.

Battling Bottles

Purpose

To observe convection using coloured water

Materials & Equipment

- 4 identical colourless plastic bottles
- masking tape or labels
- marking pen
- water
- food colouring
- 2 file cards

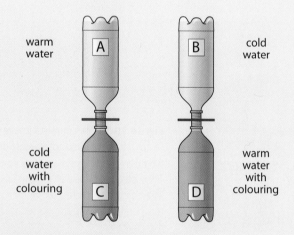

warm water — A
cold water — B
cold water with colouring — C
warm water with colouring — D

Figure 10.37 Set-up for Quick Lab D18

Procedure

1. Label the four bottles A, B, C, and D.
2. Fill bottles A and D with warm water.
3. Fill bottles B and C with cold water.
4. Add enough food colouring to bottles C and D so that you can see it easily. Mix thoroughly.
5. Cover the openings of bottles A and B with the file cards. Place bottles A and B upside down on top of bottles C and D. Make sure the bottles are centred — right on top of each other.
6. While one partner holds bottle A and another partner holds bottle B, carefully remove the file cards. Continue to hold the upper bottles.
7. Observe what happens to the coloured water.

Questions

8. At the beginning, in which bottles were the particles of water moving more quickly?
9. Describe what happened to the colour in both sets of bottles.
10. Draw two diagrams of the four bottles. Label one "Before removing the file card." Label the other "After removing the file card."
11. Write a paragraph or two to describe your observations. Use "convection" and "convection current" in your descriptions.

You're Getting Warmer

In this activity, you will be able to observe and measure the effects of radiant energy.

Purpose

To observe and measure changes in temperature caused by radiant energy

Materials & Equipment

- 2 large test tubes
- tape
- black paper and white paper
- ring stand
- 2 test tube clamps
- water
- 2 one-holed rubber stoppers
- 2 thermometers
- bright light bulb or sunlight
- a clock or watch for timing

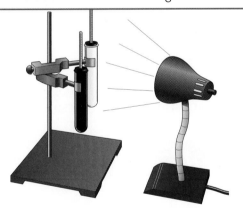

Figure 10.38 Set-up for Inquiry Activity D19

Hypothesis

Suggest what happens to dark- and light-coloured objects when a strong light shines on them.

Procedure

1. Draw Table 10.3 in your notebook.

2. Tape white paper to completely cover one test tube and black paper to completely cover the other. Set up the test tubes.

3. Place equal volumes of water into the two test tubes and insert the thermometers, supported by the rubber stoppers.

4. Measure the starting temperature of the water in each of the test tubes. Record the results in your table.

5. Turn on the light. Let it shine equally on both test tubes.

6. Measure and record the temperature of the water every minute for 20 min.

7. Turn off the light when you have completed your measurements.

Table 10.3 Temperature change

Time (min)	Temperature of Water in White Test Tube (°C)	Temperature of Water in Black Test Tube (°C)
0		
1		

Analyzing and Interpreting

8. Suggest a reason for the temperature differences you observed in this activity.

Skill Builder

9. Use the data from this activity to draw a graph that will have two separate coloured lines. One line will represent the black test tube. The second line will represent the white test tube. Use graph paper. Be certain to label the *x*-axis and *y*-axis and to give your graph a title. Include a legend for the colours you use.

Forming Conclusions

10. Suggest how you could modify this activity to find out how infrared waves are absorbed by other colours.

Key Concept Review

1. In what state of matter can conduction occur?

2. Can convection occur in both liquids and gases? Suggest a reason for your answer using the particle theory.

3. List two things that happen when invisible waves of radiant energy come into contact with a solid.

Connect Your Understanding

4. Think about how a microwave oven heats food. Do you think this type of heating is due to conduction, convection, or radiation?

5. Describe a situation not mentioned in this section in which energy transfer by conduction is important.

Practise Your Skills

6. A heat lamp was shining on two test tubes of water in a way similar to Inquiry Activity D19. The test tubes were covered with either black paper or white paper. The table below shows the data that were collected when the heat lamp shone on the two test tubes. Decide which column of data represents the black test tube and which represents the white test tube. Provide reasons to justify your answer.

Time (min)	Temperature of Water in Test Tube A (°C)	Temperature of Water in Test Tube B (°C)
0	20	20
3	22	21
6	25	22
9	28	23
12	30	24
15	33	25

For more questions, go to PearsonScience.

D20 *Thinking about Science and Technology*

Hot or Not?

Figure 10.39   **(a)**   **(b)**

Discuss the following questions.

1. What differences will there be in what the student feels under the conditions shown in Figures 10.39(a) and 10.39(b)?

2. How would your answer change if the cardboard in Figure 10.39(b) were replaced by a glass plate?

Phil Nuytten – Engineer and Deep-Sea Explorer

Figure 10. 40 Phil Nuytten

If you have ever been swimming in ocean or lake water, you know that keeping warm when in cold water can be a problem. Scientists who explore the ocean depths in Canada's northern waters are even more concerned about staying warm. That is the problem that Canadian Phil Nuytten decided to solve.

Phil Nuytten is a sub-sea engineer, inventor, and diver who lives in Vancouver. He operates Nuytco Research Ltd., a world leader in developing underwater technology. Nuytten has developed underwater submersibles — mini-submarines that can be used for exploration and other tasks. But he is most famous for developing the Newt Suit — a flexible hard suit that protects the wearer to depths of 300 m (Figure 10.41). His more recent Exosuit is even lighter.

These suits are used during undersea exploration and construction. They are standard equipment used by the navies of many countries. Astronauts from the Canadian Space Agency use Nuytten's underwater suits to train for their work on the International Space Station.

Figure 10.41 The Newt Suit

Questions

1. One of Phil Nuytten's goals is to design and manufacture exploration equipment that will help to keep divers safe. Suggest two or more ways that the Newt Suit protects divers.

2. Which aspect of Phil Nuytten's work do you find the most interesting? Explain why.

3. Research careers in underwater exploration. Find out what education or training you would need for these careers. Begin your search at PearsonScience.

Key Concept Review

1. What does the particle theory suggest about the motion of the particles of solids, liquids, and gases when they are heated? 🅚

2. What happens to the volume (size) of solids, liquids, and gases when they are heated? 🅚

3. What happens to the volume (size) of solids, liquids, and gases when they cool? 🅚

4. Name three types of energy transfer and provide an example of each. 🅚

Connect Your Understanding

5. Suggest a reason why many frying pans have plastic handles. 🅣

6. The diagram below on the left shows two beakers of water at the same temperature. Which beaker would have more thermal energy? Give a reason for your answer. 🅣

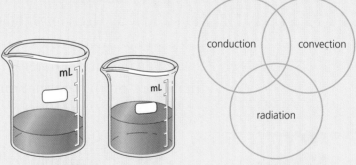

These beakers contain the same volume of water.

A three-circle Venn diagram

7. Copy the Venn diagram shown above on the right. Then, use the information you gained in this chapter to complete the diagram. 🅒

8. Describe three or more applications (uses) scientists have for infrared radiation. Then, try to suggest at least one more application that was not mentioned in this chapter. 🅐

After Reading Thinking Literacy

Reflect and Evaluate

Revisit the mind map you created in the Before Reading activity at the start of this chapter. Add any new information you have learned. Explain your mind map to a partner and listen to your partner share her or his information. Is there any important information you heard from your partner that you need to add to your mind map? What strategies and text features did you use to determine what was important when you read?

ACHIEVEMENT CHART CATEGORIES
🅚 Knowledge and understanding   🅣 Thinking and investigation   🅒 Communication   🅐 Application

9. Copy the "heat" phrases and expressions in column A of the table below into your notebook. Select the matching description from column B of the table. In your notebook, record the description beside the "heat" phrase it matches. ⓒ

Column A: Heat Phrases and Expressions	Column B: Descriptions (Scrambled)
If you can't stand the heat, get out of the kitchen.	A popular location
Dead heat	Right out of the oven
Piping hot	Getting into trouble
Hot off the press	Everybody is buying one!
Hot spot	The latest news
Hot button issue	Tied score or evenly matched
Getting into hot water	A person who gets angry easily
Strike while the iron is hot.	An issue people rather not deal with
Selling like hot cakes	Complete the task while you are able.
A hot potato	To stop an activity that is causing you stress
Hot headed	A concern held by many people

Practise Your Skills

10. Examine the scene on the right. Name as many examples as you can for each of the three types of energy transfer. ⓣ

11. Suggest how you might use metal and plastic spoons to determine which of these materials conducts heat more quickly. ⓒ

Unit Task Link

Insulation is the opposite of conduction. A good insulator does not conduct heat well.

With an adult, talk to staff at a hardware or builders' supply store. Find out about the types of insulation materials that you could use to cover a 2-L plastic soft drink bottle.

D21 Thinking about Science and Technology

Heating Past and Present

Where and how do we use ideas about heat and the particle theory to make our lives easier? Create your own Devices InfoBox. In Section A, brainstorm a list of five appliances, machines, or devices that are related to the ideas in this chapter. In Section B, suggest what devices were used (if any) before the devices in Section A were invented. In Section C, describe the benefits of using each device in Section A. In Section D, suggest new devices that might be developed in the next 20 years.

The beautiful image of Hurricane Katrina from space does not suggest the destruction that Katrina caused on Earth.

What You Will Learn

In this chapter, you will:

- identify the layers of Earth's atmosphere
- describe the effects of radiant energy on large bodies of water and land
- explain the relationship between heat, the water cycle, and weather patterns

Skills You Will Use

In this chapter, you will:

- use appropriate equipment and tools
- record and organize data
- analyze patterns and report results

Why This Is Important

Natural events affect human lives. Learning about Earth's structure and environmental processes will help you understand the events and changes that influence your life and the lives of people in your family and community.

Before Reading

Thinking Literacy

Asking Questions

Asking questions before starting to read helps readers set a purpose for reading, as well as get more involved with the text. Scan the pictures, diagrams, and summary boxes in this chapter to get a sense of the heat and weather topics being covered. Develop some questions you have about these topics. Revisit your questions during reading to see which ones have been answered in the text.

Key Terms

- atmosphere
- ocean current
- volcano
- water cycle
- wind
- rock cycle

Heat plays an important role in nature. **313**

Figure 11.1 Severe storms can cause great damage to natural and mechanical systems.

August 2, 2006, was a day that many Ontario residents will remember for a long time. That day, much of Ontario was hit by severe thunderstorms and high winds, resulting in floods and outages of the electricity supply. The violent weather came after three days of extreme heat and humidity over southern and central Ontario. Trees were uprooted and power lines brought down, causing power outages in an area from Toronto north to Bracebridge and east to Tweed (Figure 11.1). About 150 000 customers were affected. It took several days to restore power to all the homes and businesses.

Minden was the area most affected by the storm, but the Tweed area, Barrie, Orillia, Huntsville, Newmarket, Peterborough, Kingston, Walkerton, Simcoe, Guelph, and Orangeville also felt the effects of winds up to 120 km/h (Figure 11.2). A tornado was reported in the middle of the afternoon in the area of Highway 401 and Highway 6.

You might wonder what causes such violent storms to happen. Scientists who study how heat affects the atmosphere also ask this question because heat is an important part of the environment and can affect weather events.

Humans produce and use a large amount of heat in their activities. The production of heat adds a variety of chemical pollutants to the environment. Canadians are among the groups of people around the world who are concerned about how these pollutants affect the environment, the living things that are part of the environment, and themselves.

Figure 11.2 The August 2006 storm covered a large area of southern and eastern Ontario.

D22 *Quick Lab*

Cycling Water and Heat

The Sun controls natural systems on Earth, including the water cycle and the weather. A model is a design, object, or idea used to explain or visualize something difficult to see. In this activity, you will create a model to show how heat plays a role in the water cycle.

Purpose

To create a model of Earth's water cycle

Materials & Equipment

- hot plate and beaker (or kettle)
- water
- ice cubes
- cake pan
- oven mitts

Figure 11.3 Set-up for Quick Lab D22

> **CAUTION:** Steam is very hot. Wear oven mitts. Do not allow the steam to touch your skin.

Procedure

1. Place the beaker of water on the hot plate or fill and plug in the kettle.

2. Place the ice cubes inside the cake pan. Wait a few minutes.

3. When the water is boiling, use the oven mitts to hold the cold cake pan over the beaker.

4. Observe the bottom of the cake pan.

Questions

5. Describe what you saw on the bottom of the cake pan when you held it over the beaker of boiling water.

6. Draw and label a diagram to illustrate the materials and equipment and your results.

Here is a summary of what you will learn in this section:

- Human activities depend on the atmosphere.
- The atmosphere has several layers; humans live in the troposphere.
- Weather on Earth depends on heat transfer from the Sun.

Quick: take a deep breath, then breathe out. While you are reading this page, you are breathing easily. You probably realize you cannot do that just anywhere — in other words, you need to be somewhere where clean air is available.

Have you considered what it is that you are breathing and that surrounds you? It is called Earth's **atmosphere** — the blanket of gases and other particles that surrounds Earth. Whether you are reading this page at school, at home, or somewhere else, the atmosphere surrounds you.

The atmosphere includes the air humans need to live. It also includes a mixture of dirt, dust, and other substances — including some that human activities release into the air as pollution. When you breathe, you take air and a mixture of these other substances into your lungs. One of the gases in air, oxygen, is the gas that animals (including you) require to live.

D23 | *Starting Point*

Skills Ⓐ Ⓒ

Coming Up for Air

Figure 11.4 shows situations where humans must be aware of the constant need for fresh air. By yourself or with a partner, give each photograph a title. Record the letter and title for each. Briefly, provide information about what is happening in each photograph. Add any personal connections that you may have to these activities.

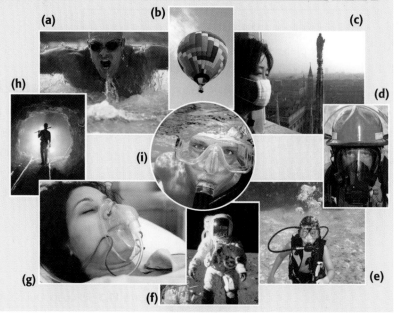

Figure 11.4 Humans need fresh air in all situations.

Question Types

When readers ask questions and look for answers as they read, they are interacting with the text in a meaningful way. There are different types of questions readers can ask:

- literal or "on the line" questions. The answer is found in the text.

- inferential or "between the lines" questions. The reader interprets information from the text along with background knowledge to answer.

- evaluative or "beyond the lines" questions. The answer may not be in the text at all. Readers need to use their background knowledge and experiences to answer.

Revisit the questions you developed at the beginning of this chapter. Use the information above to determine whether each of your questions is literal, inferential, or evaluative. Where will you find the answers to each of your questions?

Learning about Layers of Air

Wherever you go above the surface of land or above the oceans, you are surrounded by the mixture of gases that make up Earth's atmosphere. Humans live in the bottom layer of the atmosphere. Of course, many types of birds, such as the peregrine falcon, and other animals who live in trees spend some of their time in the atmosphere at a higher level than humans. Trees like the eastern white pine (Figure 11.5) extend many metres up into the atmosphere.

Conditions in the atmosphere, including rain, wind, and temperature, all affect human life. Think about thunderstorms and blizzards. Also think about sunny days at the lake, and plants growing in the spring. All of these examples show how changes in the atmosphere above Earth's surface are important not only to scientists but also for everyday life.

Scientists who study the atmosphere divide it into five main layers according to the changes in temperature as you go higher above Earth's surface (Figure 11.6 on the next page):

- the troposphere — from 0 to 20 km
- the stratosphere — from 20 to 50 km
- the mesosphere — from 50 to 85 km
- the thermosphere — from 85 to 690 km
- the exosphere — from 690 to 10 000 km

Figure 11.5 The eastern white pine is the provincial tree of Ontario. It is the tallest tree in eastern North America. The record height for this species is more than 60 m.

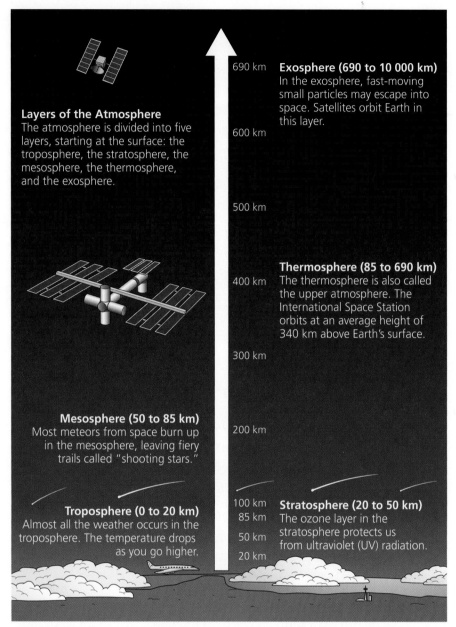

Figure 11.6 The atmosphere is divided into five layers, starting at the surface: the troposphere, the stratosphere, the mesosphere, the thermosphere, and the exosphere. Data are from National Oceanic and Atmospheric Administration (NOAA), U.S. Dept. of Commerce.

The Troposphere

Humans live in the lowest level of Earth's atmosphere — the **troposphere.** Almost all human activity, including air travel, goes on in this layer. As the word troposphere suggests, constant changes occur in the troposphere. In fact, it is the layer of the atmosphere in which Earth's weather occurs. But what is weather? **Weather** refers to the conditions of Earth's atmosphere at a particular time and in a particular place. The study of weather and weather patterns is called **meteorology**.

WORDS MATTER

Troposphere: The word troposphere comes from *tropo* (turning, changing) and *sphere* (ball-shaped).

Meteorology: The word meteorology comes from a Greek word meaning the discussion of things that happen in the sky.

Heat Transfer and Earth's Weather

What causes changes in our weather? For the answer, you have to consider not only Earth but also the source of much of Earth's energy — the Sun. The energy from the Sun that reaches Earth contributes to changes in Earth's weather systems and affects the weather in your local area.

Although it is an average-sized star, our Sun is the source of a huge amount of energy. Only a small fraction of it reaches our planet. Even so, the amount of energy reaching Earth's surface every day is more than 6000 times the amount of energy used by all humans on Earth in a day. Are you wondering what happens to this energy? Study Figure 11.7 to find out.

Take It Further

Scientists have learned a lot more about Earth's atmosphere. You can, too! Begin your search at PearsonScience.

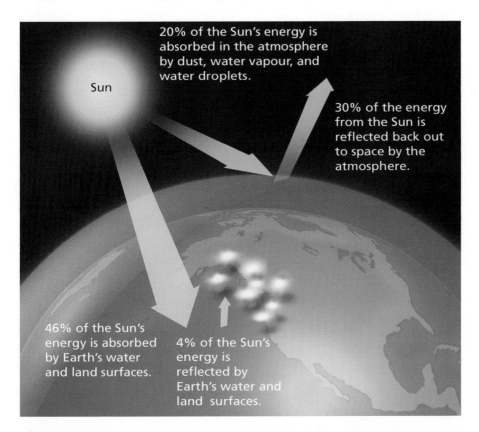

20% of the Sun's energy is absorbed in the atmosphere by dust, water vapour, and water droplets.

Sun

30% of the energy from the Sun is reflected back out to space by the atmosphere.

46% of the Sun's energy is absorbed by Earth's water and land surfaces.

4% of the Sun's energy is reflected by Earth's water and land surfaces.

Figure 11.7 Scientists estimate that less than one-billionth of the Sun's total energy output each day actually reaches Earth. Even this small portion represents a huge amount of energy.

D25 Learning Checkpoint

Reflecting on the Sun

Draw a two-column chart in your notebook as shown in Table 11.1. Refer to Figure 11.7 to complete the table. Summarize what happens to the energy that reaches Earth.

Table 11.1 The Sun's energy

What Happens to the Sun's Energy?	Percent of the Sun's Energy

Curious Candle

Air contains a mixture of gases, including oxygen. How long can a candle burn inside a closed container? How does the size of the container affect the time for a burning candle to go out? In this activity, you will use several beakers to observe the effect of heating different volumes of air inside the beakers of different sizes.

Question

How long can a candle burn under beakers of different sizes?

> **CAUTION:** Do not touch the hot beaker after the candle has gone out.

Materials & Equipment

- pie plate
- small candle
- matches
- beakers of different sizes
- oven mitts
- modelling clay
- water
- clock or stopwatch

Hypothesis

Suggest how the size of a beaker might affect the time a candle can burn inside it. Record your answer.

Procedure

1. Copy Table 11.2 into your notebook.

2. Place a small piece of modelling clay onto the centre of the pie plate.

3. Stand the candle upright in the modelling clay.

4. Fill the pie plate with water.

5. Your teacher will light the candle.

6. As you place the smallest beaker over the candle, start timing. Closely observe the spout of the beaker and record your observations.

7. When the candle goes out, record the time in minutes and seconds in your table.

8. Use an oven mitt to lift the beaker out of the pie plate. Do not let water drip on the candle.

9. Repeat steps 5–8, replacing the small beaker with the middle-sized beaker.

10. Repeat steps 5–8 using the largest beaker.

Figure 11.8 Set-up for Inquiry Activity D26

Table 11.2 Effect of beaker size

	Size of Beaker (mL)	Time That the Candle Lasted (min and s)
smallest beaker		
middle-sized beaker		
largest beaker		

Analyzing and Interpreting

11. Compare the three results you recorded in your table. Record your comparison.

12. Why did you need to start this activity by adding water to the pie plate?

Skill Builder

13. Predict how long the candle flame would last under a beaker twice as large as the largest beaker you used in step 10.

Forming Conclusions

14. What effect does the size of the beaker have on how long the candle will burn?

Key Concept Review

1. Define "atmosphere" in your own words.

2. Name several locations where humans need technology to breathe.

3. Name the five layers of the atmosphere in order, starting from Earth's surface.

4. In which layer of the atmosphere do we find the most human activity?

5. What percent of the Sun's energy that reaches Earth is absorbed by Earth's water and land surfaces?

Connect Your Understanding

6. A friend tells you: "The atmosphere is just a bunch of gas." Do you agree with this statement? Defend your answer.

7. Invent a mnemonic sentence for the five layers of the atmosphere using the letters T — S — M — T — E.

8. The word atmosphere comes from *atmo* (vapour, smoke) and *sphere* (ball-shaped). Why is this a suitable name for the blanket of air that surrounds you?

9. A simile is a comparison that uses the words "like" or "as." Write sentences to compare something in your life with the layers of the atmosphere. Refer to the description of the atmosphere in this section. Start with the sentence: "The atmosphere is like a _____ because _____."

10. Scientists estimate that less than one-billionth of the Sun's total energy output each day reaches Earth. What do you think happens to the rest? (**Hint:** Consider the size of Earth.)

Practise Your Skills

11. Draw a bar graph of the data for the Sun's energy, shown in Figure 11.7. Use graph paper, a ruler, and coloured pencils.

12. Create a mini-poster using your mnemonic sentence from question 7. On your poster, include your mnemonic sentence along with the names of the matching five layers of the atmosphere. Add a colourful illustration for each layer. Give your mini-poster an original, creative title.

For more questions, go to PearsonScience.

D27 *Thinking about Science and the Environment*

Mapping the Atmosphere

You have learned what happens to the Sun's energy that reaches Earth. Human activity adds gases and small particles to the air that can trap heat and warm the atmosphere. Create a consequence map with the central question, "What are the consequences of humans adding gases and other substances to Earth's atmosphere?" The first level of your map will be the positive and negative consequences you think will result. The second and third levels of your map will provide more information for each positive and negative consequence.

Here is a summary of what you will learn in this section:
- Water is continuously moving and changing states in nature.
- Heat creates the water cycle and affects weather.
- The water cycle and ocean currents depend on convection.

Air and water are valuable resources that humans need and use every day. The health of your family and the success of many businesses depend on these important natural resources. Just like air, water on Earth is a shared resource. How we use water or misuse it can affect people and human activities far away from us. Think about all the ways you use water or depend on water every day. It is a long list.

Water is important for farmers everywhere (Figure 11.9). A farm cannot exist without water for crops and animals. At one time, farmers may have been less concerned about the amount of water they used. Today, with technology like computers and satellites, farmers are able to monitor and closely control their water use. In addition, new farming techniques mean that farmers may need less water to grow crops.

Water use in Ontario and in all locations on Earth is influenced by the **water cycle** — the movement in nature of water from the surface of Earth to the atmosphere and back. How farmers use and recycle water affects how much water sinks into the ground, how much water flows over the surface, and even how much water evaporates from their cropland.

Figure 11.9 Water is an important consideration for farmers.

D28 *Starting Point*

Skills Ⓐ Ⓒ

Wonderful Water

It's time for some quick writing. Grab a pen or pencil. Record the title of this activity. Then, write non-stop for two or more minutes. The topic is: "How Do I Depend on Water?" Ready? Set? Write.

Heat Flow in the Water Cycle

The energy of the Sun is directly responsible for three very important natural systems that affect life on Earth — the water cycle, weather patterns, and ocean currents. Think about the water cycle. You have seen that adding heat to water by boiling causes the water to change from a liquid to a gas. But it is not necessary to boil water to cause this change of state. Adding a smaller amount of heat has the same result; it just happens more slowly. Figure 11.10 shows one example of this idea.

Water in a puddle slowly seems to disappear, even on a cloudy day. In fact, it evaporates — turning into invisible water vapour. On the other hand, when hot steam touches a cool surface, it condenses, changing from water vapour to liquid water that can cover or drip from the surface (Figure 11.11).

These observations indicate a **cycle**, a continuous movement of materials in nature that repeats. The mist on the bathroom mirror is a home version of part of Earth's water cycle — the movement in nature of water from the surface of Earth to the atmosphere and back (Figure 11.12).

Water in the atmosphere is not always invisible. When the temperature high above Earth starts to decrease, water droplets join together. Slowly, the smaller droplets become larger droplets, forming a cloud that we can see. As the water droplets grow even larger, they also become heavier and will begin to fall as rain, also called **precipitation**.

Puddles of water evaporate due to heat. As the temperature drops, water droplets in clouds join together and fall as rain. You can see that heat plays a role in the two changes of state in the water cycle:

- evaporation (liquid water on Earth absorbs heat and changes into water vapour)

- condensation (invisible water vapour in the atmosphere cools down and changes back into drops of water that fall as rain).

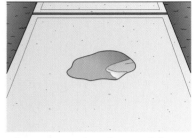

Figure 11.10 There is enough heat in the air on a warm day to evaporate the water in a puddle.

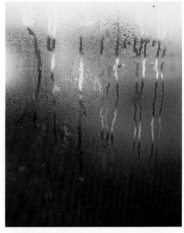

Figure 11.11 The mist is caused by water vapour that condensed on the cool mirror.

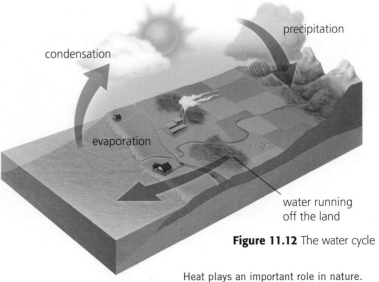

condensation

precipitation

evaporation

water running off the land

Figure 11.12 The water cycle

Weather and the Water Cycle

Draw a chart in your notebook as shown in Table 11.3. In column A, print or write the three questions to consider. In column B, try to answer these questions. After reading "Weather and the Water Cycle," complete column C.

Questions to Consider

1. How does the Sun shine down on different parts of Earth?

2. What causes ocean currents?

3. How do ocean currents affect life in the oceans?

Table 11.3 Weather and the water cycle

Column A Questions about Weather and the Water Cycle	Column B What I Know before Reading	Column C What I Know after Reading

Weather and the Water Cycle

Since Earth is roughly a sphere the Sun's radiant energy does not fall evenly on Earth's land and seas (Figure 11.13). All year round, even though Earth is moving through space, the Sun shines more directly down on the land and ocean at and near the equator, heating them more strongly.

Ontario and the rest of Canada are north of the equator. This means that in Canada the Sun's rays fall less directly than at the equator. The same amount of heat is spread over a larger area on Earth's surface. Also, in winter, Canada receives far less sunlight, making most of Canada cold and snowy.

The differences in temperature between regions near the equator and northern and southern regions set in motion a continuous movement of air across Earth. This movement distributes heat from the Sun across the planet. The movement of air in the troposphere is called **wind**.

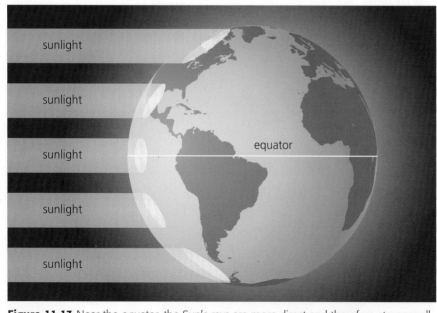

sunlight

sunlight

sunlight

equator

sunlight

sunlight

Figure 11.13 Near the equator, the Sun's rays are more direct and therefore stronger all year round.

When air in one region is warmer than the surrounding air, it becomes less dense and begins to rise, drawing more air in underneath. A convection current is set up. For example, during the day, land heats up more than water. The air above the land near large lakes or an ocean heats up and rises. Cooler air from above the water rushes in, creating a cool sea breeze. At night, when the land cools down more quickly than the water, the opposite is true. Warm air above the water rises while cooler air from the land takes its place, creating a cool land breeze.

All the while, air is carrying water vapour and water droplets that circulate from Earth into the atmosphere and back again in giant convection currents. The water cycle is one of several factors that influence the weather in your region of Ontario and around the world. In one location, the weather may be warm and sunny; only a few kilometres away, it could be raining and windy.

Take It Further

Be an amateur weather watcher! Track Canada's weather patterns yourself. Environment Canada posts weather maps for regions in Canada on the Internet. You can find 5-day forecasts for your region of Ontario as well as any region in Canada. Begin your search at PearsonScience.

Heat and Ocean Currents

An **ocean current** is a pattern of movement of the water in a large region of the ocean. Ocean currents contribute to the movement of thermal energy from the warm regions of Earth near the equator to the colder regions in the Arctic and Antarctic. In effect, these convection currents partially balance the extremes of temperature on Earth's surface.

An ocean current is like a river of warm or cold water moving in a more or less circular pattern. This pattern influences the **climate**. The climate is the long-term weather conditions over large areas of Earth. Ocean currents affect the land areas that form Canada's western, eastern, and northern coasts, as well as the routes taken by ships carrying products and people (Figure 11.14).

Ocean currents flow in convection patterns that depend on wind, the minerals dissolved in the water, the shape of the ocean floor in different locations, heat from the Sun, the pull of the Moon's gravity, and even Earth's rotation (spin).

Figure 11.14 Major ocean currents

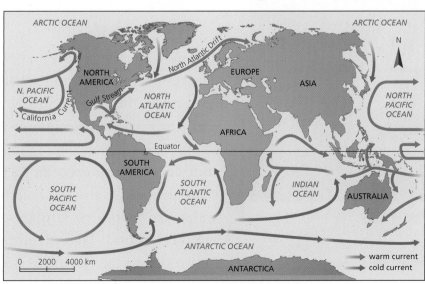

Scientists have discovered more than 50 different ocean currents. Ocean currents and their patterns are of interest in studies of Earth's air and water systems and changes in climate, such as global warming.

Keeping It Warm, Keeping It Cool

Ocean currents flow in a circular pattern — clockwise in the northern hemisphere, where Canada is found, and counterclockwise in the southern hemisphere, south of the equator. There are three categories of ocean currents (Table 11.4).

Table 11.4 Categories of ocean currents

Category of Current	Ocean Layer	Flow Direction	Factors That Drive Current
warm surface current	at and near surface	from near equator toward north and south poles	wind spinning of Earth
cold surface current	at and near surface	from polar regions toward equator	mainly wind
deep ocean current	deep ocean	form at poles; flow toward equator and rise to surface	density of water differences in temperature between layers

Ocean currents influence life in the oceans. The ocean is layered: warmer on top, cold at the bottom. The range of water temperatures in each layer controls which organisms can live there. Ocean organisms are sensitive to changes in temperature. A change in temperature of even a few degrees may be enough to cause these organisms to change their location. Other organisms that depend on them for food must also move or die of starvation.

Spinning Systems

The moving atmosphere and oceans circulate continuously. The results are wind and storms in the troposphere and currents in the oceans. Strong winds can be very destructive and may produce **hurricanes** and **tornadoes.** A hurricane is a strong, spinning weather system over the ocean that has continuous winds exceeding 119 km/h. Hurricanes form and grow stronger as they pick up heat from warm tropical ocean water. Tornadoes are strong, spinning columns of air in contact with the ground. They are unpredictable, usually local, and last only a short time (Figure 11.15).

Figure 11.15 A tornado may form as the result of a thunderstorm, at the boundary between warm, moist air and hot, dry air.

Bottled Weather — Teacher Demonstration

A 2-L plastic bottle with some smoke particles inside can provide a model of a common event that occurs every minute in the atmosphere.

Question

How can you model cloud formation?

Materials & Equipment

- 2-L or smaller colourless plastic bottle with cap (remove the label)
- warm water
- booklet of matches
- black paper

CAUTION: Be careful when using matches.

Figure 11.16 Set-up for Inquiry Activity D29

Hypothesis

Predict what might happen when you squeeze a 2-L bottle that is filled with smoke and water vapour.

Procedure

1. Place just enough warm water in the bottle to cover the bottom. Replace the cap.

2. Shake the bottle vigorously for one minute.

3. Light a match and let it burn for a few seconds. Blow out the match and immediately place the head of the match into the bottle. Let the smoke fill the bottle. Remove the match.

4. Observe that, after a few seconds, the smoke will seem to disappear.

5. Screw the cap on the bottle, being careful not to let too much smoke escape.

6. Hold the bottle over a dark surface such as a dark counter top or black paper. Quickly squeeze the sides of the bottle really hard, then release. Do this six or seven times (more squeezing may be necessary). Hold the last squeeze for a few seconds, and then quickly release it. As soon as you release the squeeze, look for a change inside the bottle.

Analyzing and Interpreting

7. Do you think that there was invisible water vapour inside the bottle before you placed the head of the match into the bottle? Suggest how you know this.

8. Interpret the changes that occurred quickly after squeezing and releasing the bottle.

9. Why do you think you needed to squeeze the bottle several times?

Skill Builder

10. Use drawings to illustrate the steps in the procedure. Include your observations of changes inside the bottle. Number each drawing with the matching step in the procedure.

Forming Conclusions

11. Suggest how your observations in this activity could help explain the formation of clouds in the atmosphere.

12. Suggest conditions in the atmosphere that might lead to more clouds forming.

Key Concept Review

1. Why is the name water cycle suitable for the movement of water on Earth?

2. How does heat cause ocean currents?

3. Suggest a reason why the oceans near the equator are warmer than the oceans closer to Earth's poles.

Connect Your Understanding

4. List several examples of ways human activity influences the water cycle.

5. Compare the steps in the water cycle to another cycle of events in daily life. You can start your comparisons with a statement such as : "The water cycle is like _____ because _____."

Practise Your Skills

6. Design, draw, and label your own illustration of the water cycle. Alternatively, plan a physical activity to represent the water cycle.

7. Design, draw, and label a series of illustrations to represent the six factors that influence ocean currents. (See page 325).

For more questions, go to PearsonScience.

D31 Thinking about Science and the Environment

Monitoring the Oceans — Argo

The International Argo Project (or Argo) is a global network of 3000 free-drifting floats that measure the temperature and salt content of the upper 2000 m of Earth's oceans (Figures 11.17 and 11.18). For the first time, scientists can continuously monitor several characteristics of the water in the upper regions of the oceans, including temperature, direction, and speed. All data are sent via satellites to centralized computers.

Figure 11.18 This image shows where many of the Argo floats were located on one particular day.

Figure 11.17 A ship installing Argo floats

Consider This

With a classmate or as a whole class, discuss the following questions.

1. What four categories of data do the Argo floats collect?

2. Why are the data gathered by Argo important to meteorologists?

Here is a summary of what you will learn in this section:

- Earth is made of several layers.
- Many of Earth's features were and are formed by heat.
- The rock cycle helps us understand how heat causes changes in Earth.

The dramatic announcement "Vancouver! Vancouver! This is it!" was made by vulcanologist David Johnston over the radio link from Coldwater Observation Post, north of Mount St. Helens in Washington State, on Sunday morning, May 18, 1980. A few seconds later, Mount St. Helens exploded because of an underground earthquake beneath the mountain (Figures 11.19 and 11.20).

Hot gases and ash shot 19 km into the sky. The top and northern side blew away, reducing the height of the mountain by about 400 m. The temperature reached 350°C, and the blast was so loud it could be heard across the Canada–United States border in Vancouver, British Columbia. For days, ash was carried east by winds, settling on cars, buildings, and houses in Calgary, Regina, and as far as Winnipeg — a distance of over 2200 km.

Volcanic eruptions grab our attention. People wonder how hot, melted rock deep in Earth can flow upward and onto the surface. But below the surface Earth is constantly changing every day — changing due to heat.

Figure 11.19 Mount St. Helens erupting on May 18, 1980

Figure 11.20 Mount St. Helens is south of Vancouver in Washington State.

D32 *Starting Point*

Skills A C

Earth's Mysterious History

The many changes in Earth's long history are closely tied to heat. It is like a mystery story. Changes on and below Earth's surface occur but we do not understand all of them. For example, heat causes mountains to form on land and on the ocean floor. Think about, and then discuss with a classmate, several reasons why scientists are interested in studying how heat causes changes on Earth. You could also describe what you know about *how* scientists research these changes.

Facts-Questions-Responses

Volcanoes and earthquakes are an interesting topic, but some information may be complex and detailed. An FQR chart can help readers interact and make sense of information while taking notes. Create an FQR chart in your notebook. Label the first column "Facts," the second "Questions," and the third "Responses." (See Figure 11.21.)

As you read the information on volcanoes and earthquakes on pages 329–333 (up to Rocks and Minerals), pause to record facts that are presented. For each fact, record a question

you have about it. In the last column, you can record your response to the fact or a connection or reaction you had. Not all facts need both a question and response. Once you have completed reading, share some of your facts, questions, and responses with the class.

Facts	Questions	Responses
Mt. St. Helen's erupted May 18, 1980	Did this affect our weather in Ontario?	

Figure 11.21 FQR chart

Questions about Earth

Humans live on the outside skin of Earth. For hundreds of years, we have asked questions similar to those you might ask before tasting a new piece of fruit (Figure 11.22). How thick is Earth's skin? Are there layers inside? What would we find at the centre? Several models for Earth are shown here (Figures 11.23–11.25). Which would you choose as a model of Earth? Why? Keep reading to see how your choice compares with the scientific evidence.

Earth — The Inside Story

You live on Earth's surface. But what about the ground beneath your feet? Scientists divide Earth into four layers. Using Figure 11.26, let us travel through these layers, starting at the surface, in an imaginary vehicle, the *Earth Explorer*.

Figure 11.22 An unusual fruit

Figure 11.23 Model 1

Figure 11.24 Model 2

Figure 11.25 Model 3

1 Earth's outer layer is the **crust**. All the features we see around us—mountains, valleys, plains, hills, plateaus—are part of the crust. You will start your trip through Earth from the bottom of the ocean because the crust is thinnest here—only about 6 km thick.

4 Finally, you reach the **inner core**. This layer is solid, even though it is very hot. The weight of the other layers has pressed the inner core into an extremely hard ball. There are still another 1250 km to the centre of Earth. But the inner core is so hard that even your special vehicle cannot drill through it.

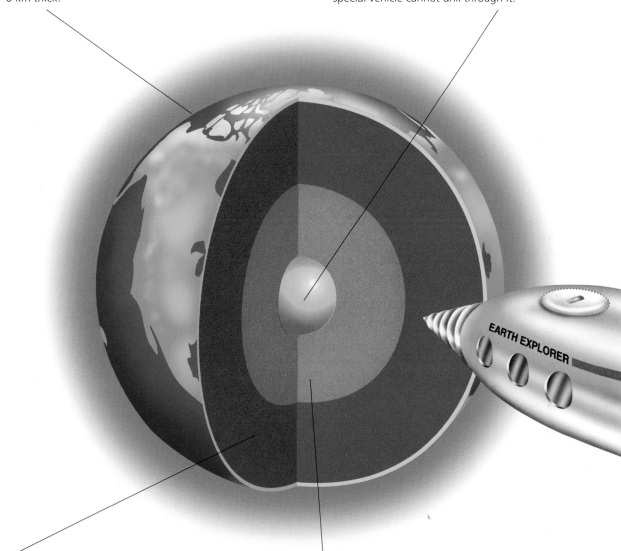

2 Now you are inside the next layer, called the **mantle**. The mantle is about 2900 km thick, but it is not the same all the way through. The upper part of the mantle is solid, like the crust. Below the solid upper part of the mantle, the temperature and pressure are higher. However, your vehicle can move more easily through this lower layer of the mantle because the rock is partly melted. This rock can flow very slowly.

3 When you leave the mantle, you enter Earth's molten **outer core**. The temperatures are so high here that the rock is completely liquid. Even though the rock is molten, it still takes you a long time to get to the inner core because this layer is also very thick–about 2200 km.

Figure 11.26 Earth's four layers

New Crust Forms All the Time

Suggested Activity •·········
D35 Quick Lab on page 336

Earth's crust is constantly changing. The three types of heat transfer (conduction, convection, and radiation) all play their part in the continuing story of the changes on and beneath Earth's surface. Conduction occurs in the solid inner core. Heat is transferred to the neighbouring molten outer core. The **magma**, that is, molten (melted) rock, in the outer core and the deeper part of the mantle is hotter than the magma in the upper part of the mantle near Earth's crust. This difference in temperature creates convection currents in the molten rock in the mantle. Hot, molten rock rises toward the top of the mantle and moves to the side (Figure 11.27). Heat is also transferred during this sideways movement by conduction and radiation. Sometimes, molten rock sinks back down toward the outer core and the cycle continues.

Earth's crust sits on large, thick sections of rock called **plates**. Because the mantle is made of hot, molten rock, these large rock plates can move apart or move together. Sometimes, the movement allows magma, ash, and gases to shoot upward toward the crust through cracks, producing rumbling in the ground and a lighting of the night sky as a **volcano** erupts (Figure 11.27). At other times, the shifting of the plates produces shaking and sliding in the crust as an **earthquake** takes place.

WORDS MATTER

Molten: The word molten means fused or liquefied by heat, from an older form of English, *melten*, meaning to melt.

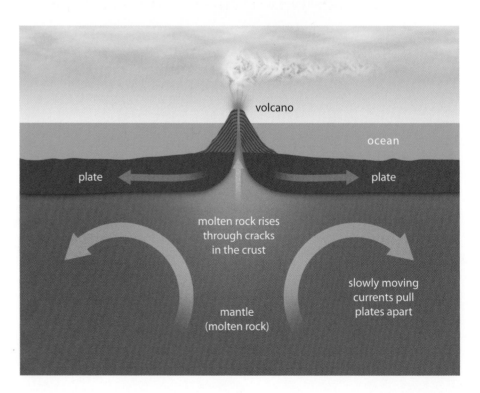

Figure 11.27 When the plates of rock that float on the mantle move apart, molten rock can shoot upward and onto Earth's surface, forming a volcano.

volcano

ocean

plate

plate

molten rock rises
through cracks
in the crust

slowly moving
currents pull
plates apart

mantle
(molten rock)

Deep under the oceans, hot magma may squeeze upward where rock plates are moving apart. The hot magma is released onto the ocean floor as **lava** (Figure 11.28). When it meets the cold ocean water, the lava begins to cool, spreads out, and then forms new crust.

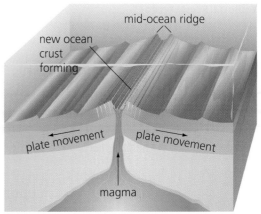

Figure 11.28 Deep under the oceans, new crust is forming continuously as hot lava reaches the ocean floor, begins to cool, spreads out, and then hardens.

Rocks and Minerals

Earth's crust is made up of rocks of different kinds. The first step in identifying a rock is to look at the **minerals** it contains. Minerals are naturally occurring solid substances that may be pure or mixed with other minerals. There are over 4000 known minerals. **Crystals** are the special shapes of minerals found in rocks made from molten rock (magma) that cooled slowly. Each type of mineral has a special crystal shape (Figure 11.29).

Three Classes of Rocks — Igneous, Sedimentary, and Metamorphic

Just as students in school are grouped into different classes, so too are rocks placed into different classes. Scientists have named three large classes (families) of rocks.

Igneous rock is the class of rock that forms from molten rock that has cooled and hardened. There are many different kinds of igneous rock. Rock that forms when magma cools slowly often contains large crystals. If the magma reaches Earth's surface, it is called lava. Lava cools quickly when it is exposed to the air or water. Lava contains small crystals or no crystals at all. Figure 11.30 shows three examples of igneous rocks. Obsidian and pumice form from lava. Granite forms from magma.

Sedimentary rock is the class of rock that forms from small pieces of rock, shells, or other materials that pile up in layers. The bottom layers pack together from the pressure of the layers above them, like snow at the bottom of a snowbank compressing from the weight of the layers of snow above it. The layers of rock at the bottom harden, forming sedimentary rock, like snow at the bottom of several layers turning to ice. Just as there are many different kinds of minerals that can pile up, there are many different kinds of sedimentary rock.

Figure 11.29 Minerals have unique crystal shapes.

(a)

(b)

(c)

Figure 11.30 Igneous rocks (a) obsidian, (b) pumice, (c) granite

Table 11.5 Rock types

Name of Rock	Class (Family) of Rock	Name of Metamorphic Rock That It Changes To
granite	igneous	gneiss
sandstone	sedimentary	quartzite
limestone	sedimentary	marble
shale	sedimentary	slate

Metamorphic rock is formed from igneous or sedimentary rocks that have been changed from their original form by heat (from Earth) or by the pressure of the rocks above them. As there are many different minerals that make up igneous rocks and sedimentary rocks, there are also many different types of metamorphic rocks. Examine Table 11.5 to find out the names of several types of metamorphic rocks. Two rocks can contain exactly the same set of minerals but look very different because they formed in different ways. The ways the minerals in the rocks are arranged and the sizes of the crystals can all give clues to how the rock was formed.

Suggested Activity •········
D36 Inquiry Activity on page 336

D34 *Learning Checkpoint*

How Rocks and Minerals Form

Match the following descriptions with the new terms you have learned.

1. the class of rock formed from layers of particles, shells, plants, or animals piled up

2. the class of rock that forms when molten rock cools and hardens

3. molten rock beneath Earth's surface

4. molten rock that reaches Earth's surface

5. the special shapes of minerals found in rocks that are made from molten rock that cools slowly

6. an opening in Earth's crust through which solid and molten rock, ash, and gases escape

---

Figure 11.31 High-quality diamonds, sold as Polar Bear Diamonds™, are mined, cut, and polished in Canada's Northwest Territories.

What Are Gemstones?

Gemstones (or gems) are minerals that are valuable because of their exceptional beauty, colour, and rarity. Their main physical properties are colour, lustre (shininess), how light passes through them, and hardness. Gemstones are often made into jewellery. Some common gemstones, like quartz and amethyst, are fairly inexpensive. Others, like ruby, emerald, sapphire, and diamond, can be very valuable. Many gemstones have important uses in manufacturing and electronics.

How and Where Are Diamonds Formed?

Diamonds, with all their beauty and sparkle, are a form of carbon (Figure 11.31). According to geologists, diamonds were first formed underground more than 2.5 billion years ago. They were crystallized in the mantle below Earth's crust at great depths, usually more than 150 km down. Here is how we believe this happens. Rocks in Earth's upper mantle were carried deeper into the mantle where they melted. These rocks contained carbon, and on melting released carbon particles. The carbon particles formed crystals under the very high pressure from the molten rock above. Under the right conditions of heat and pressure, diamond crystals formed. The diamonds were carried toward the surface by volcanic eruptions of flowing magma in the mantle. Below the volcano, carrot-shaped deposits of rock (called kimberlite pipes) formed. These deposits contain diamonds, volcanic rock, and fragments of the mantle.

Take It Further

The newest rocks on Earth are found around active volcanoes. Find out where these rocks are forming and what they are made of. Begin your search at PearsonScience.

The Rock Cycle

During an Ontario spring, it is common for ice to melt during the day and then freeze back into ice overnight. The next day, the ice can melt again and freeze again. This back-and-forth behaviour is an example of a cycle.

Rocks also go through cycles. The **rock cycle** is the repeating pattern in which one family of rock changes into a different family. Figure 11.32 shows the role that heat plays in the rock cycle. The rock cycle occurs because of the heat produced, stored, and released inside Earth. Earth is not the unchanging planet it might appear to be. Old rock is continuously being pushed into the mantle, where it melts. Hot magma reaches the crust, cools, and forms new rock. Rocks change constantly. For example, pressure from the weight of layers of rock pushing down may change one form of rock into another. Water, wind, chemicals, and even living things, lead to **weathering**, or wearing away, of rock. This is the first stage of **erosion** — the breakdown and movement of rocks and soil by wind, water, or ice.

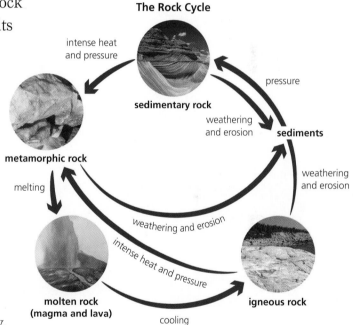

The Rock Cycle

intense heat and pressure

sedimentary rock

pressure

weathering and erosion

sediments

metamorphic rock

weathering and erosion

melting

weathering and erosion

intense heat and pressure

molten rock (magma and lava)

igneous rock

cooling

Figure 11.32 The rock cycle

Colour in a Beaker

Purpose

To create a model of the convection currents that cause molten rock to move in Earth's mantle

Materials & Equipment

- large beaker
- hot plate
- water
- food colouring
- long medicine dropper

Figure 11.33 Set-up for Quick Lab D35

Procedure

1. Add water to the large beaker until it is half full.

2. Set the beaker on the hot plate. Allow the water to become still.

3. Use a long medicine dropper or hollow glass tube (with your thumb on the end) to pick up some food colouring. Place the food colouring inside the beaker so that it forms a layer of colour at the bottom (Figure 11.33).

4. Slowly heat the beaker of water. Observe what happens to the food colouring.

Questions

5. What did you observe in the beaker as it was heated? Illustrate your answer with labelled "before" and "after" drawings of the beaker and food colouring to show the changes that occurred.

6. Compare the results of this activity with the information you have learned about convection currents in Earth's mantle. How is this activity similar? How is it different?

SKILLS YOU WILL USE
- Using appropriate equipment
- Reporting results

Crystallize Your Thinking

What happens when molten rock from deep in Earth's mantle travels upward toward the crust? It cools — in two different ways, depending on where it stops flowing. In this activity, you will observe both types of cooling by using a common element — sulphur.

Question

What happens when molten rock cools quickly or slowly?

Figure 11.34 How does quick cooling affect the appearance of solid sulphur?

CAUTION:
- Use a fume chamber or adequate ventilation.
- Be careful when using a hot plate or Bunsen burner.
- Place the glass funnel upside down so that it will not roll off your lab surface.
- Do not remove any powdered or solid sulphur from the classroom.

Materials & Equipment

- powdered sulphur
- metal scoopula
- test tube holder
- 2 test tubes
- hot plate or Bunsen burner
- 400-mL beaker (if using a hot plate)
- 250-mL beaker of cold water
- circle of filter paper
- glass funnel
- test tube rack
- paper towel
- water

Hypothesis

When molten sulphur cools quickly, it will look like...
When molten sulphur cools slowly, it will look like...

Procedure

Part 1 — Quickly! Quickly!

1. Using the metal scoopula, add powdered sulphur to a test tube to about 6 cm depth.

2. Gently melt the sulphur following your teacher's directions.

3. When the sulphur has melted, quickly pour it into the 250-mL beaker of cold water.

4. Cool the test tube in the test tube rack.

5. When the sulphur has cooled, pour off the water from the beaker and place the solid sulphur on a piece of paper towel.

Part 2 — Slow as Can Be

6. Fold a piece of filter paper to form a cone.

7. Fit the filter paper into the glass funnel. Add a few drops of water to stick the paper to the glass. Place the funnel into the test tube rack.

8. Using the metal scoopula, add powdered sulphur to a test tube to about 6 cm depth. Melt the sulphur.

9. When the sulphur has melted, quickly pour it into the filter paper. Allow the sulphur to cool slowly.

10. Place the test tube into the rack to cool.

11. Compare the two samples of cooled sulphur. Break them open and observe the inside of each piece. Record your observations.

12. Clean up. Leave all pieces of sulphur in your classsroom.

Skill Builder

13. Compare the insides of the solid sulphur samples from Parts 1 and 2. Draw and label a diagram of each sample of cooled sulphur.

Analyzing and Interpreting

14. Suggest reasons to explain any differences between the sulphur samples from Parts 1 and 2.

Forming Conclusions

15. Consider your answers to points 14 and 15. Suggest how your observations in this activity might explain differences in rock formed in the mantle and at the surface of Earth.

Key Concept Review

1. Name the four layers of Earth in order, from the outside to the centre.

2. Why is the term "crust" suitable for the layer of Earth where you live?

3. What are the names of the three classes of rocks?

4. What are the differences between magma and lava?

5. Suggest reasons why scientists are interested in studying Earth's layers.

6. A classmate suggests that heat is involved in producing all three classes of rock. Do you agree or disagree? State reasons to support your answer.

7. Suggest reasons to explain why garnet, opal, and topaz are considered to be gemstones.

8. Describe two differences between Earth's inner core and Earth's outer core.

Connect Your Understanding

9. Schist, shown on the right, is a type of rock formed when certain minerals are changed by heat and pressure. Which of the three classes of rock includes schist?

10. Compare the rock cycle to a cycle of events in your daily life. How are they similar? How are they different?

Practise Your Skills

11. On Page 330, three possible models are shown for Earth. One of these models is an accurate comparison. Which one is it? Explain the reason for your choice. Then, choose two or more additional examples that you could use to explain the layers of Earth to a friend.

12. Figure 11.32 on page 335 illustrates the rock cycle. Explain how weathering, erosion, heat, and pressure all cause changes in rocks. Design and draw a separate illustration for each part of your explanation.

For more questions, go to PearsonScience.

D37 | *Thinking about Science and the Environment*

A Volcano in the Neighbourhood

People in many parts of the world (like Hawaii) live on or near an active volcano. Suggest several reasons to explain why people choose to do this. List the costs and benefits of such a life choice. Share your ideas with a partner, a group, or the whole class. Your teacher may ask you to research communities where people live close to volcanoes. Add the results of your research to your cost-benefit analysis.

Hurricane Katrina

Figure 11.35 A hurricane is a strong, spinning weather system over the ocean that has continuous wind speeds exceeding 119 km/h. Hurricanes form and grow stronger over tropical regions of the ocean as they pick up heat from the warm ocean water. This photograph shows Hurricane Katrina in August 2005.

At the end of August 2005, a devastating hurricane, Katrina, destroyed portions of the U.S. coast from southeast Louisiana to Alabama (Figure 11.35). Katrina was one of the worst natural disasters in North American history. Katrina's journey began in south Florida. While moving northward toward the central Gulf coast, Katrina strengthened into a Category 5 hurricane. Category 5 means continuous wind speeds greater than 250 km/h.

Katrina's winds became weaker before she touched down. But they were still strong enough to cause a near-record storm surge of ocean water. The winds and water caused widespread destruction and loss of life. The city of New Orleans was particularly hard hit when the dikes surrounding the city broke. Large sections of the city were flooded. Over 80 percent of the city and many areas of neighbouring communities were under water for weeks.

At least 1836 people lost their lives in Hurricane Katrina and in the flooding. Damage to buildings and farmland due to the storm is estimated to have been more than $80 billion (Figure 11.36).

Questions

1. You have read about the destruction caused by Hurricane Katrina. Propose at least three questions about the storm and damage. Record your questions in your notebook.

2. Hurricanes rarely strike Ontario. But on October 16, 1954, Hurricane Hazel, one of the most notable hurricanes in history, moved into Ontario as a powerful storm from the United States. Flash flooding from Hazel in Canada destroyed 20 bridges, killed 81 people, and left more than 2000 families homeless. Suggest several ways Ontarians can protect themselves from such powerful storms.

3. Imagine that you are a radio, television, or newspaper reporter. Write a script in which you describe the effects of a powerful hurricane on your community. Include the names of landmarks, cities, towns, and events that are affected by the hurricane you are describing.

Figure 11.36 Some of the flooding in New Orleans caused by Hurricane Katrina

After Reading Thinking Literacy

Reflect and Evaluate

Revisit your original questions from the beginning of the chapter. Have they all been answered? Summarize what you have learned about the value of asking questions as you read using the following organizer:

3-2-1 Review

• 3 things I learned about the comprehension strategy of asking questions
• 2 ways this strategy helped me as a reader
• 1 question I still have about asking questions

Share your 3-2-1 Review with a partner and discuss similarities and differences. Try to answer each other's final question.

Key Concept Review

1. Suggest several ways in which human activities depend on the atmosphere. *k*

2. The atmosphere is a mixture of materials. Name several of them. *k*

3. What is the name of the layer of the atmosphere in which we live? *k*

4. Which of the following would be a more accurate statement? Provide reasons for your answer. (a) The weather in Sudbury is warm and cloudy. (b) The weather in Ontario is warm and cloudy. *t*

5. What is the main source of Earth's energy? *k*

6. Name the two changes of state that are part of the water cycle. *k*

7. A classmate tells you that a meteorologist studies meteors (chunks of rock that travel through space). Explain why this statement is not accurate. *c*

8. Do the Sun's rays fall more directly on Ontario or on Florida? Explain your answer. Include a drawing with labels. *t*

9. How is heat distributed across Earth? Suggest two ways. *k*

10. How is weather different from climate? *k*

Connect Your Understanding

11. Name and describe two situations or machines in which it is important to filter air before it is used. You may want to use some of the items shown on this page in your answer. *a*

12. Ocean currents flow in patterns. Name several factors that influence these patterns. *t*

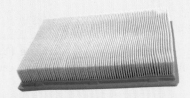

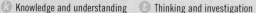

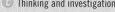

ACHIEVEMENT CHART CATEGORIES
k Knowledge and understanding   *t* Thinking and investigation   *c* Communication   *a* Application

13. A chart of numbers, similar to the one below, can help you summarize new information. Draw your chart and fill it in, using information in this chapter. You may include more than one set of information in each box. The first box has been filled in for you. t

Number	New Information and Descriptions
2	two types of melted rock: magma (underground) and lava (on the surface)
3	
4	
5	

14. Summarize the three categories of ocean currents. Copy the chart below into your notebook. k

Type of Ocean Current	Description
warm surface currents	
cold surface currents	
deep ocean currents	

Practise Your Skills

15. Design and create a chart for the activities you have completed in this unit. In your chart, include:

- each activity's number
- each activity's name
- a brief description of each activity
- a summary of your observations for each activity t

Unit Task Link

Driving cars, producing consumer goods, using electronic devices: all these use energy. Using energy releases heat into the air and into the bodies of water. Improved insulation in buildings would prevent or reduce heat loss. This would reduce the amount of energy used. Go to PearsonScience to research systems of insulation used in homes, schools, and office buildings.

D38 *Thinking about Science and the Environment* S T S E

Disaster Preparedness

Think about several ways that families and local communities can prepare for disasters such as hurricanes, ice storms, and wind storms.

What to Do

1. Draw a four column chart with the following column titles: Type of Emergency or Disaster, How Can My Family Prepare? How Can My Community Prepare? and, Why Is It Important?

2. Fill in the chart for several types of emergencies and disasters.

Consider This

Share your chart with a classmate. Add information to all four columns. Then, share your chart with a group or the whole class. Your teacher may ask you to prepare a poster so that other students can learn more about disaster preparedness.

Use the Internet to learn more about preparing for disasters and emergencies.

Begin your search at PearsonScience.

This photograph is a thermogram. It shows the distribution of heat over the surface of a house. White to yellow areas are warmest. Red to purple and green are coolest. The thermogram shows that the roof and windows of the house are poorly insulated, while the better-insulated walls lose less heat to the environment.

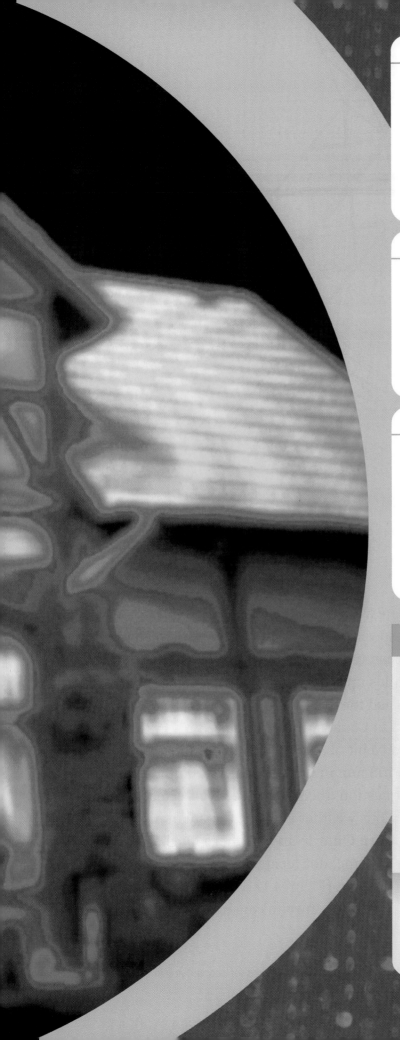

What You Will Learn

In this chapter, you will:

- demonstrate energy transformations that involve heat
- determine how you can reduce your use of energy
- discuss ways to decrease global warming

Skills You Will Use

In this chapter, you will:

- use scientific inquiry/experimentation skills to investigate heat transfer
- use a variety of ways to communicate with audiences

Why This Is Important

Heat has both positive and negative effects on the environment. Each of us has an important role to play in protecting the global environment. Canadians should be able to understand how technology can reduce heat loss. By reducing energy use, we make fewer negative changes in the world.

Before Writing

Thinking Literacy

Cause and Effect Pattern

Writers of non-fiction text use a variety of patterns to provide a structure for expressing their ideas clearly. Cause and effect pattern is one way to organize information. Think about what you know about cause and effect and look through this chapter for headings that might fit with this pattern. What other subject texts use this pattern for writing?

Key Terms

- energy converter
- heat island
- global warming
- heat pollution
- greenhouse gases
- climate change

Figure 12.1 These electrical transmission towers, and hundreds of others, were destroyed in the ice storm in 1998.

Ice storms are a common experience in most parts of Canada. They are especially common from Ontario to Newfoundland. The danger that an ice storm presents depends on the amount of ice that builds up and how long the storm lasts. The ice storm that lasted for five days in January 1998 was the worst ever recorded in Canada. From January 5 to 10, freezing rain, ice pellets, and a bit of snow fell — 85 mm in Ottawa, 73 mm in Kingston, 108 mm in Cornwall, and 100 mm in Montreal.

Without question, the storm directly affected more people than any previous weather event in Canadian history. The damage in eastern Ontario and southern Quebec was so severe that major rebuilding, not repairing, of the electrical system had to be undertaken (Figures 12.1 and 12.2). What it took human beings half a century to construct took nature a matter of hours to knock down.

Figure 12.2 The ice storm also caused problems for people living in big cities.

Farmers were especially hard hit. Dairy and hog farmers were left without electricity needed to keep animal shelters warm and to run milking machines. Many Quebec maple syrup producers lost the entire supply of their sugar bush.

What caused such a severe storm? Canadian scientists think that a worldwide weather pattern called El Niño may have played a role in the ice storm of 1998.

Winter disasters such as the ice storm disrupt the delivery of energy that we use to heat our homes and places of work. This use of heat is very important for daily life, business, and industry. Being prepared for such disasters is therefore an important part of life in Canada.

D39 Quick Lab

Keep Your Cool

If it's not protected from warmer temperatures, ice will melt quickly. There are different ways to prevent melting.

Purpose

To compare ways of preventing ice from melting

Materials & Equipment

- 10 ice cubes
- tote cooler
- paper towel
- triple-beam balance or kitchen scale
- plastic cooler
- newspaper
- towel

Figure 12.3 These pictures offer four ways to protect ice from the heat of the Sun and the air.

Procedure

1. Divide the class into five groups to test four possible ways to prevent melting of ice cubes.
   A: a plastic cooler   B: a tote cooler
   C: a towel   D: three sheets of newspaper
   E: no protection for the ice cubes
2. In groups, find mass #1 of two ice cubes, using the triple-beam balance or a kitchen scale. Record the mass.
3. Depending on your group letter, place the ice cubes in a cooler, or wrap them in the towel or the sheets of newspaper, or leave them sitting on paper towel.
4. Wait 30–45 min. Then dry the ice cubes with the paper towel.
5. Find mass #2 of the ice cubes using the triple-beam balance or scale.
6. Calculate the percent of ice remaining, using the following formula.

$$\% \text{ ice remaining} = \left(\frac{\text{mass \#2 (g)}}{\text{mass \#1 (g)}} \right) \times 100\%$$

Questions

7. Which method was most effective in preventing the ice from melting?

8. How was heat transferred in this experiment?

Here is a summary of what you will learn in this section:

- Heat is often released to the environment when energy is transformed.
- Producing energy can release heat and gases into the environment.
- Heat pollution of land, water, and the atmosphere affects the environment.

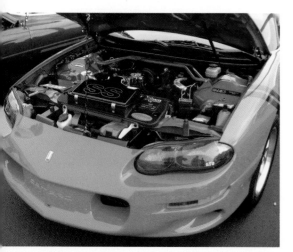

Figure 12.4 Sometimes energy conversions, like those in this vehicle, produce a lot of heat that is released into the environment.

Any device that transforms energy from one form to another is called an **energy converter**. The engine in your family car, a hair dryer, a computer hard drive, and a light bulb are all examples of energy converters (Figure 12.4). Energy converters can be much larger than these items. For example, the power plant that produces energy for your region is a very large energy converter.

Depending on where you live in Ontario, your community may obtain its electrical energy mainly from a thermal power plant that burns a fuel, such as coal or natural gas; a nuclear power plant that uses the energy stored in atoms; or a hydroelectric power plant that uses the energy of falling water.

D40 | *Starting Point*   Skills Ⓐ Ⓒ

Go with the Flow

Since the 1970s, Canadians have been paying close attention to the energy we use (Figure 12.5). In 1973, the Organization of Petroleum Exporting Countries (OPEC) dramatically raised the price of oil by cutting back production. This caused the price of gasoline to jump in a few weeks from about 9 cents per litre to about 13 cents per litre. Compare that with today's prices and you will see that energy costs a lot more today! Starting at PearsonScience, collect and prepare a collage of images to illustrate the uses we have for fuels.

Figure 12.5 In 1973, drivers of vehicles with odd-numbered licence plates could buy gasoline only on odd-numbered days of the month. Even-numbered licence plates were limited to even-numbered days.

Hidden Costs of Power Plants

Each method of producing electricity has disadvantages. All of Ontario's power plants that burn coal may soon be closed or rebuilt to reduce air pollution and heat pollution (Figure 12.6). Nuclear power plants such as the Pickering, Darlington, and Bruce Nuclear Power Generating Stations use the energy stored in uranium atoms to produce electricity without air pollution (Figure 12.7). But there are other problems with nuclear energy. The disposal of heated waste water and how and where to store the nuclear waste that these plants produce are problems that need long-term solutions.

Ontario has more than three dozen hydroelectric generating stations. Hydroelectric power generation does not create air pollution (Figure 12.8). However, hydroelectric projects that include large dams may affect conditions in surrounding ecosystems. The hidden costs of power plants have led to the search for alternative sources of energy.

Figure 12.6 The Nanticoke coal-fired power plant on Lake Erie burns coal to produce electricity. It is Ontario's worst-polluting power plant.

Figure 12.7 The Pickering Nuclear Power Generating Stations

Figure 12.8 The Lac Seul Generating Station, a hydroelectric power plant in northwestern Ontario

D41 Learning Checkpoint

Energy Conversion

1. What is the purpose of an energy converter?

2. Name several energy converters that you or your family use regularly.

3. Name three kinds of power plants that produce electricity in Ontario.

4. Describe the method of energy production for each of the three types of power plant you suggested.

Human Activities Produce Heat

You have learned that, in most energy transformations, the end result is the production of heat. A large quantity of heat may be produced, as in the engine of a car, or a small quantity, as in a student running a race. In all cases, the heat that is produced during an energy transformation is released into the environment.

Some human activities produce and release very large amounts of heat. This is particularly true in factories. Ontario manufacturers produce and ship hundreds of billions of dollars' worth of products every year. Most of this activity is found in the production of automobiles, metal, plastic and rubber products, computer products, chemical and petroleum products, machinery, and foods and beverages (Figure 12.9).

Figure 12.9 Manufacturing products for human use produces a lot of heat. **(a)** An auto assembly line **(b)** The blast furnace in a steel plant **(c)** Crushed limestone stockpiled for use in iron ore smelting **(d)** A baked-goods assembly line

(a) (b) (c) (d)

Take It *Further*

Think about the different ways in which people produce energy to run our cities and farms. Then, use the Internet to gather information on the energy transformations that occur. Begin your search at PearsonScience.

Adding Heat to the Atmosphere

Ontario has many factories. The easiest way to cool down a factory is to release hot air directly from the building into the environment. This is done by bringing fresh air into the building with large fans, circulating it, and sending the warm air back outside the building (Figure 12.10).

A second method is to use an air-conditioning system. This allows control over the indoor temperature. A third method for cooling buildings and machines is to circulate cool water from a water system such as a river. The cool circulating water absorbs the heat of the building. The hot water then circulates outside, releasing the stored heat into the air. Sometimes, the hot water is released into water systems, as in the nuclear power generating stations described earlier.

Figure 12.10 Large fans such as these remove hot air from some buildings.

Adding Heat to Natural Water Systems

Heat from human activities is added to the environment. If the release of heat has negative effects on an ecosystem, the added heat may be described as **heat pollution**. Living things are very sensitive to changes in temperature. Adding heat to a river or lake may cause a big problem for organisms that live in the water and cannot easily find another place to live.

Adding heat to a water system poses another problem. Organisms in water systems breathe oxygen, just like you do. Adding even a small amount of heat to a water system causes less oxygen to be available in the water for the organisms that depend on oxygen for survival. The result is that the organisms can suffer from a lack of oxygen and may die (Figure 12.11).

Figure 12.11 Fish and other organisms die when there is not enough oxygen in a river or lake.

D42 *Quick Lab*

Heat Transfers Between Containers

Purpose

To measure and record changes in temperature between warmer and cooler liquids

Materials & Equipment
■ two 400-mL beakers or small containers
■ pail or large container
■ thermometer
■ warm water and cool water

Procedure

1. Add warm water to the pail to a depth of several centimetres. Half-fill the beaker with cool water.

2. Draw a data table to record the temperature (every minute for 20 min) of the warm water in the pail and the cooler water in the beaker.

3. Predict how the temperature of the water in the pail and in the beaker will change over 20 min. Record your predictions.

4. Use the thermometer to measure the starting temperature of the water in each container. Record your results in your data table.

5. Use the second beaker to add cool water to the pail and warm water to the beaker.

6. Measure and record the temperature in each container every minute for 20 min.

7. Draw and label a graph to show the change in temperature of the water in the pail. Colour your line. On the same graph paper, use a different colour to draw a graph to show the change in temperature of the water in the beaker. Include a legend and a title.

Questions

8. What happened to the thermal energy of the warm water added to the beaker?

9. Describe what happened to the temperature of the water in the pail.

Key Concept Review

1. What happens to the heat that is produced during an energy transformation?

2. Name two or more ways in which buildings can be cooled.

3. What are two of the disadvantages of using coal as a fuel in power plants that produce electricity in Ontario?

Connect Your Understanding

4. How does a hair dryer act as an energy converter?

5. Name several energy transformations that release heat into the environment.

6. Describe two ways in which adding heat to water systems can be harmful to fish and other organisms that live in the water.

7. Why do you think Canadians have become concerned about gases and heat that are released into the environment every day?

Practise Your Skills

8. A student set up an experiment similar to the one in Quick Lab D42. Suggest how this situation is similar to changes that occur when a factory releases hot water into a river or a lake.

For more questions, go to PearsonScience.

D43 *Thinking about Science and the Environment*

Extra Energy

You have learned that human activities produce heat that ends up in the environment. This release of heat can affect living things.

Canada's population increases every year. How might this increase affect the amount of energy used and the amount of heat produced?

Consider This

With a classmate or as a whole class, discuss the following questions.

1. In what ways can Canadians reduce their personal use of energy?

2. How can individual Canadians and communities be encouraged to use less energy? Suggest several ways.

Here is a summary of what you will learn in this section:

- Heat islands influence local weather conditions.
- Human activities release gases that might contribute to global warming.
- Climate changes are occurring in the environment.

Hot summer days can be a big problem for some city dwellers. In North America, more than 1000 people die each year due to high environmental temperatures. Many more are rushed to hospitals, suffering from heat-related illness.

Each year, the Toronto Public Health Department issues Heat Alerts and Extreme Heat Alerts. For example, in 2007, from May through August, 15 of these alerts were issued. To prepare for and respond to these serious situations, Toronto has developed the Hot Weather Response Program.

Figure 12.12 Help in the heat

D44 | *Starting Point*

Skills Ⓐ Ⓒ

Heat Islands

In large cities, human activity can add a significant amount of heat to the environment. However, the way a city is built also has a big influence on the temperatures in and around it.

Look at Figure 12.13. Compare the rural areas, suburbs, and parks with the downtown areas. Suggest three or more reasons for the temperature differences that you observe.

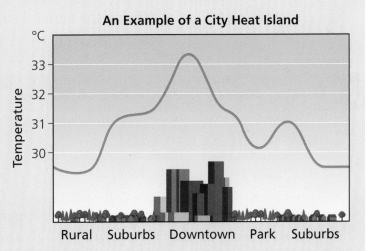

An Example of a City Heat Island

Rural   Suburbs   Downtown   Park   Suburbs

Figure 12.13 This graph shows how a typical city is warmer than the surrounding areas. Air temperatures are usually measured about 1.5 m above the ground.

Heat Islands

A **heat island** is a region of a city that has higher air and surface temperatures than its surroundings. The temperature difference is usually greater at night than in the day and greater in winter than in summer. It is most obvious when winds are weak.

Heat islands form as cities grow and replace natural land cover with buildings and pavement (roads and sidewalks). The increase in temperature in and above a heat island depends on an area's natural weather and climate, closeness to water bodies like lakes and oceans, and land forms like nearby mountains and valleys.

Climate scientists use infrared satellite photographs to measure the size of heat islands (Figure 12.14). This information allows city planners to prepare for heat emergencies during hot summers, to determine regulations for building sizes and heights, and to gauge how much parkland and green spaces a city needs.

Heat islands also affect the surrounding areas. For example, scientists have found that partly as a result of the heat island effect, monthly rainfall is about 28 percent greater in areas 10–20 km downwind of some cities compared with upwind. In the winter, some cities in cold climates may benefit from the warming effect of heat islands. In general, the harmful summertime effects from heat islands are greater than the wintertime benefits.

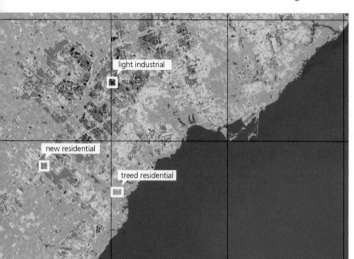

Figure 12.14 A satellite infrared image of Toronto. Yellow and red colours indicate higher temperatures.

light industrial

new residential

treed residential

D45 *During Writing*

Thinking Literacy

Cause or Effect or Both?

Cause and effect writing gives reasons for why something happened or is happening. You have just read about heat islands. What features of cities cause heat islands to form and grow in size? Develop a simple graphic organizer to show the cause and effect relationship between heat islands and their causes.

Extend your thinking further. Can heat islands also be a cause for something else? In another organizer, show some of the effects of heat islands on local weather conditions. Reread the last paragraph on heat islands to find signal words the writer used. Can you think of other signal words a writer might use in cause and effect pattern?

Monitoring Gases in the Atmosphere

Each time you breathe out, you release carbon dioxide and other gases. Each time your family drives you to school or a shopping centre, the family car releases carbon dioxide and other gases. One person, one family, and one automobile may not seem to be a problem. However, each of us adds many thousands of litres of carbon dioxide to the atmosphere every year. Millions of Canadians with millions of automobiles and billions of people on Earth add billions of litres of carbon dioxide to the atmosphere each year.

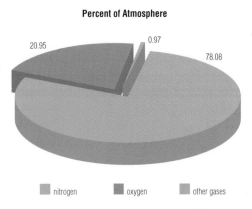

Percent of Atmosphere

20.95   0.97   78.08

■ nitrogen   ■ oxygen   ■ other gases

Figure 12.15 The main components of the air we breathe

You might wonder if this large amount of additional carbon dioxide affects the planet. You would not be alone. Scientists in many countries are investigating this question.

Earth's atmosphere contains many gases, including nitrogen, oxygen, and argon. These three gases make up about 99 percent of the air we breathe (Figure 12.15). Carbon dioxide normally makes up only 0.037 percent of air. Because carbon dioxide is naturally present in air, it is not considered to be a pollutant. But the amount of carbon dioxide that humans are adding to air has become a concern for scientists, governments, and citizens in many countries, including Canada.

What Is the Greenhouse Effect?

If you place a sealed glass container in sunlight or under a strong light, the air inside the container quickly becomes hot. This is like the inside of an automobile becoming hotter than the air outside on a cold, sunny day in winter (Figure 12.16). It is also like a greenhouse, where the glass sides and roof allow the Sun's radiation to enter, trapping the heat, warming the air, and helping plants to grow.

In some ways, our planet also acts like a greenhouse. Earth's atmosphere is like the glass sides and roof of the greenhouse or the glass windows of an automobile. The atmosphere allows radiation from the Sun to reach Earth's surface. Several of the gases in the atmosphere, like carbon dioxide, trap this heat, warming the land and oceans (Figure 12.17 on the next page).

Figure 12.16 The air inside this automobile is much warmer than the air outside.

Heat technologies offer benefits and require choices.   **353**

Figure 12.17 The greenhouse effect. Some of the radiant energy from the Sun is trapped near Earth's surface by gases in the atmosphere that act like the glass in a greenhouse.

Some of the energy that reflects back into the atmosphere from the land and oceans also warms the air. Gases in the atmosphere that trap heat are called **greenhouse gases**. Water vapour, carbon dioxide, methane, and nitrogen oxides are all examples of greenhouse gases.

The **natural greenhouse effect** is the natural range of temperatures that Earth experiences because the greenhouse gases in the atmosphere trap energy from the Sun. Without these gases, heat would escape back into space and Earth's average temperature would be about 16°C colder.

The Enhanced Greenhouse Effect

Human activities, such as burning non-renewable fuels like gasoline and coal release greenhouse gases into the atmosphere. Most scientists who study climate support the theory that these activities are contributing to an **enhanced greenhouse effect** (Figure 12.18). This effect is due to the build-up in the atmosphere of higher than normal amounts of greenhouse gases.

Table 12.1 shows some of the common sources of greenhouse gases, natural and related to human activity. It also shows some ways of reducing emissions of these gases.

*Take It **Further***

What is Canada doing to meet its commitments under climate change agreements such as the Kyoto Protocol? Begin your search at PearsonScience.

Figure 12.18 The enhanced greenhouse effect: Human activities are adding more greenhouse gases to the atmosphere. Many scientists agree that this causes more heat to be trapped, causing Earth's temperature to rise. This is called global warming.

Table 12.1 Greenhouse gases

Greenhouse Gas	Common Ways the Gas Is Released into the Environment	Possible Ways to Reduce Emissions
Water vapour (H_2O)	• Through the water cycle	• Reduction of water vapour is not needed.
Carbon dioxide (CO_2)	• When humans and other animals breathe out • When non-renewable fuels are burned in power plants and in vehicles	• Decrease use of non-renewable fuels, and increase alternative methods of energy production. • Use alternative fuels to power vehicles.
Methane (CH_4)	• From natural sources: wetlands, termites • When grazing animals digest food • When non-renewable fuels are extracted from deep underground by drilling	• Decrease use of non-renewable fuels, and increase alternative methods of energy production. • Develop ways to use natural methane.
Nitrogen oxides (NO_x)	• From natural sources in soils • From fertilizers on farms • When gasoline is burned in vehicles	• Use alternative fuels to power vehicles. • Reduce fertilizer run-off.

Global Warming

Scientific data indicate that Earth's climate has become warmer over the past 150 years. This worldwide average increase in temperature of Earth's atmosphere, land, and oceans is called **global warming**. The warming has been increasing more quickly over the past 20 years. This change in the climate has become a concern for Canadians and for citizens in many countries.

Most scientists agree that the rise in average temperature is related mainly to increases in greenhouse gases in the atmosphere over the same period, since about 1860 (Figures 12.19 and 12.20). These scientists believe that we must quickly and significantly decrease or change human activities that release greenhouse gases or that prevent nature from controlling the gases.

What Are We Doing? What Needs to Be Done?

Most Canadians, as well as citizens around the world, believe we must take action now. Agreements like the **Kyoto Protocol**, signed by more than 160 countries in 1992, call for countries such as Canada to reduce greenhouse gas emissions from all sources. Unfortunately, the levels and deadlines that have been agreed to will be very difficult for countries, including Canada, to meet.

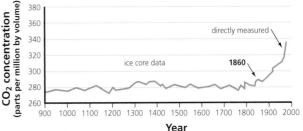

Figure 12.19 Changes measured for carbon dioxide gas in Earth's atmosphere.

Figure 12.20 Scientists use ice cores from the Arctic and Antarctic to obtain information about carbon dioxide levels in the atmosphere over hundreds of years. They analyze gases in air bubbles trapped in the ice.

Make Your Own Greenhouse

Question

What happens to the temperature inside a sealed glass container when a strong light shines on the container?

CAUTION: Do not tap the glass thermometers against other objects.

Materials & Equipment

- 2 large Erlenmeyer flasks
- 1-holed rubber stopper to fit the flask
- thermometer to fit the hole in the rubber stopper
- second thermometer
- watch or timer

Figure 12.21 Set-up for Inquiry Activity D45

Hypothesis

Suggest what might happen when sealed and unsealed flasks are placed in a strong light. Then, propose a reason to explain your statement.

Procedure

1. Your teacher will provide you with a rubber stopper for one of the flasks. A thermometer has been carefully pushed through the hole in the stopper.

2. Gently push the rubber stopper onto the neck of one flask. The thermometer should be several centimetres above the inside bottom of the flask.

3. Leave the second flask open (Figure 12.21).

4. Prepare a data table similar to Table 12.2. Measure the temperature of the air inside the sealed flask. Ask a partner to check the measurement, and then record the temperature in your data table.

5. Hold the second thermometer so that it is not touching the inside surface of the open flask. Measure the temperature of the air inside the open flask. Ask a partner to check the measurement. Record the temperature in your data table.

6. Place the two flasks in a safe place under a strong light or in sunlight for two minutes.

7. Repeat steps 4 and 5, without moving or shading either flask.

8. Take further measurements until your data table is complete.

Table 12.2 Temperature in two flasks

Time (min)	Temperature of Sealed Flask (°C)	Temperature of Open Flask (°C)
0 (starting)		
2		
4		
6		
8		
10		

Skill Builder

9. Follow your teacher's directions for drawing a graph for the data you have collected.

Analyzing and Interpreting

10. Describe the pattern(s) shown by the two lines on your graph.

11. Compare this activity with the description of the greenhouse effect earlier in this section. How are they similar?

12. Compare this activity with the description of the greenhouse effect earlier in this section. How are they different?

13. Suggest a reason for using the open flask in this activity.

Forming Conclusions

14. Suggest one or more reasons to explain the two patterns in temperature measurements that you have observed in this activity.

D47 *Decision-Making Analysis*   Toolkit 4

Reduce, Re-use, Recycle, Recover

Issue

To find personal choices that might affect greenhouse gas emissions. To consider ways to use fewer products, reduce waste, and decrease energy use.

Background Information

Every day, Canadians buy, use, and throw away huge amounts of material in all types of useful products and the packaging that comes with them. Heat is involved in manufacturing, packaging, transporting, and storing these products. And then we must deal with what we throw away. For example, Ontario produces more than 9 million tonnes of garbage per year. The City of Toronto alone produces more than 1 million tonnes of garbage per year.

1. Use a mind map or chart to brainstorm examples of how we produce garbage. Set up four categories: at home, at school, in the workplace, and in leisure activities.

2. Draw a two-column chart. Print titles for each column: column A: Examples of Garbage; column B: Methods to Reduce Garbage.

3. Transfer your brainstorm ideas to column A using the four categories. Leave several blank lines at the end of each category.

4. Use column B to suggest how individuals, families, businesses, and institutions, such as your school, can reduce waste.

Analyze and Evaluate

5. Share your chart with a classmate or group. Use a checkmark to indicate which of your ideas were also listed by other students. How many of your ideas from column A or column B were listed by others?

6. Using the lines you left blank, add more ideas for each category to your columns.

7. With your group, select several of the ideas from column B. Prepare a short class presentation in which each member of your group plays a role in explaining and demonstrating the points your group has selected. In your presentation, include pictures, samples, or video clips of products that you are describing.

Key Concept Review

1. Suggest ways in which heat islands contribute to city temperatures.

2. How do heat islands affect the surrounding regions?

3. Which three gases make up most of Earth's atmosphere?

4. Name four greenhouse gases in Earth's atmosphere.

5. What do scientists measure to estimate global warming? You may have several answers to this question.

6. How is the enhanced greenhouse effect different from the greenhouse effect?

Connect Your Understanding

7. Suggest reasons why rural areas (away from cities) cool off faster than cities.

8. How is a greenhouse a good model for Earth and its atmosphere?

9. Unlike humans, dogs do not sweat. How can we help dogs to stay cool when outdoor temperatures rise?

10. Planners estimate that, by the year 2025, two-thirds of the world's population will live in cities. What effects do you think this will have on urban heat islands?

11. If carbon dioxide makes up only 0.037 percent of Earth's atmosphere, why are scientists so concerned about the amount of carbon dioxide that humans add to the atmosphere each day?

Practise Your Skills

12. The word "implications" refers to the possibly good and possibly bad results of a situation or process. What are the implications of international agreements such as the Kyoto Protocol?

For more questions, go to PearsonScience.

D48 *Thinking about Science and the Environment* S T S E

Read All About It

In this chapter, you have read how human activities add heat and greenhouse gases to the atmosphere. Now it is time to find out how this information has been reported to the public. Begin your search for "greenhouse gases" at PearsonScience. Select at least three websites. Read as much as you can and, using your own words, summarize the information. Record all the websites you have selected. Be prepared to discuss your summary in class.

Here is a summary of what you will learn in this section:

- Global warming and climate change affect the environment.
- Wise use of heat and other forms of energy helps the environment.
- Ontario is developing a variety of alternative methods for energy conservation.

Ontario and the other provinces, as well as the government of Canada, are all concerned about reducing the use of fossil fuels and the release of greenhouse gases. Many projects, such as wind farms, involve an alternative energy source. Erie Shores Wind Farm is one of the most advanced **wind power** development projects in Ontario. It includes more than 13 000 acres in Norfolk County and Elgin County along a 29-km stretch of Lake Erie (Figure 12.22). Other alternative energy sources are the Sun's rays, which provide **solar power**, the heat deep in Earth, which provides **geothermal power**, and the force of tides and waves in the ocean, which produce **tidal power**.

A *renewable fuel* can be replaced in a short period of time. **Biofuels** are fuels that are produced from living things such as plants. Biofuels can be used as an alternative to non-renewable fuels such as oil and natural gas. Ethanol and biodiesel are the two main biofuels widely used today. In Canada, ethanol is made from wheat in the western provinces and from corn in Ontario and Quebec. An Ottawa-based company is a world leader in using straw to produce ethanol.

Figure 12.22 Erie Shores Wind Farm

D49 *Starting Point*

Skills Ⓐ Ⓒ

Sorting Things Out

Your teacher will provide you with a set of energy tags. Each tag contains a tip for saving energy in your home. By yourself or with a classmate, follow your teacher's directions for classifying the energy tags. Classify by sorting the energy tags into categories so that the tags in a category are somehow related. Give each category a title. Then, record the information on the tags in your Energy Tag Recording Page. Have fun reading, learning about, and classifying your energy tags!

Energy Use in Canada

In Canada, energy is used to produce:

- all the products you use, and all the containers you throw away (Figure 12.23)
- your share of the gasoline and other fuels that keep our vehicles moving (Figure 12.24)
- your share of fuels that produce the electricity that you use at home
- your share of the heat used to produce hot water for washing dishes and clothes and for showers and baths

The energy industry and transportation contribute the greatest share of emissions. For individual Canadians, transportation accounts for almost half of greenhouse gas emissions, mostly due to automobile use. Energy use in homes accounts for the other half. We might ask:

- How willing will Canadians be to reduce their use of automobiles and their use of energy at home?
- Are Canadians prepared to reduce energy by recycling and reducing waste as much as possible?
- Are Canadians willing to use and throw away fewer products at home, at school, and on the job?
- Should Canadians and Americans take these actions even if citizens in other countries choose not to?

Figure 12.23 Energy is used to produce recreation equipment.

Figure 12.24 Gasoline and other fuels power a variety of vehicles.

D50 *During Writing*

Thinking Literacy

Point, Proof, Comment

Writers use different strategies to help them record, sort, and identify relationships among the information they gather for their writing. Use a "Point, Proof, Comment" organizer to record notes as you read the next page on the impact of climate change. Your point will be that global warming seems to be causing climate change.

As you read, write down information that supports your point this — is your proof. Record your own thoughts and ideas in the "Comment" part. Use the information in your organizer to write a cause and effect paragraph. Use signal words appropriate to this type of writing to connect your ideas.

The Impacts of Climate Change

Global warming seems to be causing **climate change**, which we can define as any major change in the climate of a region of Earth that lasts for a long period of time. Changes in Earth's wind patterns, average temperature, precipitation including rainfall, and the number and strength of extreme weather conditions such as floods and hurricanes, may be indicators of climate change. Figure 12.25 shows some of the effects of rising sea levels, increased temperature, and changes in rainfall. Every part of life will be affected.

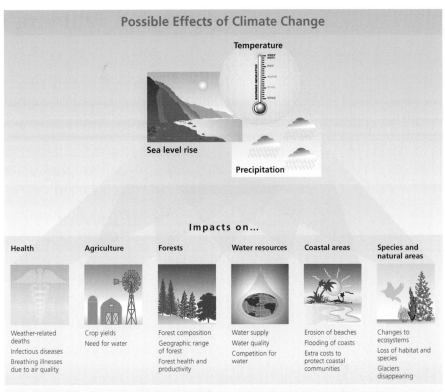

Figure 12.25 Possible effects of global climate change on Earth

Canada at Risk

Some results of climate change are already here. Canada's Arctic is warming faster than anywhere else on the planet. Certain regions have already experienced average temperature increases of as much as 3°C in the past 50 years. Nearly 1 million square kilometres of ocean ice have already disappeared, posing serious problems for seals, polar bears, and people who live in the Arctic.

Canada's forests are also at risk. For example, due to many years of warm winters, a tiny insect called the mountain pine beetle has been slowly moving through the forests of British Columbia and has now entered Alberta. The result? Since 1993, millions of lodgepole pine trees are dead or dying. Scientists have not found a way to combat this tiny killer (Figure 12.26). By 2013, it is expected that the beetle will have wiped out 80 percent of the pine forest.

Figure 12.26 The mountain pine beetle is only the size of a grain of rice but in huge numbers can have a very big effect. Mountain pine beetles and a fungus they carry kill trees. The needles turn a bright red, showing where the tiny insects have been. Colder winters are needed to stop the beetle's spread.

Solving the Problem of Too Much Heat

If adding carbon dioxide and other greenhouse gases contributes to global warming, then the solution would seem to be obvious — decrease the activities that produce and release greenhouse gases. But this is not a simple problem.

First, all countries do not contribute equally to the problem. Canada and the United States are two of the largest emitters of greenhouse gases. The United States produces 25 percent of the carbon dioxide pollution from fossil-fuel burning—by far the largest share of any country. Also, millions of tonnes of methane are released, due to drilling for oil and gas. And, according to a study by the United Nations, Canada's total carbon dioxide emissions for the year 2002 made Canada eighth on a list of almost 200 countries. Canada is one of the greatest consumers of energy per person, with each of us burning the equivalent of roughly 7700 L of oil per person each year.

One scientific report suggests that major reductions of carbon dioxide emissions will be required by all nations. For example, the United States would need to reduce by at least 80 percent below year 2000 levels by the year 2050. The question is: is such a large reduction possible in so short a period of time?

Global Warming – The Good News

Listening to the news and reading newspapers and Internet articles may make the current global warming situation seem hopeless. But, it is not. What can one person do?

- First, you can learn more about and support scientists who are studying climate change. Every year, measuring technology improves. This allows us to take different kinds of measurements and to make our measuring more accurate.
- Second, support politicians, organizations, and individual Canadians who are concerned about global warming and who are making efforts to inform Canadians. These efforts should help us begin to repair the environment.
- Third, become aware of the positive steps that countries, organizations, and citizens are taking to inform people and to help make the changes needed to reduce global warming.

- Fourth, continue to learn about Canadian issues related to global warming. Read newspaper, magazine, and Internet articles that discuss greenhouse gases.
- Fifth, discuss your concerns with your friends, family, school community, and local government representatives. Writing letters that contain accurate scientific information is often a useful means of communication.

The images in Figure 12.27 will help you to understand other aspects of the global warming issue and to see that some positive steps to combat global warming are being taken.

(i)   (ii)

Figure 12.27 (a) Ontario has banned the sale of incandescent light bulbs (i) after 2012. New efficient lighting such as compact fluorescent bulbs (CFLs) (ii) use around 75 percent less electricity than standard old-fashioned incandescent bulbs.

Figure 12.27 (b) The farmers who grow crops in this field may benefit from global warming. Warmer atmospheric temperatures could produce longer growing seasons. As well, we might be able to grow new crops due to warmer temperatures and a longer growing season.

Figure 12.27 (c) A study conducted in 2007 indicates that warmer atmospheric temperatures result in fewer colds in the winter. However, this result was obtained from only a single study; more research is needed.

Figure 12.27 (d) Climate change and rising temperatures can lead to drought and the loss of farmland to the desert. Canadian technology is helping scientists in Israel to make clean water available. This technology can then be used in other places where a lack of water currently prevents crops from being grown.

Figure 12.27 (e) Technologies that exist today have already produced hybrid automobiles. These vehicles consume less gasoline than other vehicles by running partly on electricity from rechargeable batteries inside the vehicle.

Figure 12.27 (f) A study conducted in 2003 in Australia found that the amount of methane gas had remained steady for four years. Methane is released into the atmosphere from the production of rice, cattle, and sheep; from landfills; from natural wetlands; and from the mining and use of fossil fuels such as coal, oil, and gas.

What Is Happening in Ontario?

Today, much of Ontario's electricity is produced by burning coal to produce electricity and by using uranium in aging nuclear power plants. These methods release greenhouse gases and heat into the environment.

Ontario is moving toward producing energy that does not involve burning fuels. These sources of electrical energy are called **green renewable power** because they do not harm the environment by producing gases or heat pollution. The newer methods of green renewable power that Ontario is developing include solar energy, wind energy, bioenergy, and geothermal energy (Figures 12.28, 12.29, and 12.30). Since 2003, Ontario has begun more than 60 renewable energy projects (Figure 12.31).

Figure 12.28 Solar energy panels such as these can produce electricity for thousands of homes.

Figure 12.29 The power of the wind is everywhere.

Figure 12.30 In winter, geothermal heat pumps, like this one in Iceland, use liquid in underground pipes to draw heat from deep within Earth. In summer, the pumps work in reverse, extracting heat from inside a building and discharging it underground. In Ontario, about 8500 homes and 500 buildings have already installed geothermal systems, which eliminate the usual heating and air conditioning systems.

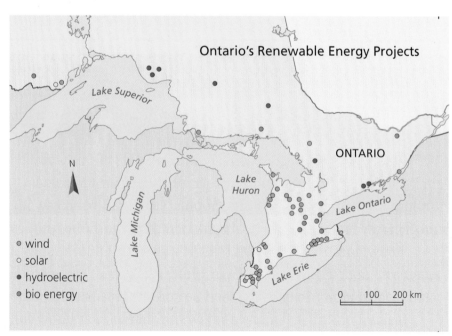

Ontario's Renewable Energy Projects

- wind
- solar
- hydroelectric
- bio energy

Lake Superior

Lake Michigan

Lake Huron

Lake Ontario

Lake Erie

ONTARIO

N

0   100   200 km

Figure 12.31 Some of the dozens of renewable energy projects in Ontario

D51 *Decision-Making Analysis*   Toolkit 4

SKILLS YOU WILL USE
- Recording information sources
- Stating a conclusion

Cutting Energy Costs

Issue

How can our community reduce the financial and environmental costs of home energy use?

Background Information

A home is more than just rooms, furniture, and a roof. It is an interactive, constantly changing set of spaces that includes a system for heating and cooling. In part, a home provides living and sleeping spaces and appliances for controlling the temperature of all spaces, water, and food.

Green buildings are structures that are built or refitted to use less energy and less water than the average structure. Many consumers and business owners realize that living and working in a green building is good for the environment, can provide a healthier living space or workplace, and can also save money.

We spend up to 90 percent of our time indoors. This requires year-round energy use for heating and cooling. In Canada, heating indoor spaces accounts for 60 percent of home energy use. Energy-reducing strategies mean that less fuel may be necessary to heat buildings, and using less fuel means producing fewer greenhouse gases. There are many ways to reduce the energy use of a building. A green roof is one way. Using new designs for windows is another. Around 20 percent of the heat lost from an average home is through the windows.

1. Select a method to reduce home energy use and/or reduce its effect on the environment from the list of homes provided. Or, choose your own method to research, after consulting your teacher.

- a home that uses geothermal heating or a heat pump
- a home that uses high levels of insulation in the attic and walls as well as energy-saving windows and a high-efficiency furnace
- a home that uses solar energy to heat water
- a home that includes a green roof

2. Research your topic. Begin your research at PearsonScience. Find out how the method you chose reduces energy use and/or reduces effects on the environment.

3. Prepare a report in your own words that provides background information and images. Include a glossary (words and their meanings) of the new vocabulary you have learned in your research. Also, include a bibliography of websites (URLs and website names) or reference materials you have used in your research.

Analyze and Evaluate

4. Form a group with classmates who have chosen other methods. Share your report. The group should try to reach consensus (agreement) on one or two of the methods that are the best choices for your community. Be prepared to report your decisions to your class.

5. How did the class groups rate the methods? Design and complete a chart to summarize the results.

6. While the groups are reporting to the class, record some of the reasons why they chose these methods.

7. Why is more energy used in Canada for indoor heating compared to most other countries? Suggest several reasons.

Key Concept Review

1. Name several predicted effects of climate change.

2. For individual Canadians, which two human activities produce the greatest proportion of greenhouse gas emissions?

3. Describe two ways that Canada's environment is at risk from global warming.

4. List four ways that individual Canadians use energy produced from oil.

5. Briefly describe how geothermal heat pumps provide heating and cooling to buildings.

Connect Your Understanding

6. Design and draw a chart to name and summarize three kinds of green renewable power being developed in Ontario. Include a small drawing or piece of clip art for each.

Practise Your Skills

7. Figure 12.27 on page 363 illustrates six categories of possible impacts (changes) due to global warming. Select one of these categories. Then, write a sample "Letter to the Editor" for your community newspaper in which you discuss this category using your own words.

For more questions, go to PearsonScience.

D52 Thinking about Science and the Environment

It's Your Choice

Dr. Jane Goodall, the well-known scientist, has remarked: "Every individual matters. Every individual has a role to play. Every individual makes a difference." This is especially true in dealing with global climate change.

What to Do

Your teacher will provide you with a list of Terrific Tasks you can do. Use the rating form provided by your teacher or develop your own rating form in your notebook. Rate each item as one of the following:

- Use 1 if you feel you can accomplish this Terrific Task.
- Use 2 if you feel that you need more information before you can accomplish this Terrific Task.

- Use 3 if you think this Terrific Task is beyond your control or if you would be unwilling to try it.

Consider This

With a classmate or as a whole class, discuss the following question.

How many of the Terrific Tasks did you rate as number 1; as number 2; as number 3?

Figure 12.32 The Energy Star label indicates an energy-efficient consumer product.

Making Connections

DAILY PLANET

Jay Ingram

Jay Ingram is an experienced science journalist and is the host of Daily Planet on Discovery Channel Canada.

The Snake and the Squirrel

Heat is something we feel. We love it in winter and try to avoid too much of it in the summer. We are pretty sensitive to heat, right? Maybe, but our sensitivity is nothing compared to that of the rattlesnake.

Rattlesnakes are superb hunters. They hunt mostly in the dark, watching out for small mammals like ground squirrels. But they are not actually *watching* in the way you might think. For one thing, they are not using their eyes. They are using pit organs in their muzzles just behind their nostrils. And they are not looking, they are *scanning* for infrared radiation — what we call heat.

Infrared is the same as light, except that its wavelengths are too long for our eyes to see. When you turn on the stove element, it is glowing in the infrared long before you can actually see it turning red.

Body heat is infrared radiation. The body heat of a small mammal like a ground squirrel is a beacon to a rattlesnake. Pitch dark or not, it does not matter—the snake can target and strike without ever using its eyes.

This ability gives the snake a deadly piece of hunting weaponry, but, as often happens in nature, there is a defense. In this case, it is employed by the California ground squirrel. When confronted by a rattlesnake, the squirrel does something called "tail flagging," waving its tail rapidly back and forth in front of the snake. At the same time, the squirrel pumps blood into its tail to make it hot.

Imagine what this is like for the snake! Instead of a tempting, vulnerable target, it is suddenly confronted with overwhelming fireworks of infrared, lashing back and forth, suggesting a much larger prey than it had reckoned with. In the lab, the snake hesitates and even backs off.

This defense is tailored specifically for rattlers: squirrels do not bother to heat up their tails when faced with gopher snakes, which lack the infrared receptors. But the irony is that the squirrel itself cannot detect infrared, so it is only doing what has worked for thousands of its ancestors in the past — without knowing why.

Key Concept Review

1. What is heat pollution? *k*

2. Describe a heat island. *k*

3. Name three greenhouse gases. *k*

4. How is the enhanced greenhouse effect different from the natural greenhouse effect? *k*

Connect Your Understanding

5. Developing Atlantic salmon (salmonids), shown on the left, prefer a water temperature of 17°C. If the water temperature varies by even 1°C, there is a reduction in growth of 8 percent. Suggest how global warming might affect the growth of salmon and other fish species. *t*

6. How is global warming different from climate change? *k*

7. How can you and your family contribute to reducing your greenhouse gas emissions? *a*

8. Why is Canada especially sensitive to climate change? Use the map below to help you suggest several reasons. *t*

After Writing *Thinking Literacy*

Reflect and Evaluate

Exchange the cause and effect paragraph you wrote on the impact of climate change with a partner. Compare the signal words you and your partner used in your paragraphs. Were there any similarities or differences?

How did knowledge of the cause and effect pattern of writing help you as you read your partner's paragraph? What other science topics would best suit a cause and effect pattern?

ACHIEVEMENT CHART CATEGORIES
k Knowledge and understanding   *t* Thinking and investigation   *c* Communication   *a* Application

9. Why do you think most of Ontario's renewable energy projects are located in southern Ontario? Suggest several reasons (See Figure 12.31 on page 364). *t*

10. Although we have many concerns about global warming, there are also positive signs. Look back through this chapter. Examine the information sections and the illustrations. Suggest several positive indicators that provide hope that humans can reduce our use of energy and Earth's resources. *c*

11. Today, many Canadians are concerned about greenhouse gases released into the atmosphere by transportation (cars, trucks, ships, airplanes). Suggest some of the changes that could be made to reduce these emissions. In your answer, consider attitudes, how we obtain data on emissions, publicity, and vehicle design. *c*

Practise Your Skills

12. Examine the pie chart on the right that shows greenhouse gas production in Canada. Identify the three major sources of greenhouse gases in Canada. *c*

13. Design and create a mini-poster or website home page to describe one type of alternative energy source that is in use or is being developed in Ontario. Begin your search at PearsonScience. For a Web page, include links to related websites. Include a relevant, creative title. *a*

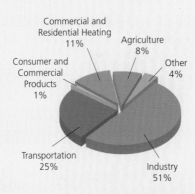

Commercial and Residential Heating 11%
Agriculture 8%
Consumer and Commercial Products 1%
Other 4%
Transportation 25%
Industry 51%

D53 Thinking about Science and the Environment

Take Action Now

In this unit, you have learned that heat causes changes in the environment. Many of these changes may not be good for the environment or for humans.

What To Do

By yourself, then with a partner or group, develop an action plan to reduce the amount of energy used and released by you, your family, and your community. In your action plan, consider what you want to do and how you will communicate your information to others.

Consider This

1. Who will your audience be?

2. Suggest a timeline for your action plan.

3. How will you "deliver your message" to your intended audience?

UNIT D Summary

10.0 Heat causes changes in solids, liquids, and gases.

KEY CONCEPTS

- Energy can be transformed and transferred.
- Heat is the transfer of thermal energy.
- Heat affects the volume of solids, liquids, and gases.
- Heat is transferred in three ways: conduction, convection, and radiation.

CHAPTER SUMMARY

- There are different forms of energy. Energy can be changed from one form to another.
- Thermal energy is the total energy of all the particles in a sample of matter. Temperature is the average energy of all the particles.
- Heating results in the expansion of solids, liquids, and gases. Cooling results in the contraction of solids, liquids, and gases.
- Heat is obtained by burning fossil fuels, from uranium, and from renewable heat sources. Heat is produced in all energy transformations.
- Cooking food and heating buildings are examples of human activities that transfer heat through conduction, convection, and radiation.

11.0 Heat plays an important role in nature.

KEY CONCEPTS

- Earth's atmosphere is divided into five layers.
- Earth's crust is constantly changing because of conduction and convection.

CHAPTER SUMMARY

- The layers of Earth's atmosphere are: the troposphere, the stratosphere, the mesosphere, the thermosphere, and the exosphere.
- Radiant energy from the Sun affects natural systems, including the water cycle and the weather.
- Ocean currents contribute to the movement of thermal energy and help to balance the extremes of temperature on Earth's surface.
- The rock cycle helps us to understand how heat causes changes in Earth.

12.0 Heat technologies offer benefits and require choices.

KEY CONCEPTS

- Human activities produce heat and greenhouse gases.
- Each person can play a role in protecting the global environment.
- Climate change may produce huge effects on ecosystems.

CHAPTER SUMMARY

- Heat pollution is heat that has negative effects on an ecosystem.
- Gases in Earth's atmosphere that trap heat and warm the planet are called greenhouse gases.
- Global warming describes the worldwide increase in average temperature that may lead to climate change.
- Ontario is developing a variety of alternative methods for energy production.

Keeping Our World Cool and Our Homes Warm

Getting Started

Insulation materials inside the outer walls of buildings help prevent heat loss to the outside air. By using insulation, Canadians can save energy and reduce the amount of greenhouse gases produced.

Your Goal

To determine how the properties of insulation materials relate to heat loss

What You Need

- 2-L clear soft drink bottle with screw cap
- selection of insulating materials
- crushed ice or snow in a large cooler
- thermometer
- hot water (50–60°C)
- elastic bands
- putty or modelling clay
- stopwatch
- ruler

CAUTION: Be careful when handling hot water.

Steps to Success

1. Create a table to record your time and temperature observations. Measure and record room temperature.

2. Punch a hole though the screw cap. Insert the thermometer so that the tip rests about halfway down in the bottle. The thermometer should extend above the cap so that you can observe the temperature readings. Use putty or modelling clay to seal the entry point.

3. Remove the screw cap with the thermometer and put it in a safe place.

4. Choose one of the materials to be tested as insulation. Wrap the bottle firmly and secure the insulation blanket with elastic bands. The insulation should be exactly **2 cm** thick on all surfaces of the bottle, including the bottom.

5. Add 1.7 L of hot water to the bottle. Immediately screw on the cap, which holds the thermometer. Start the stopwatch. Record the time and water temperature. Place the bottle into the snow (ice) cooler.

6. Record the temperature every 2 min for 20 min or until it approaches room temperature.

7. Pour the water out of the bottle. Repeat steps 3 to 5 with the other insulating materials.

8. Finally, repeat the procedure with a bottle that has not been wrapped in any material. This is your control.

9. Using the data in your table, graph your results for each insulating material you tested and the control.

10. List the samples in order from best insulator to worst insulator.

11. Examine the physical properties of the samples. Are there any common traits among the good insulators? The poor insulators? What makes a material a good insulator?

How Did It Go?

12. Would the insulating materials that you tested be equally effective in preventing heat from entering a building? How would you test this? Why would builders or homeowners be interested in knowing this?

13. Were all of the groups' results the same as yours? What might cause your findings to be different from those of others?

Key Terms Review

1. Design and draw a mind map that includes the terms below and any other new terms you have learned in this unit.

   - heat
   - thermal energy
   - temperature
   - atmosphere
   - ocean current
   - volcano
   - energy converter
   - greenhouse gas
   - climate change

   - conduction
   - convection
   - radiation
   - water cycle
   - wind
   - rock cycle
   - heat pollution
   - global warming
   - particle theory of matter

   Give your central idea an original title, and use the titles of the three chapters as the main headings on your map. Use dashed lines to connect similar ideas that occur in more than one part of your map. Write a phrase or sentence along each connecting line to explain why you connected these ideas. *k*

Key Concept Review

10.0

2. Provide three or more examples of energy transformations in which thermal energy is produced. *t*

3. What are some examples of fossil fuels? *k*

4. Explain the differences between thermal energy, heat, and temperature. *t*

5. Explain how convection heats up your bedroom in the winter. *t*

6. Identify the form(s) of energy described in each of the following situations. You may need to list more than one form of energy for some of these situations.

   (a) studying for a science test at home
   (b) eating an apple as a snack
   (c) toasting bread
   (d) using a microwave oven
     (**Hint:** Think carefully here.) *k*

7. Use a Venn diagram with two circles to compare and contrast fossil fuels and renewable energy sources. *c*

8. Describe and illustrate three situations in which heat is transferred by conduction, convection, and radiation. *t* *c*

11.0

9. What is the atmosphere? *k*

10. List the steps in the formation of raindrops in the atmosphere. *t*

11. Name the changes of state that are part of the water cycle. Indicate the change(s) that release thermal energy and the change(s) that require thermal energy. *k* *t*

12. Why is it important for scientists to study ocean currents and their patterns? *t*

13. List the geographic features that make up Earth's crust. *k*

14. Name two events that may occur as a result of the movement of the plates below Earth's crust. *t*

ACHIEVEMENT CHART CATEGORIES
k Knowledge and understanding   *t* Thinking and investigation   *c* Communication   *a* Application

15. How does heat play a role in the formation of igneous and metamorphic rocks? *t*

16. Less than one-billionth of the Sun's energy reaches Earth. What happens to this energy? (**Hint:** check Figure 11.7.) *k*

12.0

17. Name three or more energy converters that you use often. *t*

18. What do we mean when we say "greenhouse effect"? *k*

19. List three common ways that nitrogen oxides are released into Earth's atmosphere. *k*

20. Describe two possible ways of reducing the emission of carbon dioxide into Earth's atmosphere. *k*

21. List three Canadian animals or plants that may be at risk as a result of global warming. Describe why each one is at risk. *t*

Connect Your Understanding

22. Chapter 12 provides an example of heat pollution that describes how heat affects the amount of oxygen in a river or lake. Describe another example of heat pollution and its effects on the environment. *t*

23. As you hold a cup of ice cream, heat transfers from your hand to the cup and then to the surface of the ice cream touching the cup. What type of heat transfer does this describe? *k*

24. Identify a human activity that uses a large amount of electrical energy. Describe its effect on the environment. *t*

25. Infrared radiation can pass through transparent solids (like the windshield of a car) and colourless gases (like the air inside a car). On a sunny day in winter, the air in a closed car can become quite warm. Suggest a reason to explain why this happens. (**Hint:** Think about the other two types of heat transfer.) *t*

26. Figure 10.31 on page 303 compares the motion of particles to that of curling rocks. Select your own real-world example to make a comparison with particle motion. *t*

27. How does the engine of an automobile act as an energy converter? *t*

28. Compare the inner and outer cores of Earth. *t*

29. The word diamond comes from the Greek word *adamas*, which means indestructible. What role does heat from Earth play in producing diamonds and other valuable gems?

30. Draw a Venn diagram with three circles. Label the circles *igneous rocks*, *sedimentary rocks*, and *metamorphic rocks*. Then, use the information you learned in this unit to fill in the circles. *c*

31. Installing double-pane and triple-pane windows on a building greatly reduces heat loss. Which of the three forms of energy transfer are reduced by these energy-efficient windows? *t*

32. Using satellite images, researchers have found that city climates influence the growing seasons of plants up to 10 km from a city's edges. Growing seasons in  70 cities in eastern North America were about 15 days longer in urban areas than in rural areas outside a city's influence. How would this affect the type of crops that farmers plant in and near cities? *a*

33. Would you expect higher air temperatures in summer above a city or above its surrounding suburbs? Provide reasons for your answers. *t*

34. Fill in a number chart similar to the one below, using information in this unit. You may include more than one set of information in each box. The first box has been completed for you. *k* *t* *c*

Number	Chapter	New Information and Descriptions
2	10	two types of melted rock: magma (underground) and lava (on the surface)
2	11	
2	12	
3	10	
3	11	
3	12	
4	10	
4	11	
4	12	

35. Could wind energy be an effective method of producing electricity in your region of Ontario? Provide reasons for your answer. *a*

36. Scientists estimate that approximately 23 billion tonnes of carbon dioxide (CO_2) are added to Earth's atmosphere every year. That is more than 700 tonnes every second.

(a) Name several human activities that produce CO_2. *t*

(b) How is CO_2 production related to the enhanced greenhouse effect? *t*

37. In April 2007, the Ontario government announced several renewable energy projects, including one of the world's  largest solar energy farms. Why is solar energy considered to be a renewable form of energy? *t*

38. Think about the human activities that are important in your region of Ontario. For example, your region might include a high level of agriculture (farming), forestry, fishing, or mining. Develop a list of five or more human activities in your region of Ontario that depend on knowing about the weather. *t*

39. Think back to the new ideas and activities related to heat and the environment that you have seen in this unit. What changes have you already made in your daily activities? What changes do you plan on making? What further ideas do you think you need to research or explore? You could respond to these questions in writing or in an original, visual form.

ACHIEVEMENT CHART CATEGORIES
k Knowledge and understanding   *t* Thinking and investigation   *c* Communication   *a* Application

Practise Your Skills

40. Along Canada's west coast, the city of Vancouver has winters with little snowfall and a lot of rain. Use your knowledge of ocean currents to explain why a west coast winter is milder than an eastern winter. ⓣ

41. Look back at the What You Will Learn box at the start of each chapter in this unit. Record each of the items in a chart as shown. Then, complete the chart. The first line is done for you. ⓣ

Chapter	Information from What You Will Learn	Details I Have Learned
10	use the particle theory to compare how heat affects the motion of particles and the volume of solids, liquids, and gases	
10		
10		
11		

Revisit the Big Ideas

42. When the Sun shines on a metal doorknob on the outside of a home, what happens to the inside part of the doorknob? Write a paragraph to explain this. Use the words "heat," "particle theory," and "conduction" in your answer. ⓚ ⓣ ⓒ

43. You have learned how humans need and use heat and about the effects of adding heat to the environment. Write a letter to the editor of your school or regional newspaper to describe how your ideas changed since you began studying this unit. ⓒ

44. Create a home page for a website that informs viewers about our concerns for the environment as discussed in Chapter 12. Add additional Web pages and links that provide further information. Start your search at PearsonScience. ⓒ ⓐ

D54 Thinking about Science, Technology, Society, and the Environment ⓈⓉ ⓈⒺ

Tie It All Together

At the beginning of this unit (Pages 274 and 275), you learned about the concept Think Globally; Act Locally. You read about the efforts and creativity of some Ontario residents who care about energy and Earth's environment. Now, it is your turn! Brainstorm a list of climate awareness projects that you, your classmates, your family, and/or your community could develop in your local area. Choose one of these projects and create your own EAP — Environmental Action Plan. Design an original mini-poster to illustrate your EAP. Consult with your teacher to determine how your EAP can be put into effect.

Toolkits

Contents

Safety Symbols

Safety symbols identify potential hazards. When you see any of the following symbols, either in this book or on a product, take extra care.

Safety Symbols in This Book

Some activities in this book have symbols to help you conduct the activity safely. Look for these symbols at the beginning of activities.

 When you see this symbol, wear goggles or safety glasses while doing the activity.

 This symbol tells you that you will be using glassware during the activity. Take extra care when handling it.

 When you see this symbol, wear an apron while doing the activity.

 When you see this symbol, wear gloves while doing the activity.

WHMIS Symbols

Here are symbols you might see on the materials you use in your classroom. You will see them occasionally in the Materials and Equipment lists for activities when a substance that needs a warning is used. These symbols are called Workplace

Hazardous Materials Information System (WHMIS) symbols. They are placed on hazardous materials used at job sites and in science classrooms. They may also be on other manufactured products bought for home use. A container may have one or more of the symbols shown below. Discuss with your teacher what the symbols mean.

compressed gas

biohazardous infectious material

dangerously reactive material

corrosive material

oxidizing material

flammable and combustible material

poisonous and infectious causing immediate and serious toxic effects

poisonous and infectious causing other toxic effects

Hazard Symbols for Home Products

You have probably seen some of the hazard symbols below on products at home. They are a warning that the products can be harmful or dangerous if handled improperly. These hazard symbols have two shapes: a triangle (a traffic yield sign) or an octagon (a traffic stop sign). A triangle means that the container is dangerous. An octagon means that the contents of the container are dangerous. Here are four of the most common symbols.

Can you identify the symbols that are similar to the WHMIS symbols above?

 Flammable Hazard: The product could ignite (catch on fire) if exposed to flames, sparks, friction, or even heat.

 Toxic Hazard: The product is very poisonous and could have immediate and serious effects, including death, if eaten or drunk. Smelling or tasting some products can also cause serious harm.

 Corrosive Hazard: The product will corrode ("eat away at") clothing, skin, or other materials, and will burn eyes on contact.

 Explosive Hazard: The container can explode if it is heated or punctured.

The Inquiry Process of Science

Scientists are always asking a lot of questions. They are always inquiring. They want to understand why the things they observe, and wonder about, happen. Experiments are important tools scientists use to help them answer their questions.

When scientists plan experiments, they usually follow a simple set of steps.

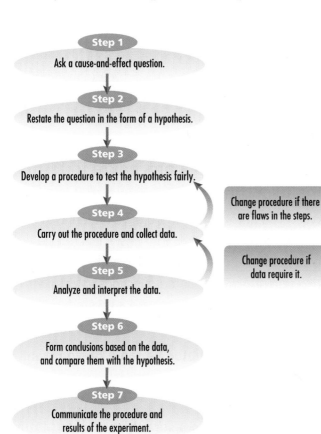

Step 1
Ask a cause-and-effect question.

Step 2
Restate the question in the form of a hypothesis.

Step 3
Develop a procedure to test the hypothesis fairly.

Step 4
Carry out the procedure and collect data.

Step 5
Analyze and interpret the data.

Step 6
Form conclusions based on the data, and compare them with the hypothesis.

Step 7
Communicate the procedure and results of the experiment.

Change procedure if there are flaws in the steps.

Change procedure if data require it.

Hints

- Answers may lead to additional questions. New questions often lead to new hypotheses and experiments. Don't be afraid to ask questions, or to re-think the ones you've already asked.

- Science grows when scientists ask questions, answer them, and are willing to question those answers. Scientific knowledge is always growing and changing.

STEP 1 Ask a cause-and-effect question.

Asking questions is easy. Asking questions that lead to reliable answers is more challenging. That's the reason scientists usually ask cause-and-effect questions. Here are a few examples.

- How does the concentration of laundry detergent in wash water affect the cleanliness of clothing?

- How do different temperatures affect the growth of seedlings?
- How does the amount of moisture affect the growth of mould on bread?

Notice how the causes—the detergent, temperature, and moisture—are things that are changeable. For example, you can have different concentrations of detergent, different temperatures, and different amounts of moisture. Causes are manipulated or independent variables. They are factors that you change when you investigate a cause-and-effect question.

The results are changeable, too. For example, some clothes may become cleaner than others, or not clean at all. Some seedlings may grow better than others, or some might not grow at all. Some bread samples may have lots of mould, some may have less, and some might not have any. Results are responding or dependent variables. They change because of the manipulated variable.

When you ask a cause-and-effect question, you should include only one manipulated variable in your question. This allows you to see the effect of that variable on the responding variable.

STEP 2 Restate the question in the form of a hypothesis.

A hypothesis is a way of restating a cause-and-effect question so that it gives a reasonable, possible answer. Basically, a hypothesis is an intelligent guess at the solution to a problem or question. It is usually in the form of an "If ... then" statement and states the relationship between the manipulated and responding variables.

Here are hypotheses for the questions outlined in Step 1.

- If the concentration of the detergent is high, then clothing will become cleaner.
- If the temperature is decreased, then the seedlings will not grow as well.
- If the amount of moisture is increased, then the bread will get mouldier.

Hints

A hypothesis is an early step in the experiment- planning process. Your hypothesis can turn out to be "right," but it doesn't always. That's what the experiment is for—to test the hypothesis.

STEP 3 Develop a procedure to test the hypothesis fairly.

When you develop a procedure, you need to ask yourself some questions. Your answers to these questions will help you plan a fair and safe experiment. Here are some questions you should think about. These questions are answered for the seedling experiment.

- **Which manipulated variable do you want to investigate?** The manipulated variable is temperature.
- **How will you measure this variable (if it is measurable)?** You can measure temperature with a thermometer.
- **How will you keep all other variables constant (the same) so they don't affect your results?** In other words, how will you control your experiment so it is a fair test? To control the experiment, these variables should be kept constant: the amount of light the seedlings receive; the amount and temperature

of water applied to the seedlings; the kind of soil the seedlings are planted in.

- **What materials and equipment will you need for the experiment?** The materials would include seedlings, soil, growing pots or containers (same size), water and a watering can, a light source, a thermometer, and a ruler or other measuring device.

- **How will you conduct the experiment safely?** What safety factors should you consider? Some of the safety factors to consider include putting the seedling pots in a place where they would not be disturbed, washing your hands after handling the materials, and making sure you don't have any allergies to the soil or seedlings you use.

- **How will you set up the procedure to get the data you need to test your hypothesis?** You could divide your seedlings into groups (e.g., three seedlings for each temperature) and grow each group at a certain temperature. You would keep track of how much each seedling in a group grew over a specified amount of time (e.g., four weeks) and calculate the average for the group.

STEP 4 Carry out the procedure and collect data.

Depending on the kind of experiment you have planned, you may choose to record the data you collect in the form of a chart or table, a labelled sketch, notes, or a combination of these. For example, a good way to record the seedling data would be in tables like the one below (one for each week of the experiment).

Week 1: Height of Seedling Grown at Different Temperatures				
Temperature seedlings grown at (°C)	Height of seedling 1 (cm)	Height of seedling 2 (cm)	Height of seedling 3 (cm)	Average height (cm)
20				
15				
10				

Hints

Analyzing the data you collect is the only way you have to assess your hypothesis. It's important that your record keeping be organized and neat.

STEP 5 Analyze and interpret the data.

Scientists look for patterns and relationships in their data. Often, making a graph can help them see patterns and relationships more easily. (Turn to Toolkit 6 for more about graphing.)

A graph of the seedling data would show you if there were a relationship between temperature and growth rate.

Hints

If you have access to a computer, find out if it has the software to help you make charts or graphs.

STEP 6 Form conclusions based on the data, and compare them with the hypothesis.

Usually, forming a conclusion is fairly straightforward. Either your data will support your hypothesis or they won't. Either way, however, you aren't finished answering your cause-and-effect question.

For example, if the seedlings did not grow as well in cooler temperatures, you can conclude that your data support your hypothesis. But you will still need to repeat your experiment several times to see if you get the same results over and over again. Doing your experiment successfully many times is the only way you and other scientists can have faith in your data and your conclusions.

If your data don't support your hypothesis, there are two possible reasons why.

- Perhaps your experimental plan was flawed and needs to be re-assessed and possibly planned again.

- Perhaps your hypothesis was incorrect and needs to be re-assessed and modified.

For example, if the seedlings grew better in the lower temperatures, you would have to re-think your hypothesis, or look at your experiment for flaws. You would need to ask questions to help you evaluate and change either your hypothesis or plan. For example, you could ask: Do certain seedlings grow better at lower temperatures than others? Do different types of soil have more of an effect on growth than temperature?

Every experiment is different and will result in its own set of questions and conclusions.

Hints

- If you don't have in-class time to repeat your experiment several times, you could ask your teacher about scheduling after-school time.

- You could also enlist the help of your classmates. If others have completed the same experiment and got the same results, the conclusions are usually reliable. If not, the hypothesis must be modified. Scientists often work this way to compare results.

STEP 7 Communicate the procedure and results of the experiment.

Scientists always share the results of their experiments with other people. They do this by summarizing how they performed the first six steps. Sometimes, they will write out a formal report stating their purpose, hypothesis, procedure, observations, and conclusions. Other times, they share their experimental results verbally, using drawings, charts, or graphs. (See Toolkits 6 and 8 for help on how to prepare your results.)

When you have finished your experiment, ask your teacher how he or she would like you to prepare your results so you can share them with the other students in your class.

The Problem-Solving Process for Technological Development

When you plan an experiment to answer a cause-and-effect question, you follow an orderly set of steps. The same is true for designing a model or prototype that solves a practical problem.

When people try to solve practical problems, they usually follow a simple set of steps.

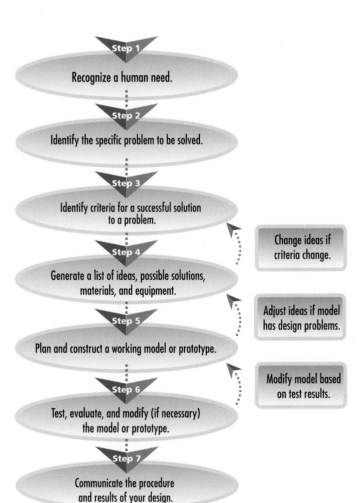

STEP 1 Recognize a human need.

This involves recognizing what the problem is. For example, suppose you observe that a rope bridge across a ravine at a local park is very unstable and swings back and forth when crossed. This might be fine for people who want a thrill, but you find that most people are not comfortable crossing the bridge and don't get to enjoy one of the nicer areas of the park. You wish there were a way to make the bridge more stable so more people would use it. That is the situation or context of the problem.

STEP 2 Identify the specific problem to be solved.

When you understand a situation, you can then define the problem more exactly. This means identifying a specific task to carry out. In the situation with the bridge, the task might be to build a new bridge or add support to the existing bridge.

STEP 3 Identify criteria for a successful solution to a problem.

You have defined the problem and now you must look for solutions. But how will you know when you have found the best possible solution? Before you start looking for solutions, you need to establish your criteria for determining what a successful solution will be.

One of your criteria for success in the bridge example would be the completion of a stable bridge. The criteria you choose do not depend on which solution you select—whether to reinforce the old bridge or build a new bridge. In this case, whatever the solution, it must result in a stable bridge.

When you are setting your criteria for success, you must consider limits to your possible solutions.

For example, the bridge may have to be built within a certain time, so rebuilding completely may not be possible. Other limitations could include availability of materials, cost, number of workers needed, and safety.

If you are building a product or device for yourself, you may set the criteria for success and the limitations yourself. In class, your teacher will usually outline them.

Hints

Always consider safety. This includes safe handling and use of materials and equipment, as well as being aware of possible environmental impacts of your ideas. Discuss with your teacher and fellow students how your solution might affect the environment.

STEP 4 Generate a list of ideas, possible solutions, materials, and equipment.

Brainstorming, conducting research, or both, are key components of this step. When you brainstorm, remember to relax and let your imagination go. Brainstorming is all about generating as many ideas as possible without judging them. Record your ideas in the form of words, mind maps, sketches—whatever helps you best.

Conducting research may involve reading books and magazines, searching the Internet, interviewing people, or visiting stores. It all depends on what you are going to design.

One idea for the rope bridge would be to anchor the bridge with strong rope or thick metal wire to large rocks or to the hillside at either end of the

bridge. Sketches and diagrams would help to generate different ideas for the bridge design.

Hints

Humans have been inventors for tens of thousands of years—so take advantage of what has already been developed. When you're solving a problem, you don't have to "reinvent the wheel." See how others have solved the same problem before and use their efforts as inspiration. You can also look for ways to "build upon" or improve on their ideas.

STEP 5 Plan and construct a working model or prototype.

Choose one possible solution to develop. Start by making a list of the materials and equipment you will use. Then make a working diagram, or series of diagrams, on paper. This lets you explore and troubleshoot your ideas early on. Your labels should be detailed enough so that other people could build your design. Show your plans to your teacher before you begin construction work.

A simple model of the bridge could be made to show how and where components such as stabilizing wires could be added.

Hints

If things aren't working as you planned or imagined, be prepared to modify your plans as you construct your model or prototype.

STEP 6 Test, evaluate, and modify (if necessary) the model or prototype.

Testing lets you see how well your solution works. Testing also lets you know if you need to make modifications. Does your model or prototype meet all the established criteria? Does it solve the problem you designed it for?

Invite your classmates to try your product. Their feedback can help you decide what is and isn't working, and how to fix anything that needs fixing. Perhaps the stabilizing wires on the bridge model could be anchored elsewhere. Maybe more wires could be added.

Hints

- For every successful invention or product, there are thousands of unsuccessful ones. Sometimes it's better to start over from scratch than to follow a design that doesn't meet its performance criteria.

- Here's an old saying you've probably heard: "If at first you don't succeed, try, try again." Remember, there can be many possible solutions to a practical problem.

STEP 7 Communicate the procedure and results of your design.

Inventors and engineers create things to meet people's needs. When they make something new, they like to show it to other people and explain to them how it works. Sometimes they will use a carefully drawn diagram of the new device and write about how they performed the first six steps. Other times, they will show the device to people and explain verbally how it works and how they built it. Your teacher will tell you how to prepare your results so you can exhibit the new device you make.

The Decision-Making Process for Social and Environmental Issues

People can have many different viewpoints or perspectives about social and environmental issues. This usually means that an issue has more than one possible solution. Scientific and technological information can be used to increase our understanding of an issue and help resolve it.

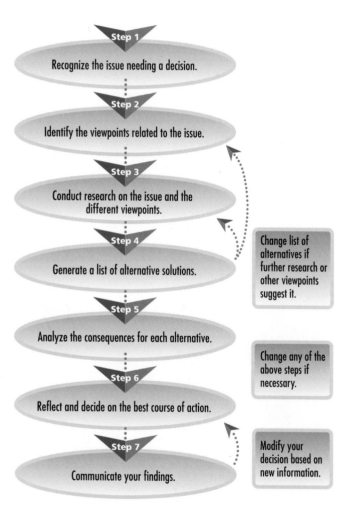

When people try to make a decision or reach a consensus about an issue, they need to use a decision-making process. Here are the steps in one possible process

STEP 1 Recognize the issue needing a decision.

This involves recognizing that an issue exists. An issue is a controversy that needs to be resolved. It may have more than one possible solution, but the chosen one is usually the one that satisfies the most people. For example, suppose you and your friends want to have some trees in a public park cut down in order to make space for a playing field. Some members of your community feel that the trees should be preserved for the birds that nest there. The local environmental specialist says that when it rains, the trees protect a nearby stream by reducing run-off, so they should be left standing. Other people say that your idea of building a playing field is too expensive.

STEP 2 Identify the viewpoints related to the issue.

The viewpoints expressed in the example in step 1 are **recreational** (you and your friends), **ecological** (people who wish to leave the trees as they are), and **economic** (people who think that the cost would be too high).

People often evaluate issues using one or more viewpoints. Some of these viewpoints are:

- Cultural: interest in the customs and practices of a particular group of people

- Ecological: interest in the protection of the natural environment

- Economic: interest in the financial aspects of the situation

- Educational: interest in acquiring and sharing knowledge and skills

- Esthetic: interest in the beauty in art and nature

- Ethical: interest in beliefs about what is right and wrong

- Health and safety: interest in physical and mental well-being

- Historical: interest in knowledge dealing with past events

- Political: interest in the effect of the issue on governments, politicians, and political parties

- Recreational: interest in leisure activities

- Scientific: interest in knowledge based on the inquiry process of science (Toolkit 2)

- Social: interest in human relationships, public welfare, or society

- Technological: interest in the design and use of tools and processes that solve practical problems to satisfy peoples' wants and needs (Toolkit 3)

STEP 3 Conduct research on the issue and the different viewpoints.

You will be able to suggest an appropriate solution to an issue only if you understand the issue and the different viewpoints. It's important to gather unbiased information about the issue itself and then consider the information provided by people with different viewpoints.

Develop specific questions that will help to guide your research. Questions for the playing field issue might be:

- How many people will use the playing field?

- Is there another more suitable site for the playing field?

- What kind of birds nest in these trees? Could they nest elsewhere in the area?

- What is run-off and why is it a problem?

- What would be the full cost of building the playing field (including the cost of removing the trees)?

Conducting research may involve interviewing people, reading books and magazines, searching the Internet, or making a field trip. It is important to evaluate your sources of information to determine if there is a bias and to separate fact from opinion. In this step, you are trying to gain a better understanding of the background of the issue, the viewpoints of different groups, the alternative solutions, and the consequences of each alternative. You will find tips on how to conduct research in the following section on researching topics.

STEP 4 Generate a list of alternative solutions.

Examine the background of the issue and the viewpoints in order to generate a list of alternative solutions. Brainstorming can be a useful component of this step. Use your research to help guide your thinking.

Examples of possible alternatives for the issue in step 1 might be as follows:

- Cut the trees and build the playing field.

- Leave the park as it is.

- Find another more suitable location

- Modify the plan in the existing park.

STEP 5 Analyze the consequences for each alternative.

Decide how you will measure the risks and benefits for the consequences of each alternative solution. You may decide to examine the importance, likelihood, and duration of each possible consequence. The importance of the consequence and the likelihood of its occurrence can be ranked high (3), moderate (2), low (1), or none (0). Duration is considered short term (S) if it is less than 50 years or long term (L) if it is longer than 50 years. Ask how many people will benefit from the alternative and how many will be affected negatively. Make sure to consider health and safety.

For the playing field example, you could analyze the consequences of each alternative solution in a table like the one shown below.

Analysis of Consequences: Alternative 1– Build the playing field in the park.

Consequence	Importance (3, 2, 1, 0)	Likelihood of occurrence (3, 2, 1, 0)	Duration (S, L)
Trees cut	2	3	1
Run-off	3	3	S
Birds move	2 to 1	3	1
Playing field well used	2	2	possibly 1
Development and maintenance cost	2 to 1	3	1

STEP 6 Reflect and decide on the best course of action.

Evaluate your decision-making process to ensure that each step is completed as fully as possible. Consider the consequences of the alternative solutions and how people will respond to each one. Then decide on what you think is the best course of action.

STEP 7 Communicate your findings.

Communicate your findings in an appropriate way. For example, you may prepare a written report, a verbal presentation, or a position for a debate or a public hearing role-play. Defend your position by clearly stating your case and presenting supporting evidence from a variety of sources.

Researching Topics

Research involves finding out something about a topic or subject. That means going to certain resources that will give you accurate information. Information can be found just about anywhere: from your home bookshelves to the public library, from asking experts to looking on the Internet. Here is the process you should follow when you do your research.

Choosing a Topic

In some situations, your teacher may give you the topic to research. Other times, you will select one of your own, such as the issue described above. If you have trouble coming up with a topic, try brainstorming ideas either by yourself or with a group. Remember, when you brainstorm, there are no right or wrong answers, just "ideas." Here are some brainstorming suggestions to get you started:

- List two or three general topics about science that interest you.

- For each topic, spend a few minutes writing down as many words or ideas that relate to that topic. They don't have to be directly connected to science.

- Share your list with others and ask them to suggest other possibilities.

- Now you have to "filter" your idea list to find a topic to research. In other words, go through your ideas until you find two or three that interest you. To

help you narrow your idea list, try grouping similar words or ideas, modifying what you've written, or even writing down a new idea. Sometimes, too, working with other people will help to focus your thoughts.

- When you settle on an idea for your topic, write it down. Try to explain it in a couple of sentences or a short paragraph. Do that for each of your two or three topic ideas.

- Have your teacher approve your topics. Now you're ready to go!

Which Topic Should I Choose?

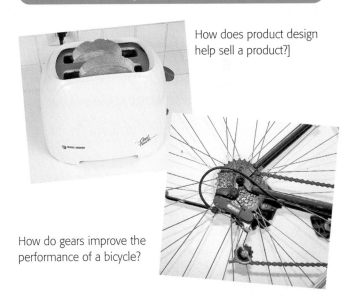

How does product design help sell a product?]

How do gears improve the performance of a bicycle?

The next thing you have to do is settle on one topic. (Remember, you should start your research with two or three topic ideas.) One way to help you decide is to determine how easy it will be to find information on your topic.

- Use some of the resources listed under "Finding Information" to do your preliminary research.

- If you can't easily find at least four good references for a topic, consider dropping it and going on to the next idea.

Hints

Sometimes topics are too broad in scope or too general to make good research reports (for example, "transportation" instead of just "bicycles"). Try rewriting your topic to narrow its focus.

If all the topics are easy to research, then you'll need some other criteria to help you decide. Think about

- which topic interests you the most

- which topic is not being researched by many students in your class

- which topic interests you the least

How Hard Will It Be to Find Information?

How Camera Lenses are Manufactured

How Mirrors Are Used in Some Optical Devices

Once you've finally chosen your topic, you might want to work with other students and your teacher to:

- finalize its wording

- make sure it matches the project or assignment you are doing

Finding Information

There are many resources that you can use to look up information. You'll find some of these resources:

- in your school
- in your community (such as your public library)
- on the Internet
- in CD-ROM encyclopedias and databases

Here is a suggested list of resources.

Resource	✓	Details
Books		
CD-ROMs		
Community Professionals or Experts		
Encyclopedias		
Films		
Government Agencies (local, provincial, and fedral)		
Internet Sites		
Journals		
Library Catalogue		
Newspapers		
Non-profit Organizations		
Posters		
DVDs and Videos		

Searching Tips

Finding Information at Your Library

Library computer catalogues are a fast way to find books on the subjects you are researching. Most of these electronic catalogues have four ways to search: *subject*, *author*, *title*, and *key words*. If you know the *author* or *title* of a book, just type it in. Otherwise, use the *subject* and *key words* searches to find books on your topic.

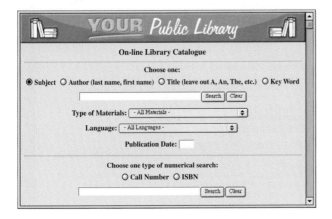

- If you're doing a *subject* search, type in the main topic you are researching. For example, if you're searching for information on solar energy, type in "solar energy." If there are no books on that topic, try again using a more general category, like "renewable resources," or just "energy."

- If you're doing a *key words* search, type in any combination of words that have to do with your topic. For the solar energy example, you could type in words such as: "renewable energy sun solar panels." Using several key words will give you a more specific search. Using only one or two key words, like "sun" and "energy," will give you a more general search.

Hints

- The library may also have a way to search for magazine articles. This is called a *periodical search*. It's especially useful for searching for information on events and/or discoveries that have taken place recently. Ask your librarian how to do a periodical search.

- Your library will probably have a reference section where all the encyclopedias are kept. There you may find science and technology, environmental, or even animal encyclopedias, as well as other reference books.

Finding Information on the Internet

On the Internet, you can use searching programs, called *search engines*, to search the Internet on just about any subject. To find a search engine, ask your teacher or click on the search icon found at the top of your Internet browser. Here are some suggestions on how to search the Internet:

- Once you reach a search engine Web page, type in key words or phrases that have to do with your topic. For solar energy, you could type in "solar energy," "solar panels," "renewable resources," or any combination of these and other similar words.

- The search engine will display a list of Web pages it has found that have these words or phrases somewhere in them. Click on any Web page on the list that looks interesting.

- Quite often you will get a long list of possible Web pages to look at. You may need to make your search more specific. This can be done by adding other key words to your search. For example, if you were looking for solar energy examples in Canada and used the key word "solar energy," you may want to do a second search of these results with the key word "Canada" added.

- Don't forget to record the addresses of any interesting Web pages you find. Why not work with a friend? One person can record the addresses of Web pages while the other person searches on the computer. Or you can

save any Web page as a *bookmark* for easy future access. Check with your teacher or librarian to find out how to save and organize your bookmarks.

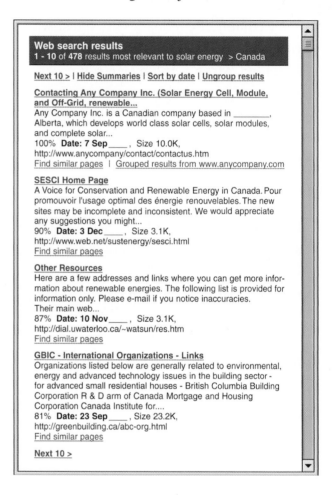

BEFORE YOU START!

Check with your teacher to find out what your school's policy is about acceptable use of the Internet. Remember to follow this policy whenever you use the Internet at school. Be aware as you use the Internet that some Web sites may be strongly biased toward a specific point of view. If you are looking for scientific or technical information, educational or government Web sites are generally reliable.

Recording Your Information Sources

An important part of researching a topic is keeping track of where you obtain information. As you do your research, you are reading through or viewing a variety of different sources. Some may be in print, such as magazines and books. Others may be electronic, such as Web sites and CD ROMs. And others may be visual, such as videos and photos. No matter what sources you use, you should keep track of them.

With this information, you can easily go back and check details. You can also use it to help you respond to any questions about the accuracy or completeness of your information. Your record of sources should include at least the following basic information:

- title or name of the source (e.g., if you read a chapter of a book, you would write down the book's title; for a website, you would include the address)

- author's name, if known

- publisher (e.g., for a website, this would be the name of person or organization who has put up the site)

- date of publication

- pages consulted

Your teacher may want you to list your information sources in a specific format. Check what this format will be before you begin your research so that you can collect the details you need to complete your reference list later. You may want to do your own research on formats for such reference lists or bibliographies.

Reading in Science

You use different skills and strategies when reading different materials such as a novel or a textbook. In a novel, you are mainly reading to enjoy the story. In a science textbook you are reading for information. A science textbook has terms and concepts that you need to understand.

Investigating Science and Technology 7 helps you with your non-fiction reading by giving you opportunities to use different reading strategies. You will find these reading strategies in the following literacy activities:

- Getting Ready to Read at the beginning of each unit
- Before Reading at the beginning of each chapter
- During Reading or Writing Checkpoints in each section
- After Reading at the end of each chapter

Using Reading Strategies

You can use the following strategies to help better understand the information presented in this book.

Before Reading

- Skim the section you are going to read. Look at the headings, subheadings, visuals, and boldfaced words to determine the topic.

- Look at how the information is organized. Ask yourself: Is it a cause and effect passage? Is it a contrast and compare passagte? Think about how the organization can help you access the information.

- Think about what you already know about the topic.

- Predict what you will learn.

- List questions that you have about the topic. This will help you to set a purpose for reading.

As You Read

- Rewrite the section headings and subheadings as questions. Look for the answers to the questions as you read.

- Use your answers to the questions to decide on the main idea in each section or subsection.

- Look carefully at any visuals— photographs, illustrations, charts, or graphs. Read the captions and labels that go with the illustrations and photographs, and the titles of any charts or graphs. Think about the information the visuals give you and how this information helps you understand the ideas presented in the text.

- Notice the terms that are boldfaced (dark and heavy type). These are important words that will help you understand and write about the information in the section. Make sure you understand the terms and how they are used. Check the terms in the Glossary to confirm their meanings.

- Use different strategies to help remember what you read. For example, you can make mental pictures, make connections to what you know, or draw a sketch,

After Reading

- Find the information to answer any review questions. Use the headings and boldfaced terms to locate the information needed. Even if you are sure of the answer, reread to confirm that your answer is correct.

- Write brief notes to synthesize what you have learned, or organize the information in a graphic organizer. You will find information about graphic organizers in the following section.

- Personalize the information. Think about opinions you have on what you've read. Consider if the new information you have learned has changed any previous ideas. List questions you still have about the topic.

Using Graphic Organizers

Graphic organizers can be used to organize information that you read, and to display ideas visually. You have probably learned and used several of the techniques shown here. Try out the ones that are less familiar to you. You may find that some help you open up your thinking in new and creative ways.

Venn Diagram

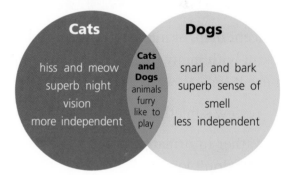

Venn diagrams are usually used to compare two things by showing their similarities and differences. To use a Venn diagram, ask yourself questions such as:

- What things do I want to compare?
- What do they have in common?
- In what ways are they different?

Hints

You can use Venn diagrams to compare more than two things. Try it and see!

Concept Map

Concept Map for Green Plants

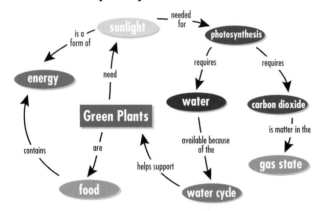

A concept map, or a mind map, is a web diagram with many uses. For example, you can use it to:

- review something you already know

- gather information about something you don't know

- explore new ways of thinking about something

- outline plans for an essay, a song, an experiment, a design challenge, a science project, and multimedia presentations

To use a concept map, ask yourself questions such as:

- What is the key idea, word, question, problem, or issue to build the map around?

- What words, ideas, objects, or questions come to mind when I think about the item at the centre of my map?

- How are the ideas, objects and concepts on my map linked or connected to each other?

Hints

If you have access to a computer, find out if it has the software to help you make your graphic organizers.

Tree Diagram

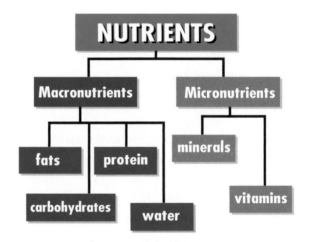

Tree diagrams allow you to see how things originate or how larger things can be broken down into their smaller components. Tree diagrams also allow you to organize or group concepts and things. Knowing about the parts of something helps you to better understand the concept or thing you are studying.

Comparison Matrix

		Characteristics			
		walk	use food	talk	swim
Things to compare	goat	X	X	X	
	tree		X		
	rock				
	person	X	X	X	X

This is often used to compare the characteristics or properties of a number of things. To use a comparison matrix, ask yourself questions such as:

- What things do I want to compare?

- What characteristics will I choose to compare?

- How are the things I'm comparing similar and how are they different?

Hints

A comparison matrix can be useful for brainstorming.

Note Taking Chart

A note taking chart helps you understand how the material you are reading is organized. It also helps you keep track of information as you read.

Your teacher will assign several pages for you to read. Before you begin reading, look at each heading and turn it into a question. Try to use "how," "what," or "why" to begin each question. Write your questions in the left hand column of your chart. Leave enough space between each question so that you can record information from your reading that answers your question.

For example, you may be assigned several pages about the scientific meaning of work. These pages contain the following headings:

- The Meaning of Work
- Calculating Work
- Energy and Work

You can see an example of a note taking chart below.

Questions from Headings	Answers from Reading
What is the meaning of the word "work"?	– work is done when a force acts on an object to make the object move – If there's no movement, no work is done – just trying to push something isn't work—it's only work if the object moves
How do you calculate work?	
How are energy and work related?	

Communicating in Science

In science, you use your communication skills to clearly show your knowledge, ideas, and understanding. You can use words and visuals, such as diagrams, charts, and tables, to communicate what you know. Some communication may be short, as in answering questions, or long, as in reports.

Writing Reports

Toolkit 2 shows you how to plan a science experiment. Toolkit 3 shows you how to do technological design, and Toolkit 4 shows you how to use a decision-making process for social and environmental issues. Here you will learn how to write a report so you can communicate the procedure and results of your work.

Here is a list of things you should try to do when writing your science reports.

- Give your report or project a title.

- Tell readers why you did the work.

- State your hypothesis or describe the design challenge.

- List the materials and equipment you used.

- Describe the steps you took when you did your experiment, designed and made your product, or considered an issue.

- Show your experimental data, the results of testing your product, or the background information on the issue.

- Interpret and analyze the results of your experiment.

- Make conclusions based on the outcome of the experiment, the success of the product you designed, or the research you did on an issue.

Give your report or project a title.

Write a brief title on the top of the first page of your report. Your title can be one or two words that describe a product you designed and made, or it can be a short sentence that summarizes an experiment you performed, or it can state the topic of an issue you explored.

Tell readers why you did the work.

Use a heading such as "Introduction" or "Purpose" for this section. Here, you give your reasons for doing a particular experiment, designing and making a particular product, or considering a specific issue. If you are writing about an experiment, tell readers what your cause-and-effect question is. If you designed a product, explain why this product is needed, what it will do, who might use it, and who might benefit from its use. If you were considering an issue, state what the issue is and why you have prepared this report about it.

State your hypothesis or describe the design challenge.

If you are writing about an experiment, use a heading such as "Hypothesis." Under this heading you will state your hypothesis.

Your hypothesis is your guess at the solution to a problem or question. It makes a prediction that your experiment will test. Your hypothesis must indicate the relationship between the manipulated and responding variable.

If you are writing about a product you designed, use a heading such as "Design Challenge." Under this heading, you will describe why you decided to design your product the way you did. Explain how and why you chose your design over other possible designs.

List the materials and equipment you used.

This section can come under a heading called "Materials and Equipment." List all the materials and equipment you used for your experiment or design project. Your list can be in point form or set up as a table or chart. Remember to include the exact amounts of materials used, when possible (for example, the number of nails used in building a model or the volumes and masses of substances tested in an experiment). Include the exact measurements and proper units for all materials used.

Also include diagrams to show how you set up your equipment or how you prepared your materials. Remember to label the important features on your diagrams. (See the following section on diagrams for drawing tips.)

Describe the steps you took when you did your experiment, designed and made your product, or researched the issue.

Under a heading called "Procedure" or "Method," describe, in detail, the steps you followed when doing your experiment, designing and making your product, or considering an issue. If you made a product, describe how you tested it. If you had to alter your design, describe in detail how you did this.

Show your experimental data, the results of testing your product, or the background information on the issue.

Give this section a heading such as "Data," "Observations," or "Background Information." In this section, you should show the data or information you collected while performing the experiment, testing your product, or researching an issue. In reporting about an issue, use only a summary of the essential information needed for a reader to understand the issue and different viewpoints about it.

Use tables, diagrams, and any other visual aids that show the results of your tests. If you performed your experiment a few times, give results for each trial. If you tested different designs of your product, give results for each design.

Interpret and analyze the results of your experiment.

Interpret and analyze the data you collected in your experiment. Calculations, graphs, diagrams, charts, or other visual aids may be needed. (See Toolkit 8 for graphing tips.) Explain any calculations or graphs that you used to help explain your results.

Make conclusions based on the outcome of the experiment, the success of the product you designed, or the research you did on an issue.

This last section of your report can be called "Conclusions." In one or two paragraphs, explain what your tests and experiments showed, or what decision you made as a result of your research.

If you did an experiment, explain if your results were predicted by the hypothesis. Describe how you might adjust the hypothesis because of what you learned from doing the experiment, and how you might test this new hypothesis.

If you made a product, explain if your design did what it was supposed to do, or worked the way it was supposed to work. If you changed the design of your product, explain why one design is better than another.

Describe the practical applications your product or experiment might have for the world outside the classroom.

If you considered an issue, explain why you made your decision. Briefly summarize your supporting evidence. If necessary, explain how you have responded to different viewpoints on the issue.

Diagrams

Have you heard the saying, "a picture is worth a thousand words"? In science, a picture can be worth even more. A carefully done diagram can help you express your ideas, record important information, and experiment with designs. Diagrams are an important tool in communicating what you know and your ideas.

Four types of diagrams you can use are a Simple Sketch, a Technical or Scientific Diagram, an Orthographic (Perspective) Diagram, and a Computer-Assisted Diagram. Examples of each type of diagram are shown. A front, side, and top view for a simple sketch and a technical diagram are shown. These different views can also be made for the other types of diagrams.

The photo on this page shows the set-up of an experiment. Practise drawing it using one or several of the diagram types presented on the next pages. What labels would you include? Would your labelling choices change depending on the style of diagram you make?

Tools of the Trade

You will need the following equipment for each type of diagram.

Hand-drawing tools

- a sharp pencil or mechanical pencil
- a pencil sharpener or extra leads
- an eraser
- a ruler

For simple diagrams

- blank, white paper

For technical and orthographic diagrams

- blank graph paper

For computer-assisted diagrams

- blank diskette
- access to computer and software

Remember!

- Give your diagram a title at the top of the page.

- Use the whole page for your diagram.

- Include only those details that are necessary, keep them simple, and identify them by name.

- If you need labels, use lines, not arrows. Place your labels in line with the feature being labelled, and use a ruler to keep your lines straight.

- Don't use colour or shading unless your teacher asks you to.

- Include notes and ideas if the sketch is a design for a structure or an invention.

Hints

If you're going to use your diagram to help you design a structure, include a top, side, and front view.

A Simple Sketch (Top View)

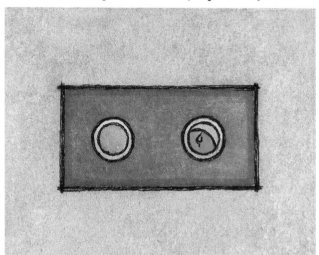

A Simple Sketch (Front View)

A Simple Sketch (Side View)

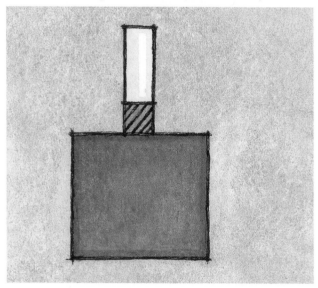

An Orthographic (Perspective) Diagram

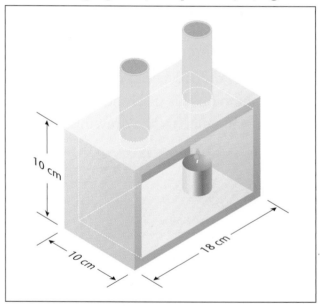

Hints

You can use the squares of your graph paper to make the scale of your orthographic diagram accurate. For example, suppose that each square stood for 1 cm. If what you're drawing is 14 cm long, you would use 14 squares to represent its length.

A Technical Diagram

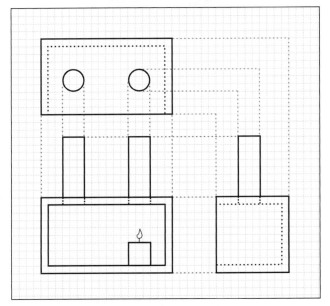

A Computer-Assisted Diagram

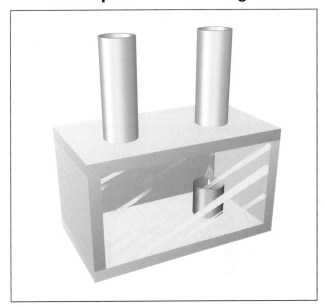

Hints

Use graph paper to help you with the details of your diagram if you don't have a ruler handy.

Hints

One advantage of using a computer is that you can easily change your work. After saving your original, practise making changes and moving the image around.

Measurement

Observations from an experiment may be qualitative (descriptive) or quantitative (physical measurements). Quantitative observations help us to describe such things as how far away something is, how massive it is, and how much space it takes up. Here are some types of measurements you might come across every day.

Length

Length tells you

- how long or short something is
- how far or near something is
- how high or low something is
- how large or small something is

Common units used to measure length include millimetres (mm), centimetres (cm), metres (m), and kilometres (km). All these units are based on a single standard: the metre.

Hints

When you use a ruler, tape measure, or metre-stick, always start from the 0 measurement point, not the edge of the measuring tool.

When you use a measuring tool such as a ruler, look directly in line with the measurement point, not from an angle.

Volume

The volume of something tells you the amount of space that it takes up (occupies). Common units used to measure volume include litres (L) and millilitres (mL). Remember, 1 mL equals 1 cm^3.

At home, you often use a measuring cup to determine the volume of something. At school, you usually use a graduated cylinder. Here, "graduated" means a container that has been marked with regular intervals for measuring. For example, a measuring cup, a beaker, and a thermometer are all graduated.

When you add a liquid to a graduated cylinder, the top of the liquid is curved near the sides of the cylinder. This curve is called a meniscus. To measure the liquid's volume

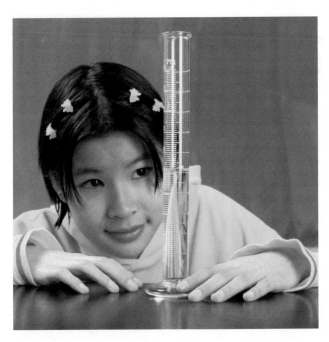

properly, you need to observe the liquid's surface from eye level so you can see the flat, bottom portion of the curve. Ignore the sides.

INSTANT PRACTICE

1. Each of the following objects takes up space. Estimate the volume of each, using appropriate units.

   (a) a cereal bowl

   (b) a test tube

   (c) a bathtub

2. Certain ancient volume measures, such as the teaspoon, are still in use today. Write a fictional paragraph describing where the ancient Japanese volume measure "koku" originated. One koku is approximately 278 L.

Mass and Weight

In science, the mass of an object and its weight mean different things. The mass of something tells you the amount of matter it has. The weight of an object is the measure of the force of gravity acting on it. We use mass more often in science. Common units used to measure mass include grams (g) and kilograms (kg).

You usually measure mass with a balance. Your classroom probably has an equal arm balance or a triple beam balance like the ones shown here.

The equal arm balance and triple beam balance basically work in the same way. You compare the mass of the object you are measuring with standard or known masses (or their mass equivalent values on the triple beam).

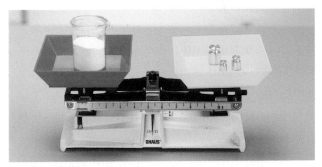

equal arm balance

An equal arm balance has two pans. You place the object whose mass you want to know on one pan. On the other pan, you place standard (known) masses until the two pans are balanced (level). Then, you just add up the values of the standard masses. The total is the mass of the object you are measuring.

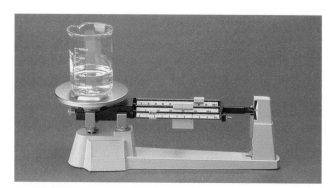

triple beam balance

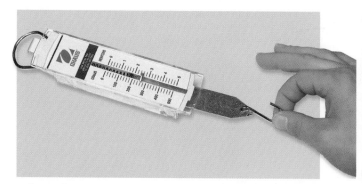

spring scale

A triple beam balance has a single pan. You place the object you are measuring on the pan. You adjust the masses on the beams until the beam assembly is level. Then, you add up the mass equivalent values of the beam masses from the scales on the beam.

You can use a spring scale to measure weight, which is the force of gravity acting on an object. A spring scale is sometimes called a force meter. A spring scale measures force in newtons.

A spring scale has three main parts: a hook, a spring, and a measuring scale. The hook at the end is used to attach the object to the scale. The spring pulls on the object. As the spring pulls, the pointer moves along the measuring scale.

To measure the weight of an object, first hang the spring scale from a clamp on a retort stand. Then hang the object from the hook of the spring scale. Once the pointer stops moving, record the measurement.

INSTANT PRACTICE

1. Describe how you would determine the mass of the amount of sand you can hold in your hands. All you can use is a small bucket and a triple-beam balance, and you cannot make a mess!

2. Explain why the following statement is false: "If I flew to Mars, my mass would be less than it is on Earth." Rewrite this sentence so it is true.

Estimating

When you estimate, you use your mind to guess the length, volume, or mass of an object. Sometimes, you can estimate by comparing one object with another object that has known measurements. For example, if you are asked to estimate the volume of your drink, you could estimate by comparing it with a large jar of mayonnaise that has its volume marked on the label.

Try to estimate the measurements of the items listed below. Include the measurement units that you think should go with your estimates. Then, measure them to see how close your estimates were to the real values. Did you choose the correct measurement units? If you don't have some of these items in your classroom, check at home.

Object	Length	
	estimate (cm)	actual value (cm)
pencil		
height of your teacher's desk		
length of your classroom		

For a large object or distance, you might divide it up into portions in your mind and guess the length, volume, or mass of one portion. You then multiply that guess by the number of imaginary portions to estimate the measurement of the whole.

Object	Mass	
	estimate (g)	actual value (g)
this textbook		
banana from someone's lunch		
piece of chalk		

Sometimes, it's useful to estimate the measurement of an object before you actually measure it. You might do this to help you decide which units of measurement and which measuring tool to use. In other cases, you might not be able to measure an object at all. In this case, an estimate of its length, volume, or mass might be the best you can do.

Object	Volume	
	estimate (mL)	actual value (mL)
amount of water poured into an empty jar		
marker cap		
drink thremos		

Graphing

Science and technology often involve collecting a lot of numerical data. This data may be recorded in tables or charts. Sometimes, however, it's difficult to see if there are any patterns in the numbers. That's when it's useful to reorganize the data into graphs. Graphs help to interpret data collected during an experiment by showing how numbers are related to one another. You have probably drawn a lot of graphs over the years in your studies of mathematics, geography, and, of course, science and technology.

Creating Line Graphs

Line graphs are good for exploring data collected for many types of experiments. Using line graphs is a good way to analyze the data of an experiment that are continually changing. For example, here are some data collected by a group of students investigating temperature changes. They poured hot water into a large container (container A) and cold water into a smaller container (container B). After recording the starting temperatures of the water in each container, they placed Container B inside Container A and took measurements every 30 s until there were no more temperature changes.

Here are the data they collected shown as a chart and as a line graph. On the graph, they put the manipulated variable—time—on the x-axis, and the responding variable—temperature—on the y-axis.

Evidence

Temperature of Water in Container A and Container B		
Time (s)	Temperature (°C) of water in Container A	Temperature (°C) of water in Container B
0	51	0
30	45	7
60	38	14
90	33	20
120	30	22
150	29	23
180	28	24
210	27	25
240	26	26
270	26	26
300	26	26

Analysis

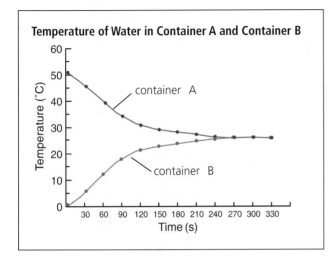

Temperature of Water in Container A and Container B

container A

container B

Creating Bar Graphs

Bar graphs are useful for showing relationships between separate sets of data. For example, the chart below shows the monthly average precipitation (both snow and rain) for a city in Canada. Compare the data in this chart with how they "look" when they are reorganized in the form of a bar graph. On the graph, they put the manipulated variable—month—on the x-axis, and the responding variable—precipitation—on the y-axis.

Month	Average Precipitation (mm)
January	50.4
February	46.0
March	61.1
April	70.0
May	66.0
June	67.1
July	71.4
August	76.8
September	63.5
October	61.8
November	62.7
December	64.7

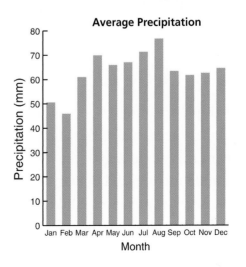

Average Precipitation

Hints

Scales for bar graphs are often rounded off to the nearest whole number.

INSTANT PRACTICE

1. Why is each bar on a bar graph the same width?

2. Which axis is used for the manipulated variable? Which is used for the responding variable? Your graph paper is 22 squares by 34 squares. December has the most precipitation of any month, with 90 mm. Describe how you would create the scales to show twelve months of precipitation.

3. How was the scale for each axis chosen? How did you decide to choose the scales that you did for the first question?

4. The yearly average precipitation for this city is 761.5 mm. How would you modify the bar graph to include this additional information? How would you need to change your graph if the yearly total of precipitation, 497 mm, needed to be added as well.

Creating Circle (Pie) Graphs

A circle graph is useful when you want to display data that are part of a whole. For example, in this circle graph, the "whole" is Earth's total land area. The "parts" are the approximate percentages of land made up by each continent.

Percentage of Earth's Land Area

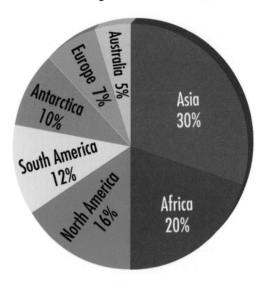

Hints

You might consider using a computer to draw your circle graphs. Some computer drawing programs allow you to use different colours for the different sections of your graph, making it easier to read.

Compare the data in this chart with how they "looked" when they were organized in the form of a circle graph on the previous page. Which can you interpret more easily and more quickly?

Continent	Percentage of Earth's Land Area
Asia	30%
Africa	20%
North America	16%
South America	12%
Antarctica	10%
Europe	7%
Australia	5%

INSTANT PRACTICE

1. Which continents, when added together, make up about half of all the land mass on Earth? Why is it easier to determine this from the circle graph than from the chart of data?

2. A survey of students in your class of 24 students showed the following:
    *   12 students usually eat cereal for breakfast
    *   6 students usually eat toast, waffles or bread for breakfast
    *   3 students usually eat a snack bar or packaged food for breakfast
    *   2 students usually only drink juice for breakfast
    *   1 student usually did not eat or drink anything for breakfast

    Sketch what this circle graph would look like.

Glossary

Note: The number in parentheses at the end of each definition indicates the page number in this book where the term first appears.

A

abiotic element non-living thing (e.g., water, rocks, soil) (13)

aeration process that mixes waste water with large volumes of air (257)

alloy solid solution; two or more solids blended in a homogeneous mixture (215)

atmosphere blanket of gases and particles that surrounds Earth (316)

B

biofuel fuel that is produced from living things such as plants (359)

bioinvasion accidental or planned introduction of a foreign species (plant or animal) into a community (49)

biotic element living thing that needs oxygen, water, food, energy, and a suitable habitat (place to live) in order to survive (13)

C

carnivore consumer that eats meat (25)

centre of gravity imaginary point in a structure where the force of gravity acts (133)

change of state change from one of the three states of matter to another (295)

chemical energy energy stored in matter such as food, fuels, and clothing (283)

chlorophyll green pigment visible in most leaves; necessary in the photosynthesis process (18)

climate long-term weather conditions over large areas of Earth (325)

climate change any major change in the climate of a region of Earth that lasts for a long period of time; change in Earth's wind patterns, average temperature, precipitation including rainfall, and the number and strength of extreme weather conditions such as floods and hurricanes, may be indicators of climate change (361)

climax community fairly stable community; features large plants and animals such as those found in a forest (64)

combination structure structure containing a combination of shell, frame, and solid structures (104)

community populations of different species that live in the same ecosystem (20)

compression type of internal force that squeezes or presses a structure together (112)

concentrated solution solution that contains a large amount of dissolved solute and very little solvent (217)

concentration amount of solute dissolved in a specific amount of the solution (217)

condensation change of state from a gas to a liquid (203)

conduction transfer of heat through a solid or between a solid and another solid, a liquid, or a gas that is in contact with it (302)

consumer 1. living thing in an ecosystem relying on feeding interactions to supply its food needs; consumes other living things (24) 2. person who buys and uses anything grown or made by producers (154)

contract (contraction) decrease in size (volume); matter contracts when heat is removed (297)

convection transfer of thermal energy by moving particles in fluids (304)

convection current circular pattern of moving particles within fluids (304)

crust Earth's solid outer layer; mountains, valleys, plains, hills, and plateaus are all part of the crust (331)

crystal special shape of mineral found in rocks made from molten rock (magma) that cooled slowly (333)

cycle repeated transformation of matter from abiotic elements into biotic elements and back to abiotic elements (43)

cycling of matter series of steps or cycle that allows abiotic elements to be used over and over again (44)

D

decomposer consumer that breaks down (decomposes) dead plants, animals, and waste products (26)

deposition change from the gas state directly to the solid state (203)

detrivore consumer that feeds off waste (detritus) (26)

dilute solution solution that has very little solute dissolved in the solvent (217)

distillation method of separating a solution into its components that involves boiling and condensation; useful for substances with large differences in boiling points (229)

dynamic load force that moves or changes while acting on a structure (110)

E

earthquake shaking and sliding in the crust produced by shifting of plates (332)

ecosystem place where living things interact with other living and non-living things (4)

elastic energy energy stored in objects that are stretched, compressed, bent, or twisted (283)

electrical energy (electricity) energy of particles moving through a wire or through an electrical device (283)

energy ability to make objects move (283)

energy converter any device that transforms energy from one form to another (346)

energy pyramid visual representation showing the amount of energy transferred in each feeding interaction (39)

energy transformation change from one form of energy to another (284)

enhanced greenhouse effect effect due to a build-up in the atmosphere of higher than normal amounts of greenhouse gases (354)

erosion breakdown and movement of rocks and soil by water, wind, or ice (335)

evaporation 1. change of state from a liquid to a gas (295) 2. method of separating a solution into its components in which evaporating solvent particles, in a container, leave the solution (as vapour) and mix with surrounding air particles, while solute particles remain in greater concentration in the container (229)

expand increase in size (volume); matter expands when heat is added (297)

external force force applied to a structure from the outside (e.g., wind, gravity) (109)

F

filtration mechanical process of separating solids from liquids (or gases) (228)

fluid substance that flows; includes liquids and gases (304)

food chain visual representation of the feeding interactions between producers and consumers (27)

food web interconnected food chains in an ecosystem (40)

force any push or pull acting on a structure (108)

fossil fuels non-renewable sources of energy formed underground millions of years ago from the remains of plants and animals (e.g., oil, natural gas, coal) (288)

fractional distillation method used to separate different substances or fractions that make up crude petroleum based on differences in their boiling points (243)

frame structure structure that is made of parts (structural components) fastened together (102)

freezing (solidification) change of state from a liquid to a solid (203)

function purpose of an object or structure (98)

G

gas flaring process in which waste gases produced by the refining process, such as methane or natural gas, are released and set aflame (249)

gemstone mineral that is valuable because of its exceptional beauty, colour, and rarity; main physical properties are colour, lustre (shininess), how light passes through it, and hardness (334)

geothermal power alternative energy source provided by the heat deep in Earth (359)

global warming worldwide average increase in temperature of Earth's atmosphere, land, and oceans (355)

gravitational energy stored energy an object has when it is above Earth's surface (283)

green renewable power source of energy that does not involve burning fuels and does not harm the environment by producing gases or heat pollution (e.g., solar energy, wind energy, bioenergy, geothermal energy) (364)

greenhouse gases gases in the atmosphere that trap heat (e.g., water vapour, carbon dioxide, methane, nitrogen oxides) (354)

Glossary

H

habitat place that provides living things with oxygen, water, food, shelter, and anything else they need for survival (14)

heat thermal energy transferred from a solid, a liquid, or a gas at a higher temperature to a solid, a liquid, or a gas at a lower temperature; also refers to the thermal energy that transfers within a solid, a liquid, or a gas (201)

heat island region of a city that has higher air and surface temperatures than its surroundings (352)

heat pollution release of heat from human activities that has negative effects on an ecosystem (349)

herbicide chemical mixture that is used to destroy unwanted vegetation, such as weeds (255)

herbivore consumer that eats plants (25)

heterogeneous term used to describe a mixture made up of many different substances, each with a different appearance and characteristics (196)

homogeneous term used to describe a pure substance in which every part of that substance has the same composition as every other part (195)

hurricane strong, spinning weather system over the ocean that has continuous winds exceeding 119 km/h (326)

I

igneous rock class of rock that forms from molten rock that has cooled and hardened (333)

infrared waves invisible waves that transfer heat (305)

inner core hot, solid centre of Earth (331)

insecticide chemical mixture that is used to destroy insects that are harmful to cultivated plants or animals (255)

insoluble term used to describe a substance that does not dissolve in a solvent (216)

internal force force that one part of a structure exerts on other parts within the same structure (e.g., shear, tension, compression, torsion forces) (109)

K

kinetic energy energy of movement; particles of matter have kinetic energy (200)

Kyoto Protocol

Kyoto Protocol 1992 agreement signed by more than 160 countries, including Canada, to reduce greenhouse gas emissions from all sources (355)

L

landfill area where garbage is disposed of and buried under layers of earth (258)

lava hot magma that reaches Earth's surface by means of volcanic eruption (333)

lifespan length of time that a product or structure is expected to function (161)

light energy form of energy that our eyes can detect (283)

limiting factor factor controlling or limiting the number and health of biotic elements in ecosystems (e.g., food availability, predators, climate, suitable habitat) (48)

load external force acting on a structure; **total load** is the sum of the static and dynamic loads (110)

M

magma (molten rock) hot liquid rock under Earth's surface (332)

magnetic property of component particles of certain metals that are attracted to particles within magnets (231)

magnetic energy (magnetism) energy that causes some types of metal to attract or push away from certain other metals; iron, cobalt, and nickel are all magnetic (283)

mantle hot, partly molten layer of material below Earth's crust, between the crust and the core (331)

manufacturer company or person who produces and sells products that consumers buy (155)

market research process in which manufacturers gather and evaluate information about consumers' likes and dislikes of products (155)

matter anything that has mass and takes up space; can be classified by its physical state (solid, liquid, or gas) and by composition (pure substance or mixture) (194)

mechanical energy energy of objects in motion (283)

mechanical mixture heterogeneous mixture; differing amounts of different types of matter throughout (196)

melting change of state from a solid to a liquid (203)

metamorphic rock class of rock formed from igneous or sedimentary rocks that have been changed from their original form by heat (from Earth) or by the pressure of the rocks above them (334)

meteorology study of weather and weather patterns (318)

mineral naturally-occurring solid substance that may be pure or mixed with other minerals (333)

mixture combination of two or more different types of matter (195)

molten fused or liquefied by heat (332)

mountaintop removal type of coal mining that begins with the clearcut and removal of the moutaintop forest; soil on top of the mountain is removed and explosives are used to blast away the land and rock above the coal; large trucks or draglines are used to transport coal to washing and processing plants (248)

N

natural greenhouse effect natural change in temperature that Earth experiences because the greenhouse gases in the atmosphere trap energy from the Sun (354)

non-renewable term used to describe something that is irreplaceable (288)

nuclear energy stored energy at the centre of particles of matter (283)

nutrient component of food that the body converts into energy (14)

O

ocean current pattern of movement of the water in a large region of the ocean (325)

omnivore consumer that eats both meat and plants (25)

open pit mining type of mining involving the removal of all materials in a large pit; used when the material being mined is uniformly scattered in overburden that is also relatively consistent in texture, and to obtain metals located near the surface (248)

organic matter made up of or coming from organisms (another word for biotic element) (43)

outer core hot, molten layer of material between Earth's mantle and the inner core (331)

overburden surface material removed during surface mining (248)

P

paper chromatography method of separating a solution into its components using paper (228)

particle very small portion of matter that cannot be seen with the eyes alone (199)

particle theory of matter theory that states that all matter is made up of particles; that all particles of one substance are identical; that particles of matter are in constant motion; that temperature affects the speed at which particles move; that particles have forces of attraction between them; and that there are spaces between particles (200)

percolation (leaching) method in which some chemicals are introduced to the water supply; chemicals seep into the ground, then later enter the water supply (255)

pesticide chemical mixture (e.g., insecticide, herbicide) that is used to destroy pests (255)

photosynthesis chemical reaction that takes place in the leaves of plants when the Sun's light is present (18)

pioneer species plant or plant-like species that is part of primary succession (e.g., lichens, grasses); plant or animal that comes to live in an area where it has not lived before (63)

plane of application side of a structure affected by a force (110)

plate large, thick section of rock that Earth's crust sits on (332)

point of application exact location where a force meets a structure (110)

population group of individuals of the same species (20)

precipitation water vapour that condenses and falls to Earth as rain or snow (323)

predator animal that hunts and consumes prey (25)

prey organism that is hunted for food (25)

primary consumer consumer that eats a producer; first level of consumer in a food chain (herbivore or omnivore) (39)

primary succession formation of a new ecosystem where no ecosystem has existed (63)

primary treatment waste water process involving the separation of a mechanical mixture, including removal of suspended solids, rocks, sand, and grit (257)

producer plant or plant-like biotic element that can make its own food to supply the matter and energy it needs to survive (18)

product recall public recall of seriously flawed products sold to consumers by manufacturers (136)

prototype model used to test and evaluate a design (143)

pure substance matter that has one type of substance throughout (195)

R

radiation (radiant energy) transfer of energy by invisible waves given off by an energy source (304)

radioactive term used to describe a substance that gives off radiation, which is a form of energy that is dangerous and possibly fatal to all living things exposed to this energy (259)

refinery industrial plant that purifies crude substances, such as petroleum or sugar (247)

renewable term used to describe something that can be reused or replaced (288)

residue chemical that comes from a pesticide (255)

rock cycle repeating pattern in which one family of rock changes into a different family (335)

S

salt pan large low-lying area surrounded by dikes into which seawater flows; used in the evaporation of seawater to obtain salt (243)

saturated solution solution that has been formed from the maximum amount of solute for a given amount of solvent at a certain temperature (217)

saturation point point at which no more solute can be dissolved in a fixed volume of solvent at a given temperature (217)

scavenger consumer that does not usually kill its own food; it feeds off the remains of living things that were killed by other consumers (26)

secondary consumer consumer that eats a primary consumer; second level of consumer in a food chain (carnivore or omnivore) (39)

secondary succession gradual replacement of one community of living things by another in established ecosystems (64)

secondary treatment waste water biological process involving aeration; living organisms, such as bacteria and protozoa, help to break apart larger particles, which then drop to the bottom of retention tanks and are removed (257)

sedimentary rock class of rock that forms from small pieces of rock, shells, or other materials that pile-up in layers (333)

sewage liquid waste water from toilets, baths, showers, and sinks; may also include run-off from roofs, urban green spaces, roadways, and liquid waste from industries (255)

shear type of internal force that pushes a structure in opposite directions (112)

shell structure structure that is strong, hollow, and light for its size (103)

sifting means of separating solids by component size; involves shaking or agitating a solid material while passing it through a screen or mesh (231)

slag byproduct of nickel and copper smelting; mixture of waste rock (258)

slurry byproduct of paper production; mixture of cellulose, chemicals, heavy metals, and other unknown solutions (261)

solar power alternative energy source relying on the Sun's rays (359)

solid structure structure that is solid all the way through (for the most part) (102)

solubility relative ability of a solute to form a solution when added to a certain solvent; maximum amount of solute that can be added to a fixed amount of solvent at a given temperature (216)

solute substance that dissolves in the solvent to form a solution (215)

solution homogeneous mixture; mixture of two or more substances that looks the same throughout (196)

solvent substance into which a solute dissolves to form a solution (215)

sorting technique that involves separating substances on the basis of appearance, which may involve colour, size, texture, or composition (230)

sound energy form of energy that we can hear (283)

species most closely related group of living things in an ecosystem that are able to produce fertile offspring (20)

stability ability of a structure to maintain its position (134)

states of matter forms in which matter can exist (solid, liquid, and gas) (295)

static load effect of gravity on a structure (weight) (110)

strip mining type of mining involving the removal of long strips of overburden in areas where the material being mined is concentrated in veins; used when the overburden is found on the sides of hills and valleys (248)

structural component part of a structure that can add strength to it (e.g., arches, beams, columns) (132)

structural failure breakdown of a structure due to the internal and external forces acting on it (135)

structural fatigue permanent changes to a structure due to the internal and external forces acting on it (135)

structural stress effect of all the internal and external forces acting on a structure over a long period of time (135)

structure any small or large object that provides support and has at least one function (98)

sublimation change from the solid state directly to the gas state (203)

succession natural replacement of one population of living things by another (63)

supersaturated solution solution that contains more solute than would normally be dissolved in the solution at a given temperature (217)

surface mining type of mining involving the removal of large amounts of soil and rock on the surface in order to access the valuable material underneath (e.g., gold ore) (248)

sustainability ecosystem's ability to continue or sustain itself (51)

symmetry balanced arrangement on opposites sides of a structure (equal halves) (143)

T

tailing pond large pool where cyanide compounds (mixed in with crushed rock) break down in sunlight (249)

temperature measurement of the average kinetic energy of the particles in a substance (201)

tension type of internal force that stretches a structure apart (112)

tertiary consumer consumer that eats a secondary consumer; third level of consumer in a food chain (carnivore or omnivore) (39)

tertiary treatment waste water process involving the application of chemicals, such as chlorine, to disinfect and kill the remaining germs and to remove phosphates (257)

thermal energy total energy of the moving particles in a solid, a liquid, or a gas (283)

thermometer instrument used to measure the temperature of solids, liquids, and gases (290)

tidal power alternative energy source produced by the force of tides and waves in the ocean (359)

tornado strong, spinning column of air in contact with the ground (326)

torsion type of internal force that twists a structure (112)

troposphere lowest level of Earth's atmosphere (318)

U

unsaturated solution solution in which more solute can be dissolved in a solvent at a given temperature (217)

V

vaporization change of state from a liquid to a gas (203)

volcano crack or opening in Earth's crust through which solid and molten rock, ash, and gases escape (332)

W

water cycle movement in nature of water from the surface of Earth to the atmosphere and back (322)

weather conditions of Earth's atmosphere at a particular time and in a particular place (318)

weathering wearing away of rock by water, wind, chemicals, and even living things (335)

wind movement of air in the troposphere (324)

wind power alternative energy source relying on the wind (359)

Photo Credits and Acknowledgements

The publisher wishes to thank the following sources for photographs, illustrations, and other materials used in this book. Care has been taken to determine and locate ownership of copyright material used in this text. We will gladly receive information enabling us to rectify any errors or omissions in credits.

COVER: Cal Vornberger/Photoresearchers/Firstlight

UNIT A: pp. 2-3 Pete Cairns/naturepl.com; p. 4 © JOHN BARKER/Alamy; p. 5 ©Bill Brooks/Alamy; p. 7 (top left) Paul J. Fusco/Photo Researchers, Inc., (middle) David Cannings-Bushell/iStock, (bottom) The Canadian Press/Bayne Stanley; pp. 8-9 Ron Hilton/Shutterstock; p. 10 (top) Christina Richards/Shutterstock, (bottom) Bill Ivy/Ivy Images; p. 11 (top left) Wendy Nero, (right) Bill Ivy/Ivy Images; p. 12 (left) Arco Images/Alamy, (middle) Jupiter Images, (right) BananaStock/Jupiter Images; p. 13 Ron Steiner/Alamy; p. 14 (top) Comstock, (middle) Yurlov Andrey Aleksandrovich, (bottom) Paul J. Fusco/Photo Researchers, Inc.; p. 16 Thomas Kitchin/FirstLight; p. 17 (top) Timofey Federov/Shutterstock, (bottom) Explorer/Photo Researchers, Inc.; p. 18 David Grossman/Photo Researchers, Inc.; p. 19 Michelle Radin/Shutterstock; p. 20 (top) John Mitchell/Photo Researchers, Inc., (bottom) Steve Skjold/Alamy; p. 23 David Boag/Alamy; p. 24 (top) Aleksander Bolbot/Shutterstock, (bottom) Wendy Nero/Shutterstock; p. 25 Millard H. Sharp/Photo Researchers, Inc.; p. 26 (top) Luis César Tejo/Shutterstock, (middle) Clearviewstock/Shutterstock, (bottom) ©PHOTOTAKE Inc./Alamy; p. 27 (top left to bottom right) Androv Andriy/Shutterstock, photos.com/Jupiter Images, liquidlibrary/Jupiter Images, Hirlesteanu Constantin-Ciprian/Shutterstock, David Lee/Shutterstock, Thomas M Perkins/Shutterstock, Dmitry Kosterev/Shutterstock; p. 28 Burke, Triolo/Jupiter Images; p. 29 Steve McWilliam/Shutterstock; p. 31 (left) Niagara Peninsula Conservation Authority (NPCA), (right) Bill Ivy/Ivy Images; p. 32 Bill Ivy/Ivy Images; pp. 34-35 Philip Lange/Shutterstock; p. 36 Brian Elliott/Alamy; p. 38 Comstock Images; p. 39 (top row) Eric Isselée/Shutterstock, (2nd row left to right) Frank Greenaway/Dorling Kindersley, Jane Burton/Dorling Kindersley, Shutterstock, Eric Isselée/Shutterstock, Comstock Images Image, (3rd row left to right) James Pierce/Shutterstock, Roman Sika/Shutterstock, Fernando Blanco Calzada, Reddogs/Shutterstock, Barbara Tripp/Shutterstock, Dorling Kindersley/Media Library, (bottom row left to right) Stephen Oliver/Dorling Kindersley, Olga Shelago/Shutterstock, Brans X Pictures/Jupiter Images; p.40 (top) Jerry Young/Dorling Kindersley, (2nd row left to right) Dorling Kindersley/Media Library, Pete Cairns/Nature Place, (3rd row Left to right) Reddogs/Shutterstock, James Pierce/Shutterstock, Frank Greenaway/Dorling Kindersley, Jane Burton/Dorling Kindersley, (bottom left to right) Dorling Kindersley/Media Library, Robin Mackenzie/Shutterstock, Brans X Pictures, Stephen Oliver/Dorling Kindersley; p. 41 (top) Richard Kellaway/PC Services, (bottom left) Stephen Oliver/Dorling Kindersley, (middle) Emilia Stasiak/Shutterstock, (right) Eric Isselée/Shutterstock; p. 42 Stock Image/FirstLight; p. 43 David Cannings-Bushell/iStock; p. 44 (top) Scimat/Photo Researchers, Inc., (bottom) Mike Dobel/Alamy; p. 46 Fisheries and Wildlife; p. 48 Jacana/Photo Researchers, Inc.; p. 49 (top) Hemera Technologies/Jupiter Images, (bottom) Andrew J. Martinez/Photo Researchers, Inc.; p. 50 Runk/Schoenberger-Grant Heilman Photography, Inc.; p. 51 Ducks Unlimited Canada/Darin Langhorst; p. 52 Steve Knell/naturpl.com; p. 55 (top) © Walter Hodges/CORBIS, (bottom) Earth Satellite Corporation/Photo Researchers, Inc; pp. 58-59 Bill Brooks/Alamy; p. 60 U.S Geological Society Survey, Denver; p. 61 CP Images/Ryan Remiorz; p. 62 Johnny Greig Garden Photography/Alamy; p. 63 Corel Stock Photo Library; p. 64 (bottom a, b, c, d) Breck P. Kent; p. 65 © Jan Baks/Alamy; p. 66 Ross Frid/Alamy; p. 67 Steven W Moore/Shutterstock; p. 68 N. McKee of IDRC International Development Research Centre; p. 69 (top) The British Columbia Collection/Alamy, (middle) The Medicine Hat News/the Canadian Press/Deddeda Stemmler, (bottom) Kari Niemelainen/Alamy; p. 70 Michael Zysman/Shutterstock; p. 71 Stock Connection/Alamy; p. 72 Bettmann/Corbis; p. 73 Paul Glendell/Alamy; p. 74 Bill Ivy/Ivy Images; p. 75 (top and bottom) Bill Ivy/Ivy Images; p. 76 (top) NordicPhotos/FirstLight, (bottom) Paul Glendell/Alamy; p. 77 (top) The Canadian Press/Bayne Stanley, (bottom) Bill Ivy/Ivy Images; p. 78 (a) Justin Sullivan/Getty Images, (b) Justin Sullivan/Shutterstock, (c) Edwin Verin/Shutterstock; p. 81 Tony Heald/naturepl.com; p. 82 (left to right) R. Gino Santa Maria/Shutterstock, Brand X Pictures/Jupiter Images, Feng Yu/Shutterstock, Rhonda O'Donnell/Shutterstock; p. 83 Wendy Nero; p. 85 suravid/Shutterstock; p. 87 Bill Ivy/Ivy Images; p. 88 (top) © DAHMER DARRYL/CORBIS SYGMA, (bottom) Paul Glendell.

UNIT B: pp. 90-91 Ashley Cooper/Alamy; p. 92 (middle centre) Imagesource/First Light, (top middle) Irwin Barrett/First Light, (top left) Photographers Choice/First Light, (bottom) Radius Images/First Light, (middle left) Jupiter Images Corporation, (middle right) Martina I. Meyer/Shutterstock Inc., (top right) Brad Whitsitt/Shutterstock Inc.; p. 93 Jupiter Images Corporation; p. 95 (bottom) Bill Brooks/Alamy, (middle right) Matt Rainey/Star Ledger/CORBIS, (top left) Mike Flippo/Shutterstock Inc.; pp. 96-97 Thinkstock/First Light; p. 98 (top) James Leynse/CORBIS, (bottom) Jody Dingle/Shutterstock Inc.; p. 99 (left) Javarman/Shutterstock Inc., (middle) Jo Ann Snover/Shutterstock Inc., (right) Philip Date/Shutterstock Inc.; p. 100 (right) Photodisc/First Light , (left) Lev Olkha/Shutterstock Inc.; p. 101 (bottom left) Alan Marsh/First Light, (bottom right) Radius Images/First Light, (top) David Hughes/Shutterstock Inc.; p. 102 (right) Mike Flippo/Shutterstock Inc., (left) Robyn Mackenzie/Shutterstock Inc.; p. 103 (top right) Charles O'Rear/CORBIS; (bottom right) Jerry Kobalenko/First Light, (top left) Alexsander Isachenko/Shutterstock Inc., (bottom left) Jiri Pavlik/Shutterstock Inc.; p. 104 Jupiter Images Corporation; p. 105 (bottom) Digitalvision/First Light, (top) Jupiter Images Corporation, (bottom left) Salamanderman/Shutterstock Inc.; p. 108 Bev Ramm/Shutterstock Inc.; p. 109 Xinhua Press/CORBIS; p. 111 Richard Kellaway/PC Services; p. 112 (bottom) Duomo/CORBIS; p. 113 Jupiter Images Corporation; p. 114 Edwin Verin/Shutterstock Inc.; p. 116 (bottom) CP-Ryan Remiorz, (top) Jupiter Images Corporation; p. 117 Ricardo Garza/Shutterstock Inc.; p. 118 Photodisc/First Light; p. 119 Jupiter Images Corporation; p. 123 All Canada Photos/Alamy; pp. 126-127 Robert Harding World Imagery/CORBIS; pp. 128-129 Dan Forer/Beateworks/CORBIS; p. 130 Digitalvision/First Light;

Jupiter Images Corporation; p. 297 (bottom 2 photos) Richard Kellaway/PC Services; p. 300 (top) Michael Dzaman/maXximages.com, (bottom) Richard Kellaway/PC Services; p. 301 (top right) Guylain Doyle/maXximages.com, (bottom centre) Bananastock/Jupiter Images Corporation, (bottom right) Tom Bochsler Photography Limited ©Prentice Hall, Inc.; p. 302 (top left) allOver photography/Alamy, (centre left) Elemental Imaging/Shutterstock, (bottom left) Richard Kellaway/PC Services, (bottom right) Michael Newman/PhotoEdit; p. 303 (top right) Reuters/Shaun Best, (top centre inset) Mike Hewitt/Getty Images; p. 305 (top right) Edward Kinsman/Photo Researchers, Inc., (centre left map) © Her Majesty The Queen in Right of Canada, Environment Canada, 2008. From http://www.weatheroffice.gc.ca/data/satellite/goes_ecan_1070_100.jpg. Satellite data provided by the US National Oceanic and Atmospheric Administration. Reproduced with the permission of the Minister of Public Works and Government Services Canada., (bottom right) Photodisc/Alamy; p. 308 (bottom left and right) Ray Boudreau ©Pearson Education Canada; p. 309 (top) Courtesy of Nuytco Research/Hard Suits Inc., (bottom) Alexis Rosenfeld/Science Photo Library; p. 311 altrendo images/Getty Images; pp. 312-313 NOAA; p. 314 CP-Jonathan Hayward; p. 316 (a) Jupiter Images Corporation, (b) iStockphoto.com/Marcel Pelletier, (c) CP/AP Photo-Luca Bruno, (d) Radius Images/Jupiter Images Corporation, (e) Gordon Swanson/Shutterstock, (f) NASA, (g) Radius Images/Jupiter Images Corporation, (h) Charles Hewitt/Hulton Archive/Getty Images, (i) John Crum/Alamy; p. 317 Steven Katovich, USDA Forest Service, www.forestryimages.org, Bugwood.org; p. 322 Marco Simoni/Robert Harding World Imagery/Getty Images; p. 323 (centre) Andrew Lambert Photography/Science Photo Library; p. 326 CP-Wayne Hanna; p. 328 (map) Courtesy of Argo Information Centre: http://argo.jcommops.org, (bottom left) John Poling, California Polythechnic and Courtesy of Argo Information Centre: http://argo.jcommops.org, (bottom centre inset) JAMSTEC and Courtesy of Argo Information Centre: http://argo.jcommops.org; p. 329 (top right) Austin Post/USGS; p. 330 (centre left) Tischenko Irina/Shutterstock, (bottom left) Alex Staroseltsev/Shutterstock, (bottom centre) iwka/Shutterstock, (bottom right) Bartlomiej Nowak/Shutterstock; p. 333 (Figure 11.29 from top clockwise) (quartz) Ricardo Miguel Silva Saraiva/Shutterstock, (blue copper sulphate) immelstorm/Shutterstock, (fluorite on calcite) Bureau of Mines, C-01685/USGS, (diamond) Harry Taylor ©Dorling Kindersley, (purple amethyst) iStockphoto.com/Emrah Turudu, (Figure 11.30) (a) Gary Ombler ©Dorling Kindersley, Courtesy of Oxford University Museum of Natural History, (b) Colin Keates ©Dorling Kindersley, Courtesy of the Natural History Museum, London, (c) Harry Taylor

©Dorling Kindersley; p. 334 Reuters; p. 338 Harry Taylor ©Dorling Kindersley; p. 339 (top) NOAA, (bottom) Reuters/Robert Galbraith; p. 340 (vacuum, centre left) Ricky Blakeley ©Dorling Kindersley, (bottom left) John Sartin/Shutterstock, (bottom centre) Jeff Banke/Shutterstock, (bottom right) Feng Yu/Shutterstock; pp. 342-343 Alfred Pasieka/Science Photo Library; p. 344 (top) CP-Robert Galbraith, (bottom) CP/Montreal La Presse-Martin Chamberland; p. 345 (centre left) iStockphoto.com/David Morgan, (centre right) Germany Feng/Shutterstock, (bottom left) Steve Gorton ©Dorling Kindersley, (bottom right) Photodisc/Alamy; p. 346 (top left) Stan Rohrer/Alamy, (bottom right) Jason Laure/Woodfin Camp; p. 347 (left and right) Courtesy of Ontario Power Generation, (centre) CP/Toronto Star-Dick Loek; p. 348 (Figure 12.9) (a) Luis Castaneda Inc./The Image Bank/Getty Images, (b) H. Mark Weidman Photography/Alamy, (c) Bill Bachman/Alamy, (d) David Mendelsohn/Masterfile, (bottom left) Thomas Sztanek/Shutterstock; p. 349 Paul Glendell/Alamy; p. 350 Gary Blakeley/Shutterstock; p. 351 CP/AP Photo-Dave Duprey; p. 352 (map) Reproduced with the permission of Natural Resources Canada 2008, and Courtesy of the Canada Centre for Remote Sensing, (bottom right) Lucas Oleniuk/First Light; p. 353 Stale Edstrom/Shutterstock; p. 355 (Figure 12.20) Reproduced with the permission of the Minister of Public Works and Government Services, and Courtesy of Natural Resources Canada, 2008, (bottom right) Roger Ressmeyer/CORBIS; p. 358 iStockphoto.com/Suzann Julien; p. 359 CP-Dave Chidley; p. 360 (centre) Design Pics Inc./Alamy, (bottom) William Mahar/Shutterstock; p. 361 (Figure 12.26) UNEP/GRID-Arendal Maps and Graphics Library, http://maps.grida.no/go/graphic/potential_climate_change_impacts. Graphic Design: Philippe Rekacewicz. Source: United States EPA, (centre) USDA Forest Service - Region 4 Archive, USDA Forest Service, www.forestryimages.org, Bugwood.org, (bottom) A. Steven Munson, USDA Forest Service, www.forestryimages.org, Bugwood.org; p. 363 (top row, left to right) FloridaStock/Shutterstock, Tom Grundy/Shutterstock, Visions of America/Joe Sohm/Digital Vision/Getty Images, Silver Burdett Ginn, (bottom row, left to right) Eitan Simanor/Alamy, CP/AP Photo-Michael Probst, Robert Harding Picture Library Ltd/Alamy; p. 364 (top left) iStockphoto.com/Grafissimo, (centre right) CP-Steve White, (bottom left) iStockphoto.com/Rhoberazzi; p. 366 Courtesy of ENERGY STAR; p. 367 (left) Kitt Cooper-Smith/Alamy, (right) Alan G. Nelson/maXximages.com; p. 368 (left) Paul Nicklen/National Geographic/Getty images; p. 372 Digital Vision/Alamy; p. 373 Harry Taylor ©Dorling Kindersley; p. 374 (left) Gregg Stott/Masterfile, (right) David Cooper/Toronto Star; p. 375 MetaPics/Alamy.